The Field Guide II for
Actively Aerated Compost Tea (AACT)

July 2003- June 2004
First Edition

by Dr. Elaine R. Ingham

President, Sustainable Studies Institute, www.sustainablestudies.org
President, Soil Foodweb Institute Pty. Ltd., Soilfoodwebinst@aol.com.
President, Director of Research, Soil Foodweb Inc. info@soilfoodweb.com
Associate Professor, Research Affiliate, Dept. Forest Science, Oregon State Univ.

Compiled and Edited by **Dr. Carole Ann Rollins**

Published by

Sustainable Studies Institute, 635 SW Western Ave., Corvallis, OR 97333
541-257-2614   Fax: 541-752-5142
info@sustainablestudies.org
www.sustainablestudies.org

and

Nature Technologies, LLC, P.O.Box 1519, Novato, CA 94948
415-898-5895   707-225-5762   Fax: 707-940-0444
info@nature-technologies.com
www.nature-technologies.com

First Printing August 2005
Second Printing October 2008

ISBN 0-9797561-2-X (Paperback)

Forward

Commercial agriculture and non-agriculture consumers are sensitive to environmental impact of toxic chemical pesticides and synthetic fertilizers on soil and plants. With government regulation and gradual removal of toxic pesticides currently and in the future, alternative non-toxic substitutes are desperately needed. The same chemical companies losing revenue from toxic pesticides sales are gearing up biotech production of disease resistant seeds utilizing genetically modified organisms (GMOs) to refill that market niche they once held. But unknown consequences of these potentially harmful GMOs introduced into the marketplace before adequate testing, has caused controversy and concern. This situation is providing a unique opportunity for non-toxic alternatives to be introduced into the marketplace and fill these gaps.

Current research from Dr. Graham Lancaster of Southern Cross University in Australia and Dr. Elaine Ingham, a microbiologist from the Soil Foodweb Labs reported in 2004 that in virtually every soil examined were enormous amounts of total nutrients, but they were not available to plants in their current form. Beneficial micro- organisms must be present in the right ratios for the specified plants to make these nutrients available to the plants at rates the plants require. If organisms are not present they must be added through inoculums such as high quality actively aerated compost tea. Plants provide foods to keep the organisms performing their functions. The organisms must also be fed properly through the times that plants are dormant through the addition of compost or other types of nutrients.

This second Field Guide to Actively Aerated Compost Tea contains Dr. Elaine Ingham's emails from the past year, since the first Field Guide, compiled and organized into a resource for people to use in the field. There are so many questions we all face when we are standing there with a new client. There is no one "blanket answer" to each unique problem that comes up --- each answer depends upon so many different variables intrinsic to each site, environmental conditions, chemical and sustainable practices. Sometimes you will not find a direct answer to your question in these field guides. You will have to piece together different bits of information to try to figure out a possible path to try to help your customer in solving their problems. We are all working together, sharing our experiences and striving to create a more sustainable environment for plants, animals and people. If you have stories to share please send them, every little bit of new information contributes to the greater knowledge and helps us all understand and make sense of the world we are trying to regenerate with Mother Nature, instead of people, in charge.

If you need more help in devising programs or answering questions, you can always consult with the Soil Foodweb Lab in your region. As Dr. Ingham is a prolific writer, the next increment of Internet correspondence is being compiled and is scheduled to be published July, 2006. A special thank you to Gladys Rollins for their hours of proofreading and editing and James Eddington for his on-going support and inspiration. The cover photo is courtesy of Newbury Rugby Club, Mike Harrington. Good luck on your journey and our joint venture into creating this new field of AACT.

Carole Ann Rollins

Dr. Carole Ann Rollins, PhD   May, 2005 Sonoma, California

TABLE

OF

CONTENTS

Table of Contents

Chapter I – Introduction 23

   1. Sustainable System 24
   2. Regenerative Agriculture 24
   3. The Ebb and Flow of Nutrient Cycles 24
   4. Conversion to Healthier 24
   5. Biology and Nutrients 26
   6. Life In Your Soil 26
   7. Controlling Diseases and Pests in a Sustainable System 26
   8. Definition of Sustainable 27
   9. Chemical versus Sustainable Approach 29
      a. Calcium Salts Insane 29
      b. Salts with Foods for Biology 29
  10. Building a Habitat for Beneficials 32
  11. General Biological Practices 32
      a. Small Gardeners vs. Large-Scale Commercial Growers 32
  12. Disturbing Soil 33
  13. Live Organisms 33
  14. OMRI Approval 33
  15. Product Claims Must be Documented 34
  16. Patent Protection 34
  17. Saved a Plantation from Bankruptcy 35
  18. Scientific Soil Food Web Literature 35
  19. Definition of AACT 35
  20. History of Compost Tea 35
      a. Actively Aerated Compost Tea 35
      b. Organisms Like Tiny Little Pilgrims 35
  21. The Scientific Method 36
  22. AACT is Beyond Observation and Hypothesis Stage 36
  23. Tea Types 36
      a. Actively Aerated 36
      b. Fermentative Teas 37
      c. Switching Tea 37
      d. Anaerobic Tea 37
  24. Tea Definitions 37
      a. Aerated Compost Tea 37
      b. Anaerobic Tea 37
      c. Plant Tea 37
      d. Manure Tea 37
  25. Why Brew Tea? 37
  26. Why Use Tea? 38
      a. Foliar Teas May Be Needed 38
      b. Soil Applications 38
  27. Teas Improve Plant Growth and Health 39

28. Tea Contains Biological NPK 39
29. Plant Teas 39
30. Not Compost Tea 39
31. Fermentation 40
    a. Anaerobic Fermentation 40
    b. Aerobic Fermentation 40
    c. Aerobic Metabolism 40
    d. Aerobic Organisms 41
    e. Anaerobic Organisms 41
32. Leachates 41
    a. You Can Harm Roots 41
33. Anaerobic Worm Caste Leachate 41
34. Regulations 42
    a. Anaerobic Brews 43
    b. Temperature 43
    c. Air Pressure 43
    d. Oxygen Concentration 43
    e. Microbial Foods 43
    f. The Set of Microbes 44
    g. The Research 44
    h. The Best Approach 44

Chapter II -- Mechanisms of Impact from AACT Applications 45
  1. Starting the Process of Building the Soil 47
  2. Microorganisms Solubilize Nutrients 47
  3. Replace the Nutrient Removed in Harvest 47
  4. Organisms on Leaf Surfaces 47
  5. Active Organisms Needed 48
  6. Biology is not like a Chemical 48
  7. Tea Contains Biology Not N-P-K! 48
  8. Biology Effect Not NPK 48
    a. Fertilizer Effect 48
  9. Deep Roots 49
10. Mechanisms for Benefits 50
11. Scientific Principles 50
12. Organisms -- Systemic Versus Living on the Surface 51
    a. Internal Contents of Plants 51
    b. Some Organisms Breach Cell Wall and Membrane 51
    c. Summary -- Systemic Versus Living on the Surface 56
13. Bacteria Not Normally in Plant Xylem 56
14. Fungal to Bacterial 52
    a. Late successional perennial grasses 52
    b. Poa, ryegrass 52
15. Bacterial Biomass 52
16. Successional Stages 52

17. Tropical Systems 54
18. Transmutation versus Transformation 54
19. Transmutation 55
20. Beneficial Microorganisms 55
    a. Disease-Causing Fungi 55
    b. Mycorrhizal Fungi 55
    c. Beneficial Fungi 55
21. Mychorrhizal fungi vs. Disease-Causing Fungi 55
    a. Mycorrhizal Fungi 55
    b. Disease-Causing Fungi 56
22. Molds and Mildew 56
    a. White molds 56
    b. Mildew 56
    c. Fungi 56
    d. Water Molds 56
    e. Oomycetes – the Bad Guy 56
23. Water Mold Reproduction 57
24. Types of Fungi 57
25. VAM 57
    a. Non-Mycorrhizal Plant Species 58
    b. Mycorrhizal Spores on Rhododendron 58
26. *Mycorrhizal* Status of Plants 58
27. *Ectomycorrhizal* and *Endomycorrhizal* Fungi 59
    a. Ectomycorrhizal fungi 59
    b. Endomycorrhizal fungi 59
    c. Glomulin 59
28. *Mycorrhizal* Requirements 59
29. *Mycorrhizal* Spores 59
30. Fungi Morphological Terminology 60
31. Fungi and Carbohydrates 60
32. How Fungi Work in Soil 60
33. *Rhizobium, Burkholderia, Bacillus* and *Pseudomonads* 61
34. *Rhizobium* and *Azotobacter* 61
35. Microarthropods 62
36. *Beauveria* and Microarthropods 62
37. Microarthropods Aren't in Tea 62
38. Copper 63
39. Copper and Salts 63
    a. Salt Problems 63
40. Microbes and Salt Levels 64
41. Microorganisms Deal with Salt 65
42. Residential Wastes, Biosolids and Water 67
43. Nitrate in Water 68
44. Mechanisms of Worms 68
45. Earthworms and Weeds 69

      a. Earthworms 69
      b. Weeds 69
46. Slowing Vegetative Growth 69
47. Chitin-utilizing Organisms 70
48. Chitin 70
49. Chitinase 70
50. Eel Worm or Nematode 70
51. Fungi Growth 70
52. Spore Waking Up... 71
53. Successful Organic Orchard................................ 71
54. Prions 77
55. Keritinase 77
56. Biological Control Methods 78
57. When Organic Approaches Don't Work 78
58. Reduced Organism Activity Conditions 79
59. Ways of Achieving Sterilization 79
      a. Plating in a Sterile Medium 79
      b. Mushroom Facilities 79
      c. Commercial Beer Production 79
60. Sterilization Required for Culturing Specific Species ... 80
      a. Sterilizing Grains 80
      b. Wine Production 80
      c. Take Home Story Number One 80
      d. Take Home Story Number Two 80
61. Bindweed and Nutsedge 80
62. Sclerotinia, Trichoderma and Crop Rotation 81
      a. Crop Rotation 81
63. Organisms and pH 81
64. Moss 81
65. Moss and Lawns 82
66. Moss Control 82
67. Weeds 83
68. Shift in Weed Species 83
69. Stop Spraying Chemicals and Weeds Exit the System ... 84
70. N Available Over Three Months 84
71. Giant Cabbages in Alaska 84
      a. Sulfate Effects on Soil Biology 84

Chapter III -- Effects on Diseases 87
  1. Tea is Not a Bio-Pesticide 89
  2. Compost Tea is Not a Fungicide 89
  3. Fungicide vs. Compost Tea 89
      a. Compost Tea Protects Leaf Surfaces 78
      b. Root Coverage of Beneficial Organisms 89
      c. Protozoa and Nematodes Consume Disease-Causing Fungi 89

       d. Antibiotics is not a Potential Mechanism 89
       e. Nothing Toxic about Compost Tea 90
  4. Undefended Plants 90
  5. Disease Occurrence 90
       a. Benefit of a Healthy Foodweb 90
  6. Toxic vs. Non-Toxic Materials 91
  7. Altering Outbreak Capacity 91
       a. If You Have Good Healthy Soil 91
       b. Disease is a Message From Mother Nature 91
       c. Using Toxic Chemicals on Weeds 92
       d. Using Toxic Chemicals on Insect Pests 92
       e. Isolating a Fungus 92
       f. Commercially Available Beauveria 92
       g. Fungus-Killing Factor 92
       h. Pathogenic Fungi 92
  8. Insect Problems and Walnuts 93
       a. Inoculate the Right Aerobic Biology 93
       b. Chloroform Fumigation to Assess Microbial Biomass 93
  9. Fungi Could be *Chitinase* Producers 94
 10. *Sclerotinia* 94
 11. Fairy Ring Fungi in Lawns 94
 12. Protozoa and Ants 94
 13. Asian Rust 94
 14. Pear Blister Mite 95
 15. Apple Scab 95
 16. Banana, Avocado and Mac Nut 95
 17. *Plum Curculio* 95
       a. Gypsy Moth, Pine Bark Beetle and Codling Moth 95
       b. Winter Dormant Stages 96
       c. PC in Outbreak Mode 96
 18. *Penicillium oxalicum* 97
 19. Insect Attacking Fungus 97

Chapter IV -- Applications for Actively Aerated Compost Tea 99
  1. Conditions for Tea for Survive in the Field 101
  2. Dormant Spores 101
  3. Soil Drench 101
  4. Air Dropped Tea 101
  5. Application of Organisms if Ground Not Frozen 101
  6. Transporting and Applying Tea 102
  7. Soil Injection 102
  8. Tea Under Vines 102
  9. Softening the Soil with Microbes 102
 10. Plant Responses 103
 11. Measuring Plant Responses 103

12. Rapid Response 103
13. How To Help You Fix The Biology 104
    a. *Outside The Normal Range* 104
14. Diluting Tea and Adding Food 105
15. Adding Food to Finished Tea 106
16. Effect of UV 106
17. Droplet Size May Be Important 107
18. Maximize Benefits 107
19. Healthy Soil 108
    a. *Kelp* 108
    b. *Greensand* 108
    c. *Egg Shells* 108
    d. *Compost* 108
20. Chelates 109
21. Organic Approaches 110
22. Molasses in Irrigation Water 115
23. What is Out-of-Whack? 115
24. Sugar Beets 116
25. Lime 116
26. Bacterial Mulch or Fungal Mulch 116
27. Inocula for Compost 116
28. Mold and Nematodes 117
29. Beneficial Nematodes 117
    a. *Predatory Nematodes* 117
30. Slugs and Tea 117
31. Slug Control and Tea 117
32. Slugs and Yucca 118
33. Slugs in the Garden 118
34. Slugs Attracted by Alcohol 118
35. Lilies 118
36. Solarization with Black Plastic 118
37. Microbes and pH 118
38. Spraying Livestock with Compost Tea 119
39. Compost Tea for Deicing? 119
40. Profits vs. Continued Application of Inoculums 119
41. Urine on Lawns 120
42. Animal 120
43. Calcium 120
    a. *Nasty Acid* 121
    b. *Eggshells for Calcium Carbonate* 121
    c. *Add Calcium to Compost* 121
    d. *Soil Biology and Soil Chemistry Interaction* 121
44. Oyster Shells 121
45. Calcium Sulfate or Calcium Nitrate 121
46. Sulfur in the Form of Biology 121

47. Elevated CO2 and Plant Growth 122
48. Hydrogen Peroxide is a Sterilant 122
49. Soil Compaction 123
        a. *Clay Soil* 123
        b. *Sheep Manure* 123
50. Clays 123
51. Flocculation of Clays 124
52. Inorganic Nutrients 124
53. *Pseudomonas Inoculum* 125
54. Fish Hydrolysate Balances N 125
55. Alternative Sources of Copper 126
56. Spreaders and Organisms 126
57. Ripping Under the Roots 126
58. *Mycorrhizal* Fungi 126
59. *Mycorrhizal* Fungi Require Roots 127
        a. *Fungi Use Molasses* 127
60. *Mycorrhizal* Colonization 127
61. *Mycorrhizal* Sample Analyzed 128
62. *Mychorrhizae* and Crop Rotation 128
63. *Mycorrhizal* Applications 129
64. *Mycorrhizal* Fungi Spores 129
65. Organic Matter Retains Spores 129
66. Spores in Different Soil Types 130
67. Spores vs. Hyphae 130
68. Fish Hydrolosate, Aloe, Pine Sap & Molasses 130
69. Rototilling is Not Evil 130
70. Strip Tillage 131
71. Herbicides and Tillage 131
72. Most Weeds Indicate Soil Information 132
73. Weed Suppression and Animal Weight Gain 132
74. Discing in Weeds 132
        a. *Green Material Recapitulates Succession* 132
75. Survival of Organisms – Temperature and Discing 133
76. Feeding Fungal Biomass in Strawberries 134
77. Rotation is a Good Idea, Eventually 134
78. Giant Veggies 134
79. Copper Sprayer 134
80. Copper Alternatives 135
81. Pyrethrum Effect on Organisms 135
82. Hot Pepper and Garlic Treatments 135
83. Antimicrobials 135
84. Test for Chemical Residues May Be Necessary 135
85. Turf Questions 135
86. Eastern Red Cedar, Osage Orange, Chinese Elm 136
87. Blackberry and Raspberry 136

88. Brambles 136
89. Peat Moss and Fungi 136
90. Did the Tea Not Work? 136

Chapter V -- Application Rates for Actively Aerated Compost Tea 139
  1. Spring and Fall and Foliar 140
  2. Application Rate to Soil 140
  3. Tea Amount Per Bush 140
  4. Fungal-Dominated Over-Story Crop Plant 140
  5. Application at Bud Swell 140
  6. Application at Bud Break 140
  7. Too Much Tea? 141
  8. Less is Sometimes More 141
  9. How Much is Too Much 141
 10. 5% Fungal Coverage 142
 11. Leaf Coverage of Organisms 142
 12. 70% Organism Coverage 142
 13. Organism Survival on Leaf Surfaces 142
 14. Organisms and Survival 143
 15. Higher Organism Numbers 145
 16. Is Biology in Tea Adequate 145
     a. Stain to Determine Leaf Coverage 145
 17. Heavy Metals and Microorganisms 145
 18. Toxic Salt Thresholds 145
 19. Extension Service N Rates 146
 20. Soybean Application Rates 146
 21. Can Tea Spraying Be Redundant? 147

Chapter VI -- Spray Equipment 149
  1. Mesh Size of Spray Nozzles and Drip Tape 150
  2. Size of Microorganisms 150
  3. PSI Rates 150
  4. Droplet Size 150
  5. Pumps and Critters 150
  6. No Copper Sprayers 151

Chapter VII -- Brewing Techniques 153
  1. Different Kinds of Compost Tea 154
     a. Good Machine 154
     b. Foods 154
     c. Temperature 154
     d. Mixing 154
     e. Spraying 154
  2. Selecting for Organism Growth in Brewers 154

    a. Sugar and Different Foods 155
    b. Fungal Foods 155
    c. Temperature 155
    d. Understanding the Variables 155
    e. Quality of Tea Machines 155
    f. Nutrient Cycling 156
3. Microorganism Growth and Reproduction in Teas 156
4. Fungi Growth Rate in Tea 156
5. Spore Don't Grow in 24 Hour 156
6. Fungi Activity 157
    a. Spores Are Important 157
    b. Fungi Survive Bad Conditions 157
7. Testing and Ratios of Fungi 157
    a. Ratios in tea - Active to total biomass 158
    b. Low Fungi 158
    c. Low Active Fungi, High Total Fungi 158
8. Equipment Design... 158
9. Brewing Configurations 159
    a. Aquarium Stones 159
    b. Brewing Time 159
10. Brewing Techniques 159
    a. Pre-composting 160
    b. Brewing Temperature 160
11. Brewing Instructions 162
12. Temperature and Organisms 163
13. Brewing Temperatures-a 164
14. Brewing Temperatures-b 165
15. Minimum or Optimum Mesh Size for Tea Bag 165
16. Mesh Size in Filters 165
17. Tradeoffs in Straining 165
18. Hyphae Build Up On Filters 165
19. Gluing Pipes 165
20. Extraction and Aeration 166
21. Aeration Pumps 166
22. Aerate Tea to Grow Huge Numbers 166
23. Difference Between Aeration and Being Aerobic 166
24. Oxygen Content 166
25. You Can't Over-Aerate 166
26. Bubbles, Oxygen and Microbes 167
27. Oxygen Concentration 167
28. Dissolved Oxygen Saturation Limits 167
29. Microbial Respiration and Dissolved Oxygen 168
30. Organism Death vs. Going to Sleep 168
31. Keep Air Blowing 168
32. Bigger Pumps 169

33. Aerator Unit Placement 169
34. Micro Bubbles 169
35. Air Filter Stones 169
36. Pipe with Simple Holes 170
37. Soaker Hoses, Cleaners and Microbes 170
38. Bad Stuff in the Pipe 170
39. Cleaning Equipment 170
40. Hydrogen Peroxide and Cleaning 170
41. Brewing Temperatures 171
42. Tea Brewing Ingredient Amounts 171
43. Maintaining Biology 172
44. Balance of Food and Aeration 173
45. Does Temperature of Tea for Various Soil Temperatures Matter? 173
46. Water Quality Issues 173
47. Chlorine and Chloramine.. 173
48. Chlorine is a Microbe Killer 173
49. Neutral pH or Water 174
50. De-Gas Water 174
51. Chlorine, Bacterial Resistance 174
52. Chloramine 174
53. Could Pathogens Slip Through? 174
54. Human Pathogen Controversy 175
55. Food Crops and E Coli 175
56. EM Ferment 175
57. Aerobic vs. Anaerobic Decomposition 176
58. Anaerobic Teas 176
59. DO Levels Dropping Down 177
60. Oxygen and Anaerobic Conditions 177
61. Rapid Microbial Growth May Cause Anaerobic Conditions 177
62. Preventing Detrimental Effects of Anaerobic Conditions 178
63. Best Way Not to Go Anaerobic 178
64. Fungi in Teas 179
65. Calculating Biomass 179
66. Food Additions after Brewing Stops 179
67. Organisms Need Tea Environment 179
68. Pathogen Survival 181
69. Human Pathogens 181
70. Getting Active Organisms in Brews 181
71. Mechanical Failure 181
72. Sludge 182
73. Bio-Film 182
74. Bio-Film and Tea Quality 182
75. Bio Film and Protection 183
76. Winter Brewing 183
77. Fish Oils 183

78. Think Biology, Not Mechanical 183
79. Stagnated Compost Went Anaerobic 184
80. Carbonization Suppresses Fungal Growth 184
81. Flow Forms 184
82. Temperature Flow Form System 184
83. Biodynamics 184
    a. Frequency Wavelength 185
    b. Stirring BD Preps 185
    c. Flow Forms are Aerator Units 185
    d. Preps Added to Teas 185
84. Yogurt-Type Organisms 185
85. Getting Good Tea 185
86. 90 Degree Turns 186
87. 90 Degree Angles... 186
88. Manufacturers are Responsible 186
89. Microscope Manual 186

Chapter VIII -- Ingredients for Actively Aerated Compost Tea 187
1. Brewing Recipes 188
2. Quantities in Brews 188
3. Different Foods Select for Different Organisms 188
4. Think Like a Microbe! 188
5. Differences in Amounts of Foods 188
6. Types of Foods 189
    a. Anaerobic Condition 189
    b. AACT Brewers 189
    c. When is AACT Ready? 189
    d. Anaerobic Processed End Products can be Toxic 190
    e. Humic Acid Testing Results 190
7. Tea Recipe 190
8. Tea Ingredients 191
9. Purpose for Ingredient Additions 191
10. Propionic Acid, Molasses, Any Simple Sugar 191
11. Carbon Sources 191
12. Sugars and Nitrogen 191
13. Bacteria and Molasses 192
14. Different Kinds of Sugars 192
15. Too Much Molasses 192
16. Molasses Concentration 192
17. Sugar Source 193
18. Sulfur 193
19. Kelp 193
20. Humic Acid in Tea 193
21. Good Compost Needed for Tea 193
22. No Fresh Manure in Compost Tea 193

23. Compost, Nutrients, and Brewing 193
24. Shelf Life and Preactivation of Compost 194
25. Compost Used in Tea Based on Purpose of Application 194
26. Diversity and Balance of Microorganisms 194
27. Increasing Fungal Growth 195
28. Fungi Need a Surface To Grow On 195
29. Beneficial Fungi 195
30. Fungi 195
     a. Anaerobic Tea 195
     b. Aerobic Tea 196
31. Grains and Fungi 196
32. Carbohydrates and Tea Brewing 196
33. Nematode Presence in Tea 197
34. Nematodes 197
35. Predatory Nematodes 198
36. Temperature and Microherds 198
37. Total Dissolved Salts 199
38. Water High in Salts 199
39. Anaerobic Waste Materials Are Killers 199
40. *Bacillus subtilis* 199
41. Live Worms in Compost Tea Sediment 199
42. Milk and Coffee and as Food Resources? 199
43. Nitrogen in an Organic Form 200
44. Guano 200
45. Fish Hydrolysate and Fish Emulsion 200
46. Bonemeal 200
47. *Beauveria* 201
48. Hay and *Protozoa* 201
49. Saponin and Ionic Associations 201
50. Aloe in Teas 202
51. Aloe 202
52. Peat Bogs 202
53. Extracted Amino Acids 205
54. Yeast 205
55. Biodynamic Preps 206
     a. Consistency in Actively Aerated Compost Tea 206
     b. Adding EM Inocula in Teas 206
56. Effective Microorganisms (EM) 207
57. EM and AACT 207
58. EM Brews and Rock Powders 207
59. *Bacteriophage* 207
60. *Mycorrhizal II* 207
61. Organic Acids and Preservatives 208
62. Organic Materials 208
63. Raccoon Scat 208

   64. Plant Tea 208
   65. Comfrey Compost Tea 208
   66. Comfrey Tea vs. Comfrey Compost Tea 209

Chapter IX Commercial Brewers 211
   1. Anaerobic Tea 212
      a. Aerobic Tea 212
      b. Buy the Manufacturer's Starting Mix 212
   2. Tests and Posted Data 212
   3. Easy To Clean 213
   4. Tea Brewing Equipment Manufacturers 213
   5. Inadequate Brewing Equipment 214
   6. Back-up Claims with Data 216
   7. Buying a Brewer 216
      a. First Step 216
      b. Second Step 216
      d. Fourth Step... 216
      e. Kind of Pump 216
      f. Ease in Cleaning 216
      g. Surfaces to Clean 217
      h. The Compost Container 217
      i. Bubble size 217
   8. Problems With Some Machines 217
      a. Inside of the Machine Needs to be Clean 217
      b. Checking the Water Source is Important 217
      c. If a Little Food Resource is Good, More is Better.... 217
   9. Soaker Hoses From Petroleum Products 217
  10. Break-down Products Pretty Toxic 218
  11. Why Buy a Commercial Machine? 218
  12. Tea Makers Compost and Nutrient Mixes 219
  13. The Point Is To Make Good Tea! 219

Chapter X -- Compost and Worm Castings 221
   1. Compost Gets Calcium in Soil 222
   2. Worms in Compost 222
   3. Human Pathogens in Compost 222
   4. Compost Has The Diversity Needed 222
   5. Worm Compost, The Better Choice 223
   6. Grey Gritty Liter 223
   7. Time versus Money 223
   8. Mulch and Vermicompost 223
   9. Green Foods 224
  10. Microbial Biomass in Manure 224
  11. Worms and Pathogens 224
  12. Worm Manure 225
  13. Dead Insect and Pathogens in Compost 225

14. Nematode Types ……………………………………………… 225
15. What Type of Fungi is It? ………………………………… 225
16. Ergot Fungi are Fungi ……………………………………… 226
17. Animal Droppings in Compost Piles? …………………… 226
18. Evaluation of Landscape Soils and Compost Materials …………………… 226
19. Compost Breakdown ……………………………………… 229
20. Resuscitating Compost …………………………………… 229
21. Composting ………………………………………………… 229
22. Molds and Fungi? ………………………………………… 230
23. Pathogens and Regrowing ……………………………… 230
24. Compost Temperature …………………………………… 230
25. Compost Moisture ………………………………………… 230
26. Eucalyptus-a ……………………………………………… 230
27. Significant Carbon in Biosolids ………………………… 232
28. Beneficials in Composting Process ……………………… 232
29. Diversity is Critical ……………………………………… 232
30. Pay for Beneficials, Not for Problems ………………… 232
31. Keep Compost Aerobic …………………………………… 232
32. Eucalyptus-b ……………………………………………… 232
33. Nematodes are Transparent …………………………… 232
     a. Nematodes are Microorganisms ………………… 232
     b. Nematodes Come in Four Functional Groups ………………… 232
     c. Bacterial Feeding Nematodes ………………… 233
34. Worms in South Africa …………………………………… 233
     a. No Worms in Organic Fertilized Areas ………………… 233
     b. Stinky Organic Matter is Not Compost! ………………… 235
35. Sell Compost to Growers ………………………………… 235
36. Compost Quality …………………………………………… 235
37. Temperature for Organisms ……………………………… 235
38. Biosolids …………………………………………………… 237
39. Inhibitory Compounds and Mushroom Compost ……… 237
40. Compost Processing ……………………………………… 238
41. Raccoon Manure …………………………………………… 239
42. Forms of Chitin …………………………………………… 240
43. Bacteria and Fungi Groups ……………………………… 240
44. Hay and *Protozoa* ……………………………………… 240
45. Compost Smell …………………………………………… 241
46. Molds, *Mycellium*, Fungi ……………………………… 241
47. Nematodes ………………………………………………… 242
48. EM, Bokashi, Chloroform Fumigation ………………… 242
     a. Fish Hydrolysate ………………………………… 243
     b. A Little EM ……………………………………… 243
     c. Chloroform Fumigation ………………………… 243
49. Balancing Nutrients ……………………………………… 244
50. Mushrooms ………………………………………………… 244

      a. *Mushrooms in Forests* 244
      b. *Mushrooms in Grasslands* 245
51. Hair, Feathers, Fungal Hyphae Enhance Keratinase 245
52. Urea 245
53. Worm Composting 246
54. Fungi Appearance 246
      a. *Fungi Are Most Likely Not in Most Soils* 246
55. Types of Pathogens in Compost 246
56. Compost Ingredients 246
57. Making Compost 247
58. So, as Fungal a Compost, or Compost Tea as Possible, is Needed 247
59. Temperature Affects Worms 247
60. Worms and Lettuce, Nitrogen Gas, Chlorine 247
      a. *High Temperature* 247

Chapter XI -- Testing and Field Trials 249
  1. Compost Tea Standards 250
  2. Biomass Levels Relative to Plant Growth 250
  3. Testing Tea 250
  4. Testing Each Batch of Tea 251
  5. Testing for Good Sets of Organisms 251
  6. Tea Definitions 251
      a. *Poor Tea* 251
      b. *Adequate Tea* 252
      c. *Very Good Tea* 252
      d. *Excellent Tea* 252
  7. Qualitative Assessment 252
  8. Organisms in Soil, Compost, Water or Tea 253
      a. *Comparing Numbers of Bacteria with Numbers of Fungi is Nonsensical*... 253
      b. *Comparing Biomass Makes Much More Sense* 253
      c. *Protozoa are Reported in Numbers of Individuals per Gram or Milliliter* 253
      d. *N is for Nematodes* 253
      e. *Desired Ranges* 253
  9. Testing Methods 254
10. Numbers of Individuals in Soil 254
      a. *Colony Forming Units* 254
      b. *Plate Count Approaches* 254
      c. *Numbers versus Biomass* 255
      d. *Field Soil* 255
11. Plate Count vs. Direct Count 256
      a. *Plate Count vs. SFI Method* 256
12. Assessing Compost Tea Quality 258

       a. *Plate Counts* 258
       b. *Bio-Log Determinations* 258
13. Plate Methods vs. Molecular Methods 259
       a. *Plate Methods* 259
       b. *Molecular Methods* 259
14. Microscope Methods 259
15. General Biological Practices 259
       a. *Test an Area* 259
       b. *Step one* 259
       c. *Step two* 260
       d. *Step three* 260
       e. *Analyzing the Chemical Data* 260
       f. *Step four* 261
       g. *General Recommendations* 261
           1) *fish hydrolysate* 261
           2) *kelp* 261
           3) *soft rock* 262
           4) *compost* 262
       h. *Standards* 263
       i. *Brewing Equipment* 263
       j. *Black Spot* 263
       k. *Conclusion* 263
16. Plate Counts Shortcomings 264
       a. *Here's an Example for You* 264
       b. *Make Sure Tea stays Aerobic* 264
       c. *Molecular Probe Testing* 264
17. Leaf Organism Assay 265
       a. *SFI Technician Wrote* 265
       b. *Elaine's further explanation* 265
18. *E. Coli* Testing 265
19. Bio-Log Samples 266
20. Testing Tea for the Home Brewer 266
21. Epi-Flourescent Microscope 266
22. Assessing Tea 266
23. Assessing Activity 267
24. Ecoli Testing 268
25. Fecal E Coli Tests 268
26. Pathogen-Free vs. Below Detection Level 268
27. *Actinobacteria (actinomycetes)* 269
28. Formazan for Dehydragenase Enzyme Test 269
29. Electrical Conductivity 270
30. Organisms in Soil 270
       a. *Chloroform Fumigation and Plate Counts* 270
31. Labs and Back-up 271
32. SFI Testing Methods 271

      a. Numbers Provide Evidence 272
      b. SFI Does Not Culture Organisms 272
      c. Most Organisms in Soil, Compost or Compost Tea Cannot be Cultured ... 272
      d. Activity Stain Determines Active Biomass 273
      e. Soil Health May Take Years 273
      f. Testing to Improve Plant Growth 273
33. Tea in Fall 273
      a. Northern Hemisphere 273
      b. Southern Hemisphere 274
      c. How to Test Tea 274
34. Pathogen Interaction Trials 274
35. Pathogen Testing 275
36. Publishable Data 275
37. Testing Particulate Settled Matter 275
38. Testing for Human Pathogens 275
39. 20% Coefficient of Variation 276
40. 5% Molasses Test 276
41. Biovolume Calculation, Not Weighed 277
42. Three Conditions for E.Coli To Be Present 277
43. DNA and Molecular Analysis 277
44. DNA Analysis 277
      a. DNA Analysis Parameters 277
      b. Plate Counts for a Specific Species 278
      c. Molecular Methods 278
45. Diverse Microbial Communities 278
46. Bulk Densities of Organisms 279
      a. Fungi 279
      b. Protozoa Values 280
47. Sampling 280
      a. Organisms in Tea 280
      b. pH 280
      c. Organic Matter 280
      d. Root- Depth 280
      e. Soil Structure 280
      f. Soil Depth 280
48. Representative Test 280
49. Testing Scrutinized 281
      a. Live organisms tests 281
      b. CT Scrutiny 281
50. Pathogens and Sugars 281
51. Academic Mind Set 281
      a. Transformation not Transmutation 282
      b. Government Funded Testing Needed 282
52. Active and Total Organisms 283
53. Anaerobic Brews 283

54. Training for Starting an SFI Lab 284

Chapter XII – Sample Templates for Replicated Trials 285
   1. Basic Information Needed for Replicated Trials 287
   2. Potted Plants Template 288
   3. Row Crops Template 289

Chapter XI11 – Dr. Elaine Ingham's Profile 291

Chapter XIV – Dr. Elaine Ingham's Publications 297

Chapter XV – References 305

Chapter I

INTRODUCTION

To
Actively Aerated
Compost Tea

INTRODUCTION

1. Sustainable System 1/3/04 8:52 AM

Most people mean by sustainable, a situation where as-much-as-possible, the materials to grow plants and keep the people on that land alive come from the land, and specifically from the land owned by the farmer. Most people mean by sustainable that toxic chemicals are used to the least degree possible. That means pesticides and herbicides are not used, except as last-ditch methods to save a crop. Use of toxic materials to routinely control disease and pests is not considered sustainable.

2. Regenerative Agriculture 7/22/05

But sustainable is a word that has been abused terribly in the last decade. Life can be sustained at very low levels, in intolerable conditions. If we take degraded agricultural lands, and merely sustain what is there, we have not solved the problems we have. We will continue to have to use toxic chemicals to sustain even the poor agriculture we have. So instead, what we really need is a whole new concept.

Let us discuss regenerative agriculture. At the Byron Bay Compost Tea Party held in June, 2005 at Regenesis Farm, we coined this term to mean agriculture that built soil, increased organic matter and nutrient status in soil to optimal levels, and resulted in nutrients in plants in the proper form and amounts to sustain human and animal life without resorting to toxic chemicals or supplements. That's the agriculture that is needed, and it is way beyond sustainable. We have repairs to do, before we can think about just sustaining our lands.

3. The Ebb and Flow of Nutrient Cycles 1/3/04 8:52 AM

Be aware of the ebb and flow of your nutrient cycles, or you can't be sustainable. Fukuoka was right, for the system he described. It is just that his particular examples do not work everywhere around the world. He didn't mean them to be, but people take his example as "THE WAY". The concept presented was entirely possible; his examples were good. He recognized the need for human comforts, outside bare meeting of food-needs. But you need a paradigm, a mental framework and understanding, to allow you to transfer what was done there to what needs doing on your land. Hopefully, as we keep incorporating more aspects into our understanding of the biology and chemistry of the soil, we fully realize that paradigm, and enable rapid recovery of not-healthy soil back to a sustainable condition, relative to the plants you want to grow.

4. Conversion to Healthier 11/15/03 8:46 PM

Nutrient cycling is something soil does just fine, all by itself, if you don't destroy the foodweb. Water retention increases, and roots grow deeper into healthy soil with the right biology to prevent compaction. Simple, but you have to remember, it takes more than just bacteria. Not only bacteria, but also fungi, protozoa, nematodes, mycorrhizal fungi and microarthropods. They are ALL required for a healthy foodweb to happen. And they all respire carbon dioxide. So how can you possibly use CO_2 to tell you which set of organisms is present and doing their job. Maybe $CO2$ could be a general measure of whether thing are respiring in the soil, but not to determine if you have the mix of organisms you need in the soil. All of the predators are aerobic organisms. You cannot achieve healthy soil with anaerobic bacteria alone! And the conversion to healthier happens rapidly. If you don't see the conversion happening (green plants without fertilizer additions, and reduced need for water) within the first year, suspect a serious residue of toxic chemicals in your soil. It is the biology, which will decompose those toxics, but you have to figure out what biology is needed first.

5. Biology and Nutrients 1/20/04 11:35 AM

Getting soil biology right for your plants lets all that happen. We've done it, so we know it's possible and "done it" in your part of the world, so we have experience there. Of course, hand-in-hand with biology, we need to make sure you have the nutrients in the soil (they may have leached out or been gassed off during abusive chemical treatment of the soil, so calcium, manganese, zinc, iron, and other nutrients may actually have to be added, even in a very young soil parent material). If you test one typical garden for nutrients left after the typical chemical approach, you get a good handle on where everyone is with their garden.

6. Life In Your Soil 10/20/03 6:48 AM

Question: So, given that there appears to be plenty of fungal activity all around us, what am I trying to accomplish with fungal teas? I know that they're really important for protecting leaf surfaces from colonization by The Bad Guys, but what am I trying to accomplish with soil drenches? If there are already fungi in the soil, seems to me that I just have to keep feeding them via compost and soil amendments like kelp, rock dust, etc. Is this right?
Answer: That's right - once you have lured the fungi into your garden soil, you just have to feed them. The point of soil drench teas is to get the whole mix of organisms: fungi, protozoa, and beneficial nematodes, to move into your soil. The teas also have some foods to feed those organisms. Compost and plant residues are longer-term food resources for these organisms, so if you have good compost, and plant residues, use those too. Many places don't have your great growing conditions, so they have to use the soil drenches to build the soil life and the foods to feed soil life. To make sure you have the life in your soil in the right balance, you might want to test your soil to make sure everyone is home. Now is a good time to check.

7. Controlling Diseases and Pests in a Sustainable System 1/3/04 8:52 AM

Question: So how do you control diseases and pests in a sustainable system?
Answer: The existing biology. You have to make the habitat in your soil support the beneficial organisms, which combat, inhibit, out-compete, prevent the bad guys from having or finding a habitat in which they can grow, relative to the plants you want to grow. If you are trying to grow cranberry, you are going to make the habitat support a certain set of organisms in the soil that would never work for corn, or tomato, or..... whatever garden vegetable you want. Cranberry is adapted to waterlogged, at times anaerobic,, conditions in the soil. Set the stage for highly productive cranberry by making the soil exactly what cranberry needs. Get rid of serious weed problems by recognizing what the weed needs to germinate and grow, and make sure those conditions are NOT met. Being sustainable means recognizing these factors. But when nature sends a whammy, as in a drought, a flood, torrential downpours, you have to respond to get the soil

life back to what your plants need. A truly healthy soil can tolerate a great deal of abuse before being forced off-target. But nature can send conditions that move that soil away from the healthy condition for your plants.

Question: Recognizing what needs to be done to move the soil back to the healthy condition is what we are working on now. So, can this be done?
Answer: Yes. We did a survey at SFI of our clients. Anyone working with us is going to be trying to get back to a healthy soil condition, which is, by definition, moving to sustainable. Pesticides are not things that can be included in building healthy soil. We asked some of our clients why they weren't sending in soil samples to be assessed. Of the approximately 60 clients we contacted, about 25% said, "We don't need to send soil samples in, because we have achieved the no-pesticide and no-fertilizer result that SFI talks about. We've achieved healthy soil". We, of course, suggested that they might want to check their soil on occasion, maybe once a year, just as a health check-up. You go to the doctor for routine health check-ups, your soil probably needs it, too.

Question: But, the question was put in a previous question, can you achieve sustainability?
Answer: Well, we can achieve healthy soil. It's a goal that can be achieved. We can document that we have achieved it. The determinant of whether you reached your goal is no more pesticide or inorganic fertilizer use. We can predict that condition by monitoring the biology in your soil.

Question; Healthy soil is MAINTAINED through making compost from your own plant material, from the human manure produced on-site (most people are eating foods from not-on-farm, so there is an import of nutrients there. Enough to replace export of nutrients in off-farm plant sales?
Answer: Hum….. The out- and in-flows have to be balanced. To be sustainable, you have to understand nutrient cycles. If you buy a farm where the soils lost nutrients through leaching, and the soil is compacted, you have to re-build soil structure, put the nutrients back into the soil, along with, and at the same time as, the biology to hold the nutrients for you once you add them. You can be sustainable, as long as you pay attention to the export of nutrients from your farm, and balance the out-go with in inputs from off-farm. If you are going to be a part of modern society, you will remove nutrients and sell them off-farm. That means I have to bring nutrients from off-farm and put them back into my soil, hold them with the biology, and be sustainable. I can fix nitrogen on-land, no problem. But I can't fix calcium, or boron, or manganese from the atmosphere. I have to get compost from off-site to balance those out-flows. This is perhaps a broader picture of sustainable than being barely sustainable. I don't think life is sustainable without a few human comforts. Darn, but I'm not living without a refrigerator, a hot water heater and a computer. I have imported metal, coolant, electricity, and the internet. I have to export enough stored energy in the form of plant material to balance those inputs. I have to bring back enough mineral nutrients to balance the minerals sold off my land in the form of plant material so I could have the money to buy my comforts. I need to get the exported nutrients back, so I have to sell more plant stored energy…… which means I need to bring more nutrients back in.

8. Definition of Sustainable 1/3/04 8:52 AM
We work with farms that are pretty much sustainable farms in various places around the world. How sustainable they actually are depends on…..your definition of sustainable. No one exists as

islands unto themselves on this planet. If nothing else, air pollution affects everyone. You can't avoid it. Sorry, not even the Amazon or Antarctica are free from air pollution anymore. The gases your plants use to fix sunlight energy and carbon dioxide into energy-storage carbon compounds inside the plant comes from off-site. You are stuck with the mineral nutrients that your soil has. Geology determined the original parent material, and succession has determined the organic matter built up in your soil. You may need to fix a lack of nutrients if you got stuck with poor soil. If conventional agriculture has gone on in your soil previously, soil nutrients were mined out, sold as plant produce, or lost to erosion and leaching and volatilization. So, when trying to resuscitate that land, the nutrients have to be put back into that soil. The fast way to fix this nutrient problem is to buy the nutrients that are lacking (you have to do a soil chemistry test to figure this out).

Question: For example, if calcium is needed, you buy calcium in some form (as lime, for example) but then that's not sustainable, is it?
Answer: You bought something from off-farm to put back into the soil.

Question: To hold onto the soil calcium, you have to get the fungal biomass going again. Where do beneficial fungi come from?
Answer: They don't just "arrive". Especially with the fungicides that are being poured on the land in today's AG world.

Question: Where would beneficial fungi come from in your neighborhood?
Answer: Think about it for a minute. Where is that inoculum coming from? Anything treated with a pesticide has lost a significant portion of the fungal community. Anything treated with normal-for-today levels of inorganic fertilizer has lost the beneficial fungi. No wonder you get stuck having to use fungicides. Don't let your mineral nutrients leach again – you have to get the fungi back. You must find a source of good fungi and get them, and bacteria, protozoa and beneficial nematodes and microarthropods going in your soil again.

Question: You can use a slower (more sustainable?) way, by buying compost from off-site, and using plant organic material and the biology that comes with the compost to put back the lost nutrients. And the biology. But is that sustainable?
Answer: The compost is from off-site. But you have to put back into the soil the nutrients and biology that are no longer there.

Question: Is it "fair" to expect someone to suffer poor plant production until they can resuscitate soil that someone else destroyed, because we want to have rules about what is or is not sustainable? Or is it "allowed" to let people do some non-sustainable resuscitation until the soil is back in decent form?
Answer: You could try to let plants grow their roots down deep into the soil, and lift the nutrients from deeper in the soil.

Question: But how long does it take to pull up the minerals needed?
Answer: But the roots won't grow down if the soil is severely compacted from conventional agricultural practices. If the soil is compacted at 6, or 12, or 18 inches (and sometimes there are separate compaction layers at EACH of those depths), roots will not grow through those layers to

get to soil where the nutrients have leached. Sometimes the nutrients are completely gone from the soil, because they reached groundwater, and have been moved downstream. When you see algal or cyanobacterial blooms in surface water, that's a result of the nutrients being leached from the land, into the water, and those nutrients are gone from the land.

Question: You have to grow roots past the water table in order to pull nutrients from deeper layers. How long will that take?
Answer: If the soil is compacted, you can't get the roots to those deeper nutrients. So, we have to let growers have a time to fix these problems before demanding totally sustainable practices. The grower has to stay alive as well, for something to be sustainable.

9. Chemical versus Sustainable Approach   1/3/04 11:42 AM
The recommendations you talk about come from people who deal with soil on the totally chemical end of the spectrum. If you have no biology in your soil, then those recommendations are what you have to do. But it is not a sustainable approach, because you will, every year, be stuck doing more chemistry.

Question: At ACRES this year, there was person saying that they have done what University of California has recommended every year for the last 13 years, and this year, again, the recommendation from his advisor was, just like every other year, "Apply 4 tons of lime per acre, 200 pounds of ammonium sulfate, some pounds of boron, etc......" The grower's question was, when does he get out of this trap? He has been applying this much lime, this much nitrogen, this much of some other set of chemicals, every year for the last 13 years. When does the drain on his checkbook stop?
Answer: The answer: Never. Chemical sales people don't want their cash cows to dry up. Biology will not return to a soil where you are killing the organisms through salt applications. And all those things in the recommendation you got are salts. Those salts ALL kill some portion of the biology, to varying degrees. Now, don't get me wrong, you have to put the nutrient elements back into the soil. But putting them in as salts is not going to fix the problem. Instead, do as Arden Anderson is showing us how to do. Get the nutrients into the compost; into the compost tea. In compost and in tea you give the biology high amounts of foods, so that they can incorporate the salts without getting killed.

a. Calcium Salts Insane
You could add calcium salts to soil, but then you'd have to be putting 200 gallons fish and 200 gallons of molasses per acre, along with the salts. Insane. Don't do it that way.

b. Salts with Foods for Biology
Salts of any kind should be incorporated WITH foods to feed the biology, making sure the correct biology is present. Salts dis-associate in water, and the nutrients are taken up and immobilized by the organisms, which make soil organic matter. The predators in the soil cycle the nutrients into plant available form, but mostly JUST in the root zone. Leaching losses do not then occur to any significant extent. Next year, you don't need to put in near as much nutrient, because you haven't lost the nutrients from last year. When adding inorganic salts into compost, you don't put in NEAR the amount of salt as you would need to add to the soil. When you add salts directly to the soil,

you have to add in a high amount, because you end up losing most of what you add. When you lack biology in the soil, there is nothing to hold the nutrient, and what the plant doesn't take up immediately leaches out of the soil. In some instances, when you add a nutrient like phosphate, or phosphorus, the existing chemistry in the soil ties that material up in plant not available, in not-going-to-benefit soil structure forms that you might as well not have bothered. Waste of time and money.

Question: OK, unless you have the biology needed to mineralize that chemically immobilized nutrient. Except you just added salt, or strong acid, to get the chemical immobilization. So, do you now have biology functioning to get the immobilized nutrient mineralized?
Answer: Nope. Now, certain approaches to dealing with lack of calcium in soil take the approach the you should add sulfur to release magnesium from the clay, so you don't have to add 4 tons of lime. Adding 4 tons of lime is expensive.

Question: But, do you really want to remove nutrients from your soil in order to improve the APPARENT concentration of calcium?
Answer: Wouldn't it be wiser to add back in the missing nutrient? Don't deplete nutrients from your soil. Don't leach something out that you are going to have to add back in sooner or later. What a poor way to fix a problem! So, add calcium. But not as tons of lime. One possible approach that homeowners like: add eggshells, about 50 pounds of eggshell per ton of compost, and then apply about a half-ton per acre of that compost. It seems to give the same plant benefit as applying 3 tons of lime per acre.

Question: Not enough eggshells?
Answer: Then use 100 pounds of calcium carbonate per 900 pounds of compost. Use a half-ton of that compost per acre, and it equals the 3 tons of lime application. Arden Anderson has data that shows adding the lime at the beginning of the composting process OR near the end works just as well, as long as you give the organisms in the compost about a week to do the immobilization. Add humic acids to help them tie things up ASAP, without negative impacts as the result of salt addition. Willikers!

Question: Will save you money?
Answer: A half ton of compost, properly made, with the added calcium, instead of 3 tons of lime out on the field, which will kill the biology you have worked so hard to improve. Is this a Duh!?

Question: Why so much less calcium needed in the compost system?
Answer: Because we KNOW you will lose about 95% of the calcium you add as lime. So, when adding a salt, in order to get any benefit, you have to add TONS of lime. What a waste!

Question: Why do you think we have the water quality problems we do? Where are all those nutrients coming from? Tons and tons of fertilizer and nutrients are poured on the soil every year? Were those nutrients exported in the plant material you sold?
Answer: Nope. So, where'd they go? If they were still there, in your soil, you wouldn't need to apply more this year, would you? I try not to get depressed when I think about what we've been doing to all the critters I care about for all these years.

Question: So, you've been advised to do inappropriate things. What do you do instead? We've been advised to apply 100# of elemental sulfur to our vineyard and crop fields.

Answer: Ask the person giving this recommendation where the data are that this sulfur is going to help anything. If the hypothesis is that this sulfur will knock Mg off the clays, and thus the ratio of Ca:Mg will be improved, you are now making $MgSO_4$.

Question: What does the $MgSO_4$ do to the plants?

Answer: $MgSO_4$ is a soil "softener"? No, calcium flocculates the soil. There's a "battle" if you will between Ca building good spaces between clays, and Mg flattening space between the clays. You need both. Remove Mg in order to improve the ratio, and you've depleted your soil of Mg. When you finally get Mg reduced low enough to make the Ca:Mg ratio ok, you now will have to add Mg. Just think this one through for a minute.

Question: How do you ever get off the chemical treadmill?

Answer: ADD calcium instead. Consider what 100 pounds of elemental sulfur will do to the biology LONG before the sulfur knocks Mg off the clays. It will kill a herd of beneficial fungi, and some pathogens too, in the soil. But you are going backwards faster than you are getting a benefit. You are playing chemistry, but it is biology that builds soil from sand, silt and clay.

Question: Also zinc sulfate and copper sulfate at lesser rates. Our soils are high in magnesium and the cal/mag ratio is not in balance. I believe the theory is that the sulfur will attach to the magnesium and dissipate, resulting in a looser soil that is relatively higher in Calcium.

Answer: Zinc sulfate is also a salt. More killing. Add copper sulfate, and there is even more killing. Anything over 3 ppm copper, and you are killing beneficial organisms in the soil. Just try to keep diseases out of your roots. If you need sulfur, add it as organic matter, which contains sulfur. The biology will make that sulfur available to your plants, and work to establish an equilibrium with Mg on the clay surfaces. Using S to remove Mg is much like the case when I say the ratio to fungi to bacteria is too low, which means there is too high bacteria compared to fungi. So people try to "solve" that problem by killing the "excess" bacteria. Whoa! No! If fungi are too low, you add fungal inocula and/or fungal foods. Kill the bacteria to get the ratio right? There's a backward attitude. Now you not only have to improve fungi, but you will have to do something to get the bacteria back. Remove your Mg by leaching as $MgSO_4$, and you will have to put Mg back into the soil. If you need to add calcium, add calcium. But do it in a way that will not mean death to the biology you have.

Question: Are you saying that more biology will bring the magnesium and calcium into balance? If so, how would this work?

Answer: The way to do this is to add calcium to the compost. You have to have calcium, but the way to incorporate it is in the biology. That way you don't leach the elements you add. You add the biology that will hold what you have and prevent further losses. I get tired of people who don't want to add soil biology into their understanding. I suspect the lab you sent your soil chemistry analysis to was one of those I asked if they would want to work together to include soil chemistry and soil biology in one package. Their response was that they would be happy to send me their soil chemistry analysis without their interpretation on it, so I could do it myself. That "don't bother us" attitude does not advance our understanding of how biology and chemistry work together. It does not give the grower the knowledge needed to stop paying so much to grow crops.

10. Building a Habitat for Beneficials 1/2/04 12:12 AM

"If you build it, they will come." It's what we are doing when we maintain aeration above 6 ppm in a cost tea. when we add good foods for fungi, or bacteria. When we make sure the temperature is in a good range to grow fungi and bacteria in a 24 hour period, we are building the habitat correctly to allow the beneficials to have the best chance to live in the house. The good guys need oxygen. They need food. As Arden Anderson likes to point out, oxygen, water, food and comfort is what makes the habitat correct. Think about how long you can live without air. Same with the beneficial microorganisms in soil, compost or compost tea. Just as people can only live a few minutes without oxygen, oxygen is the most critical with respect to that fact that you can't live long without it. When it is gone, the habitat rapidly changes, and thus the organisms living there will rapidly change. Water is second on this list. You can go without water for a couple days. Beneficials will go to sleep within only slightly longer time periods as compared to oxygen when the moisture level moves off target. Then consider food.

Question: How long can you go without food?
Answer: A few weeks. So in terms of a critical factor for surviving, food isn't as important as air or water. But as a factor that selects for growth and reproduction, it is very important. Build the habitat correctly and the beneficial organisms will move right in, if they are around. Unfortunately in most soils, we have killed most of the beneficials that should move in. So, compost and compost tea provide the organisms to move into the habitats we start to build by adding the foods in the compost and compost tea or cover crops. We all know that anaerobic conditions kill plant roots, that compaction results in anaerobic conditions, which will result in plant root death, and thus plant death, through a number of possible mechanisms. Anaerobic conditions result in volatilization of N, P, S, and a number of bad-news-for-your-plant organic acids.

Question: So, why would you want to make and apply a compost tea that went anaerobic?
Answer; You will not benefit biology in the soil if you add anaerobic bacteria to your soil. Things will move backwards.

Question: Even if anaerobic teas kill a few pathogens, why push the rest of the system backwards, when if you use an aerobic tea, all plant surfaces will have improved protection?
Answer: As well as all the other benefits I talk about being possible. There is more to biology than disease suppression. Please hold that in mind when explaining compost tea. Actively aerobic compost tea is way beyond just protecting leaf surfaces from black spot being able to find a foothold.

11. General Biological Practices 1/20/04 11:35 AM

a. Small Gardeners vs. Large-Scale Commercial Growers
Most small gardeners don't need to consider all the complex issues that large-scale, commercial growers need to be concerned about. Consultants, as well, have to worry about making sure their advice is the best there is, and when we can drop water use between 30% to 75% in the first crop

after improving soil biology, it can be critical to get the biology right. If you don't get the biology back into the soil, and get it right for the plant you want to grow, you may not get the benefits you desire. I tend to want to get people there ASAP, and in the commercial world, it is critical to get people there ASAP. So, getting things right in the compost and the tea is critical - and we get picky about having things "right".

But that is different for most back-yard gardeners since they would just like to see the seeds germinate, grow, be pretty, and have a good crop. Not quite as "tootsies to the fire" as commercial growers. Back-yard gardeners aren't going to lose their house and yard if they don't make top-yields. Commercial growers will, and so we get very into-the-details when we work with those folks. It is still important to get as many of the benefits to your small scale growers as possible, however. Reduce their water use, reduce (and most likely completely eliminate) pesticides and inorganic fertilizer use (and therefore reduce costs as well as toxic material), improve soil structure so roots go deeper, and survive the summer dry period without watering, or requiring a whole bunch of fussing.

12. Disturbing Soil 1/16/04 1:34 PM
Consider that when we till soil (plow, rototill, disc, whatever word you want to use, when you disturb soil), fungi are more negatively impacted than bacteria. Good guy protozoa are more impacted than fungi. The beneficial nematodes are even more impacted (but not the root-feeders, they are small nematodes), and the microarthropods (which are the fungal-feeders which keep the fungi in line) are the MOST impacted. When we disturb soil, we lose the beneficial fungi and fungal-feeder part of the foodweb. So, most often, what has to be put back is the fungal part of the system. When you till, you lose the fungi and the things that fungi feed on. So, even though most lawn grasses are on the slightly bacterial side, you still need to replace the fungi and the bigger critters.

13. Live Organisms 2/21/04 2:31 AM

Question: I am a VISTA volunteer doing some research for my project. I am not at all scientific, but I am fairly intelligent. I have just finished reading The Compost Tea Brewing Manual. Am I correct in understanding that compost tea has live organisms in it and so cannot be bottled and stored?
Answer: Compost tea has live organisms in it, and these organisms cannot be stored, or the tea will lose its efficacy for many of the benefits I talk about. Bottle active tea, and the bottle will blow up. Put the tea to sleep, and while you lose species diversity, you can then store it.

Question: I would also like to know how compost tea and worm tea are the same and how they are different.
Answer: Many people mean worm compost EXTRACT and not true tea, when they SAY worm tea. TEA is brewed for a period of time. Extract is not.

14. OMRI Approval 2/1/04 6:46 PM
OMRI approval does not mean anything with respect to impact on organisms. After all, OMRI approves copper sulfate, and that is a pesticide. It does a great job of killing bacteria and fungi. To

learn if something will kill the organisms in the tea, you need to make a tea, and do a test on that - say just the ACTIVE bacteria and ACTIVE fungi. Then, add the product to SOME of the tea, and send in that sample again, assessing for active bacteria and active fungi. You could do protozoa on both samples, also, to see what effect the material had on the protozoa. Then you would know for certain if it hurt, was neutral, or helped the biology.

15. Product Claims Must be Documented   12/17/03 10:28 PM

It is a good idea to be wary of products that just say they are biological stimulants, without any data to back up that claim. Any product that claims they make nutrients appear from nothing should also be scrutinized closely. It just isn't possible. Organisms in soil can solubilize, or mineralize, the non-plant available nutrients and make them plant available, but there needs to be some data to show this is happening in order to document the claim. If you want to go to my website, I have something approaching 100 references in peer reviewed, scientific journals, books and articles to show that what I talk about with respect to the benefit possible from the right biology is the case. But you have to document that your soil has the right biology in order to KNOW that what I talk about is happening in your soil, or compost or tea.

We are in the position of moving the work we have done into practical field applications. The Soil Ecology Society has over 300 scientists working on these kinds of projects. Their journal is Applied Soil Ecology. Get the journal to see the constant information coming out that documents lab testing of the kinds of things I talk about, and some field work as well. Biology and Fertility of Soils is another good journal, as well as Soil Biology and Biochemistry. So, products HAVE to show that they have the right biology, and they need solid documentation of benefit to plant growth. I think we've done enough research to show that if the biology is present in the soil, then plant production will be befitted, through one or more of the mechanisms discussed previously. Solid science is needed. If you are going to spend your money, you need to have information that shows what the product does to the biology, and therefore, to improve the potential benefits. I think I harp on this a great deal. Data are necessary. If you can't get data showing comparison of the product with a control (conventional) field from the company selling you that product, don't buy the product.

16. Patent Protection   10/18/03 9:19 AM

We need people willing to spend the money to patent things, and then let the rest of us be able to use those processes without fear of reprisal from some larger company. The patent holder does get the commercial right to extol the process, and we have to recognize that we can't infringe on that commercial right. Advertising is everything in our current western culture. The claims you make are what will get you in trouble. And be very aware of that when selling compost or tea. No statements about tea will suppress disease. Tea can protect surfaces. Tea can put back organisms on the leaf surface and the plant will then feed the proper organisms and the disease organisms will have nothing to eat. Tea will put the "cats" back onto the plant surfaces, so the "mice" can be reduced to non-pest levels. Read protozoa and nematodes for plant surface "cats", and disease-organisms as "mice". The EPA and USDA don't register cats as biocontrol agents. Dogs don't have to be registered. Yogurt hasn't been required to be labeled as a digestive-system biocontrol agent, but that's what it does. It does much the same thing for your digestive system that compost tea does for plant surfaces. Just be careful about what you say and how you say it.

17. Saved a Plantation from Bankruptcy 2/28/04
Amazing results from OZ and NZ! We saved a plantation from bankruptcy by showing the grower how to get biology back in the soil.

18. Scientific Soil Food Web Literature 5/6/04 8:07 PM
Any clue on where to obtain the "Web of Life" by John Storer? I'm sure you have read Sir Albert Howard's book on compost, and Lady Eve Balforth's books on soil and compost. They pretty much knew, without the solid scientific data, what I talk about. Steiner and Pfeiffer had a really good idea that the critters were there; they just couldn't count them the way the microscopes we have allow us to do. If you do some reading in the scientific literature in the 1930's, you can see that the work I have continued, which grew out of David Coleman and Don Klein's programs at Colorado State University, was being done in the 1920's and 1930's. And then fertilizers and pesticides happened, and within four to five years, all funding for work looking at biology in soil stopped. The last 50 to 60 years will be regarded as a horrible, odd, insane time in the annuals of human history -- the time during which humans did their best to make sure humanity would not survive. Scary part is, we aren't really out of the woods yet. Global climate change is happening, but our government is still ignoring the fact. Oh well, there are some things you just can't allow yourself to think about too much. We all just do what we can, when we can, and hope for the best

19. Definition of AACT 11/16/03 8:35 AM
AACT stands for Actively Aerated Compost Tea. This is to differentiate it from teas that go anaerobic during the tea brewing process, and thus have highly variable metabolic products present, and quite questionable, biology.

20. History of Compost Tea 11/25/03 7:45 AM
I started looking at compost tea in 1978, and really only had funding to study it since 1990 or there about. Compost tea has been around since the Roman Empire in various guises. People have used and applied tea with variable results all through the history of agriculture. That's the problem - the methods of production were so random that the end results were not reproducible. What is new and different NOW is the use of science to try to understand compost tea. We have carved off a section of the methods used to make compost tea, and started to become consistent.

a. Actively Aerated Compost Tea
Actively aerated compost tea gives you the same product, within certain parameters, time after time. You need to make sure the compost has the organisms needed, that the foods you give them feed the good guys, that aeration maintains aerobic conditions, and temperature remains in the range where the organisms will grow. Mixing is important as well.

b. Organisms Like Tiny Little Pilgrims
You have to make sure the way you apply the organisms doesn't kill them too. A little extra food as they are sent out and establish homes on your leaf or root surfaces helps a lot too. Think of your organisms in the tea as tiny little Pilgrims on their way to the New World. Help them out as much as you can, but not too much, or they won't be able to survive in that new world on the leaf surface.

You want them to be tough enough to survive (no luxury items going with them), but they need some basic survival gear in order to make the trip, and survive at the other end.

18. The Scientific Method 11/24/03 9:05 PM
The scientific method is:

1. Observation
2. Formation of an hypothesis based on those observations
3. Testing that hypothesis
4. Using observation from that testing to re-formulate the hypothesis over and over again until the hypothesis is generally accepted
5. Formation of theory, based on repeated testing.

22. AACT is Beyond Observation and Hypothesis Stage 11/24/03 9:05 PM
AACT is beyond the observation stage, and past the hypothesis stage, well into the testing, trying to figure out the parameters that define what is and what is not compost tea. We have some clear hypotheses, some not-so-clear ones, some assumptions, poor logic and mis-conceptions. The gamut is there, and they will be cleared up as continued testing is done. There is what is possible with the best of all healthy biology in the soil, and there is the transition to get to that biology. We have never failed to get our clients off pesticides and end high inputs of inorganic fertilizer IF the biology in the soil reached what we have seen as being the best for the plant species involved. Fully proven? Ah, but you can't do that in science. There's always the next set of conditions, variations, etc. Could be the next situation is the one where the rule does not hold. To do science is to test, test and test again, defining the parameters of the testing condition ever more rigorously. Reductionistic science means taking a single factor by single factor approach. If a farming practice requires water, plant species, and N additions, the reductionistic approach says each factor has to be tested individually and in all combinations. That's just ONE WAY of doing science. Useful in certain conditions, but not in others. A more rational approach is to delete from the testing scheme all the management combinations that don't make sense from a real world point of view. If we always put kelp and fish hydrolysate into our teas, and thus don't care what the effect of each individually actually is, why test each separately?

23. Tea Types 12/7/03 1:38 PM
Active fungi are very prone to damage by passing them through a screen, mesh, strainer, etc. So are protozoa. Fungal spores are not damaged by passage through a screen, etc., but they will still be caught in the sludge build-up on the surface of a screen, fabric, etc. That's why the Compost Brewers with a compost bag doesn't work - the fungi stay inside the bag. In-line screens can be problems in that regard too. Larger size nozzles are the way to go. The e-zine archives will be in place soon, plus a whole new tea section. I've separated compost tea into different kinds, based on method to make the tea.

a. Actively aerated - being the most repeatable, and the method with the best documented results.

b. Fermentative teas - using the EM or bokashi approach. Less data available, but some pretty interesting results. We need to work with people doing bokashi to understand the production methods better.

c. Switching tea - where the tea starts aerobic, goes anaerobic for a time, and comes back aerobic. Not at all well documented, some really bad results from using it. E. coli abounds. So how would you know it to be good? Can it be turned into a useful approach?

d. Anaerobic tea - smells terrible. Can it be useful? Highly variable results on this. I don't think I want to go there, but just to make certain the whole range is covered, I do mention it.

For example, SFI has done testing on about 150 plus compost teas made, using actively aerated methods, and none had E. coli. Not-properly tested teas? There were E. coli. We have to get the production methods separated in the NOSB literature.

24. Tea Definitions 8/12/03 5:25 AM
Actively aerated compost is aerated to make sure the liquid does not become anaerobic, even if foods are added into the brew.

a. Aerated compost tea may not be aerated more than by just a stir or two. Highly variable results have been documented. Sometimes it is beneficial, sometimes not. I've killed a plant or more when using teas we just stirred.

b. Anaerobic tea can have toxins that could, or might not, cause problems. Lots more to do to document repeatability of the product.

c. Plant tea - no compost involved here. If plant material is used, like horsetail tea, then that's what that is. But not compost tea. May be aerobic, may be anaerobic. Lots of research to do here too.

d. Manure tea - again, no compost. Not a compost tea. Contains human pathogens to start out with, may or may not be out competed, consumed during aerobic or anaerobic tea production.

25. Why Brew Tea? 3/17/04 11:00 AM
So the brews were run subsequently, which may explain the differences in oxygen use. If the temperatures during one run were higher, that means the organisms grew more rapidly in the tea using the foods you added. There is a direct relationship between oxygen use by growing organisms and temperature. The higher the temperature, the less efficient the growth of bacteria and thus the more rapid their growth, but the more energy that is expended in respiration. There is a cost to rapid growth. And if temperature is higher, then the precise species mix is different in the different brews. So, different species growing, different efficiencies on those food resources. If we were dependent on a few species to do the job to improve plant growth, then we'd be up a creek without a paddle as temperatures shifted. Luckily, one of the major things in good compost is that we have literally tens of thousands of bacterial species, and maybe ten thousand species of fungi. They ALL get transferred to the compost tea. They all get to the plant surfaces, and the ones that

the plant is going to feed get to grow on the plant surface. That may be a different set of species than what we grew up in the tea brewer.

Question: So why do we brew?
Answer: We need to overwhelm the surfaces of the plants with those organisms that will occupy the infection sites on the leaf surfaces. Just a few hundred, maybe as many as a thousand, species actually grow to high number in the tea during brewing, but we need that so the leaf surfaces get fully covered. Putting on lots of species means that even if they are not exactly the right set, some of them will be close enough to protect the leaf, and some of them are ready to grow ASAP. That's why most compost extracts don't work that well - they don't concentrate the organisms enough, and the organisms are not awake and ready to grow when they reach the leaf surfaces that need protecting. Compost leachates don't generally get the organisms out of the compost - just the soluble nutrients, enzymes and growth hormones come out. So, different growth conditions mean different species mix of bacteria and fungi growing, so the oxygen curve may be different as a result. But notice how similar the curves are with respect to shape. The maximum oxygen use occurs at about 6 hours, so your compost must be pretty well activated, or you are adding something where the organisms are already active and growing to get peaks in oxygen use that early on. As temperature was lower in the other runs, the peak in use of oxygen occurred later and later, as organism wake up and growth was less and less rapid.

26. Why Use Tea? 11/17/03 4:12 PM

Question: So, why use tea?
Answer: To add the microbes and the foods to feed them. Right. But, if you have already added the good organisms to the soil by using good compost (testing once in awhile might be a good thing - like once every 5 years?), maybe adding more good organisms in the tea isn't going to do much. Adding more good organisms to an already good foodweb won't hurt, but it might be un-necessary.

a. Foliar Teas May Be Needed
But putting out foliar teas may still be needful, to get the protective organism layers on the plant surfaces. That way diseases can't get established and the improvement can only be seen in comparison to conventional systems where the diseases occur. Diseases don't occur because there's a lack of pesticides, it's because of a lack of the right biology, which results in plant stress. Arden Anderson always points that out, and it is an eye-opener when you finally get it.

b. Soil Applications
So, as a soil application, people using good compost applications to the soil likely don't need to be using tea. BUT, if you have neighbors that spray pesticides, if dust occurs in your area, or if air pollution is significant in your area, you need to apply foliar compost tea. All summer. So, before being negative, try thinking through why something is being recommended. I try very hard to avoid telling people to do things "just because". There's always a good reason why I recommend something. Usually several good reasons. If they aren't clear to you, then ask.

27. Teas Improve Plant Growth and Health 2/23/04

The bottom line is how teas improve plant growth, or plant health. What we do with tea needs to have that goal in mind. Plant response needs to be assessed, but usually plant responses are down-the-road, so we need a set of "early warning signals" to let us know if the tea we are making now is going to give the plant response. So, the biology in the tea at the beginning, when the tea is finished, is immediate information that we can use to know that the tea will give the response we want. Documenting the actual plant response is important, too.

28. Tea Contains Biological NPK 11/3/03 8:52 PM

Compost tea does not contain much N,P,K, but it does contain the components of the normal nutrient cycling system that is supposed to exist in soil, and is what plants have used for the last billion years as their source of plant available N. So while tea does not contain N as nitrate or ammonium, or P as inorganic phosphate, or K as ash, potash or other inorganic form, tea contains a great deal of protein, amino acids, lipids, phospholipids, carbohydrates containing N, P, S, K, Fe, etc. and so on. If you have decent numbers of protozoa, nematodes and arthropods in your soil, then biologically held N, P, K, etc. will be made plant available in the root zone of the plant, and will be easily taken up by your plant in the right amounts, etc.

So, long-term use of inorganic N,P,K is a sure pathway to toxic water, unhealthy plants and sick soils. We have to hold the nutrients in the organisms, and let the predators do their job. That way things stay in balance.

Tea contains biological N,P,K, not inorganic N,P,K. The chemists missed the important stuff, because they didn't have the means to measure it. We now have a useable way to measure the important things, it's what we do at SFI.

29. Plant Teas 1/10/04 1:45 AM

When I've looked at what is in most plant teas, they are bacterial, or they don't have much microbial life at all. Maybe there is a limited set of microbes on the leaf surfaces because of pesticide drift or dust? Plant teas can have direct, immediate impacts on AACT, IF the tea has really toxic materials in it (low pH, high concentration of phenols, tannins, terpenes, organic acids, toxic plant materials.

Question: Consider that some plants make some very toxic compounds (think of deadly nightshade, hemlock, poison ivy). What affect might those compounds have if extracted from a plant?

Answer: So, testing might be a good idea so you know what effect occurs. Testing for mineral content in plants, especially if a plant is thought to be elevated in certain nutrients. Alan Capular did a study on lots of the different plants and the amino acids, and maybe some on minerals, about 5 years ago. Maybe Alan would be a good person to ask about some of this information. I understand that Will Newman (newman@osalt.com, I think) is working on the book to be published from this. Check with Oregon Tilth about this too.

30. Not Compost Tea 11/15/03 1:45 PM

We do need to stop calling them compost tea, ok? No compost? Not compost tea. They are plant teas when you take the plant material, put it in a container, add water, and let ferment. And make no mistake, it is fermentation. You have to learn the right "smell" for the brew, or you kill things. I know, I have killed many plants this way. The brew usually goes anaerobic while the bacteria are using the simple sugars from the plant material, but as the simple sugars get used up, growth rates decline, and oxygen diffuses into the brew faster than it is used up, and the tea returns to the aerobic condition. The aerobes that could make dormant stages fast enough when the brew was going anaerobic (so the speed of going anaerobic is critical) wake up, and the brew can now be ok. And the toxic materials made during the anaerobic brew are indeed pesticides.

Antibiotics in the truest sense of the word. And as you might guess, we don't know the conditions that make primo plant teas. One time, the tea will be hot stuff, the next, no effect, the next, kills your plants.

The variability of actively aerated compost teas is significant, as we all know. But the factors involved in plant tea brewing are even greater. So we started with actively aerated compost tea because it is easiest to get a firm
handle on what is working, and what is questionable. Aeration, good compost, good organisms present, we have a usable, repeatable product. Once we have AACT under our belts, then let's move into plant tea production. Maybe clean up the anaerobic tea production end of things.

Clear, uniform production conditions have to be established. With plant teas, you first have to document that the plant material you are using has the sugars, proteins, carbohydrates, or other compounds that are important in antibiotic or phenol production. Then, precisely which bacterial species do you need? Or is that a mix of species? Which fungi? Are they needed? What is the oxygen concentration required for the best brew? When should the brew return to aerobic? How aerobic? When do you stir? How much? Phew! The production factors boggle the mind. But we do need to document these methods, if we want to use them reliably.

31. Fermentation 8/12/03 5:25 AM

a. Anaerobic Fermentation
Fermentation is a word, which has had different meanings over time. To ferment something used to mean the same as to grow, basically. A ferment was a culture of something. With brewing of alcoholic beverages, fermentation gained a connotation of being involved with the production of alcoholic beverages. And therefore, restricted to anaerobic conditions. Confusing? Especially as some people who are un-aware of the change in usage have been using fermentation in the earlier use of the word, which is just "to grow". I prefer to use terminology that is more precise, and avoid the use of a term compromised with different traditions.

b. Aerobic Fermentation
So, an aerobic fermentation is a nonsensical combination in some people's lexicon. Aerobic alcohol production? Not likely. Alcohol production is an anaerobic process. But only if you use fermentation in the sense of alcohol production. So, can we please leave fermentation to the beer industry?

c. Aerobic Metabolism, requiring oxygen as the last electron acceptor in the cytochrome system. Or anaerobic metabolism where something other than a molecule of oxygen is used as the final

electron acceptor in energy production. There's also photosynthesis, which produces oxygen as a waste product.

d. Aerobic Organisms
There are aerobic organisms, which always use aerobic metabolism. There are facultative anaerobic organisms, which can switch from aerobic metabolism, to anaerobic metabolism. The oxygen concentration where they convert from one to the other varies.

e. Anaerobic Organisms
There are anaerobic organisms, which always use anaerobic pathways.

32. Leachates 8/10/03 12:06 AM
First of all, it is not compost tea. It' is the leachate coming through the piles of organic matter. There is no extraction of organisms from the compost, and no effort to assure that the leachate has beneficial organisms. If the organic matter has pathogens growing in it, those pathogens could well be in the brown liquid they sell. We have tested some of this material, and my understanding is that the people who had us test it will soon be putting that data on their website. A year or so ago, we tested the brown liquid they produce on our own dime,
and the liquid had no organisms in it. Typical of leachates. Therefore, it is ok to bottle and put in sealed containers. No organisms, why worry? Maybe there are some nutrients, some humic acids, maybe some enzymes in the material. Maybe it can benefit plant growth. But if what you buy stinks, you would want to be very careful about what you put it on. Do not put directly on your plant surfaces. Adding to soil might be beneficial, because the organisms in a good soil will consume the anaerobic products long before getting to the plant.

a. You Can harm Roots
But if your soil isn't in good shape, then look out. You can harm your roots with materials that contain alcohols, phenols and organic acids produced under anaerobic conditions. I've been poked at about scenically replicated data to show these results. Scientists don't publish negative data, and when you test something meaning to do beneficials things and the plants die, you tend not to publish those data. We've killed quite a few plants with anaerobic tea, but all it did was make us try to figure out what was going on, not try to publish the data. And really, Cedar Grove needs to document what the quality of their materials are. SFI should not have to do that, they should. If they are doing a fermentative process, then they should say that, and document the lactic acid bacteria they are putting into the piles. DOCUMENTATION that is what is required. The public needs to know. As always, don't just believe a salesperson. Ask for data. If they don't have data, don't buy the product. Do be careful though about plate count data. That doesn't mean anything except there were dormant spores in the liquid. That isn't going to help your plants. You need data showing active bacteria, active fungi, and protozoa. OK?

33. Anaerobic Worm Caste Leachate 6/2/04 9:47 PM
Anaerobic worm caste leachate - not really a tea as you describe it - should be held until it is no longer anaerobic. You could stir or aerate it to speed aeration. Make sure the bad smells are gone before you put it on your plants. A biodynamic approach -- use your nose. You really don't want to have your worm compost get so wet that water runs out of the pile. Cover the pile when it starts

raining a lot. A Top-Tex fabric that lets gases through, but sheds water, is a good choice. Try putting cardboard on the top of the pile. It works when it gets really rainy. The worms love the cardboard as the fungi start to break it down. The water that comes out of a worm pile usually doesn't contain many organisms. It usually has some good nutrients and enzymes, hormones, proteins, etc. That's what the organisms that come out of the pile grow on. So, aerate that leachate, or hold it until it gets over the anaerobic phase and returns to aerobic conditions.

34. Regulations 8/9/03 11:49 PM

If the compost used to make tea is documented to be made according to certification requirements (i.e., made according to regulations, whether organic or USDA),
OR
if the compost is tested for human pathogens and found to contain fewer than the acceptable levels as established by EPA or USDA standards,
THEN
Compost tea made from those sources can be used without restriction. So far so good. If you make sure your compost was made correctly, no problem -- with or without manure.

The CURRENT USDA - NOP regulations are for compost tea MADE WITH MANURE-BASED COMPOST, the 120 day rule applies. Tea made with compost that does not contain manure can be used without restriction. If certifiers are making rules different from that, they need to talk to Bob Pooler, of the USDA - NOP.

Again, if composted correctly, pathogens should be out-competed, consumed, and reduced below levels of concern in the compost. The tea from such compost can be used without restriction.

The USDA just finished a study - from Pat Milner's program - that showed that compost that reached temperature for an adequate period of time resulted in reduction to acceptable levels of the human pathogens. Problem is, the USDA doesn't recognize that things other than temperature can be involved in reduction in pathogens.

Why hasn't the USDA recognized this? Because there are more than one or two factors that have to be determined to know that the habitat is not appropriate for the growth of human pathogens. My view - which not everyone agrees with - is that you have to have adequate aeration, adequate microbial activity, and adequate protozoan numbers in order to know for certain that the human pathogens, if present to begin with, have been reduced.

We have some data to show that is the case, but we haven't tested all the possible situations. We have data to show that molasses does NOT "cause E. coli to grow" as has been claimed by one other researcher. Don't pick on molasses as the only thing that E.coli can utilize. Human pathogens can grow using a number of different sugars. But it has to be more than just that one factor that will allow E. coli to grow. The other factors have to be correct for E. coli to grow. So, lack of proper aeration and lack of the other competitive organisms that outcompete and consume human pathogens. Aerobic organisms - in high diversity and in high numbers - outcompete and consume human pathogens most readily.

42

a. Anaerobic Brews

OK, one more caveat - if the conditions in the brew are very anaerobic, human pathogens are also not able to grow. But, very anaerobic brews will not remain anaerobic. There will be a period of time when that anaerobic brew will be back in range to allow human pathogen growth. Are the human pathogens then able to reach high enough numbers to be a problem? Don't know. Need data. My feeling is, let's not allow use of those anaerobic brews until someone does the necessary research to let us all know what's going on.

Now, a couple other things to think about - When you start to deal with aeration, you have to pay attention to temperature and air pressure because they determine maximum oxygen concentration in the water. You have to pay attention to microbial growth, because microbes use oxygen and respire carbon dioxide. Microbial growth may drop oxygen low enough that human pathogens can outcompete the aerobic microbes. When you deal with microbial growth, you have to pay attention to temperature (microbial growth rate increases with temperature typically) and amounts of foods added (more food, more microbes). So really, in order to assess the habitat and make sure it is not conducive to human pathogen growth, you have to assess:

-- temperature
-- air pressure
-- oxygen concentration
-- microbial foods
-- bacteria, fungi
-- protozoa

b. Temperature should be monitored hourly through the brew. How fast will the organisms grow, and how much oxygen can the water hold?

c. Air pressure should be known at the beginning of the brew (temp and air pressure will tell you the max oxygen possible in the brew. There may be times, with compost that you know contains pathogens, where you will not be able to brew, because the temperature is too high, and therefore oxygen concentration will be too low at the start of the brew to select against the pathogens)

d. Oxygen concentration should be monitored throughout the brew. We have seen 5.5 to 6 ppm to be the "cut-off" when dealing with typical aerobic microbe to facultative anaerobic microbe growth conditions. Valid in all situations? What you have is a fermentative lactic-acid bacteria community of organisms?

e. Microbial foods should be added relative to the set of microbes in the compost, which will determine the growth achieved during the brew cycle, given that oxygen concentration that can be maintained by the machine through the brewing cycle. This is information machine manufacturers should determine, and which all the tea machine manufacturers of AACT have performed. They haven't all put their data on their websites. The machine makers that don't have data on their websites are the ones whose machines can't achieve the microbial growth to prevent pathogens from growing. The people showing their data are the ones doing the work to make sure their machines CAN maintain aeration, microbial growth, and suppress human pathogens.

43

f. The set of microbes, including protozoa, in the compost and thus the tea should be known. Plate counts are not appropriate for assessing bacteria or fungi in any environmental material since viability is not what is needed, but activity and total biomass. As methods are developed, molecular methods must be used to assess species composition. Typically production methods for commercial composting should be such that each batch of compost produces the same set of microbes, within certain ranges. There may be variation based on starting materials and initial chemical content, but these can be determined, and the variation in microbial content known as seasons change.

g. The research that needs to be done is on composts that are of questionable microbial content, where some level of significant human pathogen contamination is left. We need research to assess what precisely is the habitat that allow human pathogens to be reduced in number and activity, and what habitat allows human pathogens to grow. I've outlined the information needed for research to do the job of figuring out what conditions select against human pathogens. If people want to do bacterial or fungal plate counts so they can prove to themselves just how pointless it is to do those determinations in order to assess the response of microbes in compost or compost tea, fine.

h. The best approach we have for assessing human pathogens is E. coli plate counts or broth MPNs. That use of plate count methods is appropriate. We know the conditions that allow E. coli to grow in lab cultures. But don't mistake those special conditions as being reflective of what happens in real world conditions. Stop imagining that lab cultures represent real world situations. So, that's where I think we're at, without being in any way specific about what's being said or done in the CTTF. Any questions, or places my logic is not clear, please discuss with me. I am putting a summary of the regulations for different state's irrigation water on the SFI website. If conventional growers can water crops with those levels of E. coli - and therefore potentially human pathogens - then higher standards should not be imposed on organic growers. The summary is based on information sent out by the USDA.

Chapter II

MECHANISMS
OF
IMPACT

From
Actively Aerated
Compost Tea
Applications

MECHANISMS OF IMPACT FROM AACT APPLICATIONS

1. Starting the Process of Building the Soil 5/2/04 12:56 PM

Of course, if there are no beneficial organisms left in the soil after pesticide and high levels of inorganic fertilizer applications, then the organisms in Commercially available microbially rich Humus will help immensely, and will start the process of building the soil so when the indigenous organisms do arrive, they have condominiums already present for them to move into. Non-natives may not be the absolute best thing to get out there, but having someone doing the work is better than no work being done. The locals can take over much more easily once the initial site construction is underway.

2. Microorganisms Solubilize Nutrients 5/2/04 12:50 PM

There is no data to show that carbon or silica are actually transmuted to calcium. Sorry, but that whole "data" set was based on someone not recognizing that chemical extractants do not extract microbial-biomass. Bacteria and fungi tie-up nutrients in forms that the extractants do not touch, and predators of bacteria and fungi make nutrients available in completely different forms, at times. If you don't recognize that exchange, then fuzzy logic leads to the kinds of conclusions that were made about "transmutation" of chemical elements in soil. No solid proof there. There are many papers on microorganisms solubilizing nutrients from parent material, or from the sand, silt, clay and rock. Please read the current issue of Applied Soil Ecology, or Biology and Fertility of Soil. There are quite a number of papers showing that predator - prey interactions release nutrients in the root zone, which improved plant nutrient concentrations. See the SFI website for a list of these papers in my CV.

3. Replace the Nutrient Removed in Harvest 5/1/04 10:39 AM

Typically, we are reducing the need to apply mineral nutrients on the soil by getting the nutrients into the compost, and thus into the tea. You will always have to replace the nutrients removed in harvest, but if you get the biology back into your soil, you no longer have to replace nutrients lost as a result of leaching, or out-gassing. Neither of these processes is significant, once the aerobic biology is back in place and soil structure has been re-built. So, if you don't have to replace leached nutrients, think of the reduction in mineral fertilizers you would see!

4. Organisms on Leaf Surfaces 11/23/03 5:59 PM

We've done LICOR readings of respiration on leaf surfaces, as well as plant tissue analysis of various nutrients. The coverage of the leaf surface with the microbes (at least 5% needs to be fungal coverage in order to deal with something like mildew in the work we have been doing on the SARE grant). There was no difference in chlorophyll concentration, or sugar produced in short term experiments with organism coverage, or without organism coverage. There was a significant increase in CO_2 evolved on leaves with the biology present on the surface. This resulted in a greater time that stomates were open, and the length of time that stomates were open. Iron, N, and potentially other micronutrients were in higher concentration in the leaves with organisms on the surface. This needs to be repeated of course. We have the results from one replication of this work, but don't have the money or time to do more. SFI could contribute these initial data if someone was interested in writing a grant to fully fund the work.

5. Active Organisms Needed 5/6/04 7:52 AM

Anaerobic conditions kill the beneficial organisms - no beneficial fungi, no beneficial, nutrient-cycling protozoa, no beneficial nematodes. You can have bacteria out the ying-yang, but they alone cannot give you the results you want to have. ACTIVE organisms are what we need, and you cannot tell activity using a bright light microscope.

6. Biology is not like a chemical 1/26/04 10:16 PM

Biology isn't just like a chemical that you can just add, neutralize and add again on-demand. Establishing the biology can take a bit of time. Diversity is important. Knowing that you have the diversity needed is important to establish, if you have to have maximum yields. If you don't have to have max yields, then you can be more relaxed about knowing that you have the food web established. Take 6 months, or a year to bring it up to speed in your yard, garden, etc. Commercial growers need to know they have it right, ASAP. So, testing is a good idea. But maybe not needed if you are a small scale grower and can walk the land and see what the plants are telling you. Use the plant response to give you information. But so many commercial growers check their land while driving 60 mph on the freeway going by their 500 acres of fields. Hard to really see what the plants are doing. Having testing done may be the way to go there.

7. Tea Contains Biology Not N-P-K! 11/1/03 9:42 AM

If you want to spend quite a bit of money to figure out what the appropriate amount of food to add to make good tea (good tea defined by the ORGANISMS you are growing in the tea, not the inorganic chemicals in the tea!), then go ahead. But please realize, compost tea is beneficial NOT because of N-P-K, but BECAUSE IT CONTAINS THE BIOLOGY KILLED BY TOXIC CHEMICAL USE. Your soil (which should often just be called dirt if it does not contain beneficial soil life) and plant surfaces have insignificant levels of beneficial organisms left if toxic chemicals have been applied. Got that? It's the biology. Not the chemicals. You want N-P-K? Go buy a chemical fertilizer. Lots of N-P-K there.

Question: But you are just killing more of your biology when you use high concentrations of N-P-K. You just make the whole situation worse, if you use inorganic fertilizers or toxic chemicals. Soluble inorganic N, P, ok K, as measured by the soil fertility kit you bought at the store, should read practically ZERO in a good tea. Why?
Answer: Because the bacteria and fungi growing so rapidly in your tea should have tied up all the soluble inorganic N, P, and K in their biomass. The fact that you had measurable N, P, or K says you weren't making really good tea. It's the biology that needs to be put back. And you need ALL the biology - not just bacteria.

8. Biology Effect Not NPK 11/15/03 11:15 AM

You don't apply compost tea based for NPK. You use compost tea to establish, and get growing, the biology that does nutrient retention and nutrient recycling.

a. Fertilizer Effect

You usually get a "fertilizer effect" with compost tea, because your plants will now control their own rhizosphere and thus the rate at which nutrients become available to the plants. On foliage, the tea organisms elevate CO_2 on the leaf surface, and thus influence stomatal responses. Elevated

CO2 causes the stomates to open sooner, and remain open longer, thus allowing nutrients on the leaf surface to move, through simple diffusion, into the plant. Please start learning the mechanisms that explain why tea does what it does,
or you end up saying something that critics latch onto and go ballistic. One Lab has said about compost tea -- that compost tea is worthless, because it doesn't have high concentrations of inorganic nutrients. They just don't get it, do they? Actively aerated compost tea contains the organisms required to immobilize and retain nutrients on leaf surfaces, in the root system, etc. But bacteria and fungi alone are not adequate to establish a healthy foodweb.

Question: What else is needed? And therefore, why is it that if the liquid goes anaerobic you can't possibly
have the benefits of a healthy foodweb added to the soil, or the leaf surfaces? It's a quiz! Do you really understand what actively aerated compost tea is all about?

9. Deep Roots 1/25/04 11:45 AM
Deep roots require good soil structure. That means compaction at a minimal degree. You should be able to drive a rod through the soil with just your hand, without grunting. Building soil structure, and building it so well that driving a tractor across the soil even when the soil is wet (but not too wet - that's the question we have yet to answer. How wet is too wet?) still doesn't compact the soil, requires a fully functional and complex food web. That means not only bacteria, but fungi, protozoa, nematodes (just the good guys, please), and microarthropods. And not just their total biomass, but ACTIVE biomass. We could expect that you would have to buy each species separately and apply them (whoa! think of the cost!), but luckily we have compost, which, if made right, supplies all the critters. Thermal compost will be a little short on the microarthropods, so a touch of worm compost too.

OR ---- Compost tea can be used to add back everything but the microarthropods (although we still need to work on how to get nematodes numbers higher in good compost, so we can extract high numbers into the tea). Easier to apply the liquid in many cases. But remember, fungi, protozoa and nematodes DO NOT SURVIVE in tea that has lost oxygen. People selling "compost tea" have to document that they have the biology in the tea, or at the very least, document that the tea did not go anaerobic during the brewing cycle. Or you have to conclude that you are getting bacteria alone. And possibly some pretty nasty bacteria. Combat black spot? Sure, they do a job on black spot. Take out mildew? Not in the studies we have run. So, if you want to have deep roots, you have to build soil structure. The biology does that. Compaction means you don't have the right biology. So fix it.

Deep roots means you don't have to water nearly as much (perhaps as great as 70% reduction, but more likely 30% reduction in water needs); you don't need the inorganic fertilizer (the roots access the nutrients you put down last year, the year before, and which leached below your compaction zone). So, to grow deep roots, you need actively aerated compost tea (AACT), not fermentative tea, not anaerobic tea, not a tea that went anaerobic for awhile and returned aerobic. An aerated compost extract can give you this as well, but you then have to add the foods for the organisms to the soil. Compost extracts don't generally work for foliar applications, as the organisms need to be active in order to stick to the leaf surface. Examples of where tea did work are appreciated. also, examples where tea did not work are useful, so we can figure out why it didn't work, Analysis of the biology, and conditions during tea production usually lets us know why something did not work. Get those roots going deep!

10. Mechanisms for Benefits 8/21/03 5:43 AM

Question: My take on anaerobic ct (also act !;) it is alive, just not necessarily aerobic;
Answer: Correct

Question: It depends on whether the organisms are beneficial or pathogenic as to whether the results would be good.
Answer: Correct; there are not-harmful anaerobic organisms

Question: I'm completely guessing, but is it possible that much of it could be ambidextrous (I mean 'facultative aerobes'?): this latter would explain how an anaerobic ct could be beneficial as a foliar spray in particular.
Answer: One of the mechanisms for benefit is that the bacteria and fungi cover the leaf surface, and keep the pathogens from even getting to the leaf, physically. If there's several layers between the disease and the leaf, there's no way the disease can cause the disease in the plant tissue. So, simple physical distance is important, and this can be a function of aerobic or anaerobic organisms. So, anaerobes might do this just, sometimes. It's just that the critters that do better under reduced oxygen conditions are usually the pathogens......

Question: I'm also guessing that if you spray leaves with true anaerobes that they will die or go inactive due to the O2 environment.
Answer: Maybe, depends. But the metabolites they produce CAN kill plant tissue. Not the case under aerobic conditions.

Question: Related to this subject, I am wondering what status the bio-dynamic preparations have - o2 wise. I hope someone can clear up the murky water..
Answer: If they are made correctly, they tend to be highly fungal preps.

11. Scientific Principles 11/25/03 7:45 AM
To document that the bacteria are inside and systemic in the plant means you have to show pictures of the plant tissues with bacteria inside the xylem. I get people claiming systemic microbial growth, but it is just the microbes being carried all over the surface of the plant by the taxicabs in the real world - microarthropods, nematodes, insects, protozoa. The bacteria or fungus are not inside the plant. There is some work on fungi that normally live in trees. Typically, this group (just a few species) live in the sap of trees. They do not grow to high densities, but they are present in many trees. Systemic, not harmful, perhaps beneficial, but no one knows.

Question: Does it make tree growing un-scientific that this fungus has not been investigated?
Answer: That's what has been suggested about compost tea. Because we haven't figured out every factor, tea-making is un-scientific? Bizarre definition of science! If you are doing science, you

have to use the scientific method. We are using that approach, and therefore being scientific about compost tea. We are just at an early stage of the scientific method with respect to compost tea.

Question: But think about the fact that we do not yet completely understand the human body and how it works. Does that make medicine un-scientific?
Answer: So, just because we have only begun to apply scientific principles to our understanding of compost tea does not mean a label of pseudo-science can be applied here.

12. Organisms -- Systemic Versus Living on the Surface 11/24/03 7:39 AM
Your example is about organisms living and surviving on the surfaces of the plant roots. I'm glad to see the research about the beneficials STAY there, if you get them growing and healthy. Different from the question about systemic bacteria. The term systemic means the bacterium has moved inside the plant, and is part of the system, i.e., part of the plant.

a. Internal Contents of Plants
Internal contents of plants, like the internal organs and muscles of animals, are sterile. The insides of living organisms tend to be great growth media. If a bacterium or fungus gets inside the tissue of an organ, or inside the muscle tissue, or inside the tissues of the plant, disease is the usual outcome. Just too perfect a growth medium.

b. Some Organisms Breach Cell Wall and Membrane
Some bacteria and some fungi have mechanisms for breaching the cell wall and cell membrane, and thus are what we think of as pathogenic. It is not normal for the SAP of a plant, or the internal tissues of the plant to have any other organism, besides the plant, present. Mycorrhizal fungi are half-way there - they breach the cell wall of the plant, but do not get through the cell membrane. I usually talk about that in the introductory lectures I give.

Question: For a paper to show that the bacteria sprayed onto a leaf surface moved inside the plant, and did not just stay on the surface of the plant, is a shock. It is not a normal occurrence. What are the conditions that allow this kind of situation to occur?
Answer: Sterile leaf surfaces, water imbalance, stomatal games being played. So, if you mis-treat plants to an extreme, you can end up with compromised plants. You can do that to animals too.

Question: So, systemic bacteria?
Answer: We don't find them in plants growing normally.

Question: Could conventional agricultural management result in the conditions necessary to have bacteria assault and move into the plant tissue?
Answer: Hum, yes.

Question: Would that happen using organic agricultural management?
Answer: I believe it would not, but darn it, there's that word believe. The only defense at this point is that there is no documentation to suggest it could happen using organic practices.

c. Summary -- Systemic Versus Living on the Surface

Just to summarize - systemic versus living on the surfaces of the roots, being present on the next generation of tuber. The first situation is not good. The second situation is great. Once a soil is inoculated AND YOU MAINTAIN THE HABITAT FOR THE ORGANISMS, allowing the PLANT to feed the beneficials, that set of organisms will survive, multiply, and be on next year's tuber. Hooray! If you do nothing to kill them, and make sure the habitat is right (food, shelter, good community), the good guys will still be there. You would not need to inoculate again.

15. Bacteria Not Normally in Plant Xylem 11/24/03 2:34 AM

Bacteria are not normally found in plant xylem. I've stared at enough plant sap to know. The paper reporting bacteria entering plant tissue is an exceptional case, because of the conditions to which the plants were subjected. If you abuse plants, or humans, long enough and strangely enough, you will get bizarre behavior. But, prove it to yourself that bacteria are not normally found in plant juices, or in the surfaces of plant leaf tissues. To see bacteria, you have to have EITHER oil immersion, 1000X or greater phase contrast objectives and a phase condenser, OR a 400X DIC microscope. Both cost about $9000 for a good one. You might be able to go to your local University and get one of the microbiologists to do some looking for you, for a minimal price.

14. Fungal to Bacterial 4/1/04 9:20 PM

a. Late successional perennial grasses

Are usually around 50 - 50 Fungal to bacterial.

b. Poa, ryegrass

Typically around 0.75, along with some bunch grasses (given that the systems we looked at were truly not-disturbed).

15. Bacterial Biomass 7/29/04 5:09 PM

Question: If I'm not mistaken, most soils have the same bacterial count...the difference is that in more mature systems the fungal biomass increases and the more mature the system, the greater the fungal biomass vs. the "somewhat static" bacterial biomass number....PLEASE CORRECT ME, DOC, if I am wrong!

Answer: You are correct when it comes to bacterial biomass. Generally there are 600 million bacteria per gram soil in agricultural soils, while there are 6,000 million per gram in forest soils. Only a ten-fold increase, while fungi go from 5 ug per gram to 5,000 ug per gram, from agriculture to forest. But when doing plate counts, very often there is no change in numbers of colony forming units going across production gradients in agricultural soils. So, scientists have assumed that means all soils have pretty much all bacteria, all the time. Just an artifact of the method, I'm afraid.

16. Successional Stages 7/29/04 7:16 Am

There appears to be a strong correlation with successional stage, based on the over 100,000 soil samples that we've looked at. That is what I base these conclusions on - we have looked at over 100,000 samples of soil, where the following conclusions hold.

If a plant is an early, weedy species, found in grasslands, in annual or bi-annual conditions, in areas that are typically highly disturbed, then those are usually bacterial-dominated plants. If plants are typically found in perennial, not-disturbed environments, then they are typically fungal-dominated plants.

The earliest colonizers in both categories (annual versus perennial) require high levels of inorganic nitrogen to germinate and maintain dominance. Thus, inorganic fertilizers will select for these weedy species in both situations. Reduce the available inorganic N levels, and these weedy species do not thrive. Your later successional plants do better in conditions where inorganic nitrogen is a limited pool in the soil.

So think of succession - which plants are earliest in the colonization process of ecosystem successional cycles? These are the weedy species, and they are highly bacterial dominated around the roots. Later successional plant species will be less bacterial dominated, and require more fungi in the balance. More fungi to suppress disease, to alter pH to result in potentially a less strongly alkaline condition. The most productive grassland situations are balanced, one to one fungal to bacterial biomass.

Remember, we measure biomass, and thus fungi and bacteria can be compared. Please realize this when you hear the recent criticisms from agricultural scientists who are saying bacteria and fungi can't be compared. If we assess biomass, then bacterial biomass and fungal biomass can be compared. If you assess numbers, then it is correct that bacterial numbers and fungal numbers are a silly thing to compare. But my conclusions are based on biomass, not numbers.

As you move into forested situations, and into HEALTHY forest soils, the soil becomes fungal dominated. The most productive forests are highly fungal. Perhaps 1000 times more fungi than bacteria in healthy old growth forest soil. But bacterial biomass is highest of any ecosystem in these old growth forests. It's just that fungal biomass is much, much higher.

Soil pH correlates with all this. Highly bacterial soil tends to be very alkaline, while highly fungal-dominated soil tends to be in the 5.5 to 6.5 range. But you have to pay attention to compaction, because if the soil compacts and goes anaerobic, then soil pH will drop, and can become VERY acidic. Highly acid soils are indicative of very sick conditions. The ecosystem may well be going "backwards" towards more bacterial conditions. Acid soils will become alkaline once the anaerobic conditions are alleviated, but that may take thousands of years to shift. Or only a decade. The environmental conditions must be paid attention to.

But then consider that when we talk about wetland, or riparian systems, things are different. Soils that are water-logged for some part of the year tend to have lower pH, because there may be anaerobic conditions during water-logged times. Anaerobic bacteria produce VERY alkaline metabolites. How anaerobic for how long?

So, think of where your plants occur in the real world. What is the ecosystem, or habitat that they normally occur in? That should give you some good clues about what they like - bacterial, or fungal-dominated conditions?

If you have specific questions about plant requirements, just ask me the specific plant species. I may have to ask back, where does the plant normally occur? In forest, or grasslands? In early successional forest, or early successional grasslands? In weed fields, or mature grasslands? Then we can typically answer the question, even if we haven't measured the ratio. It is safest, however, to actually measure the ratio.......

17. Tropical Systems 7/29/04 5:25 PM

Question: Doc, you wrote, "But bacterial biomass is highest of any ecosystem in these old growth forests. It's just that fungal biomass is much, much higher. This doesn't make sense. Did you mean the bacteria NUMBERS
are higher but the biomass of fungi is higher? Another question: In tropical forests the numbers of ants is like nothing I have ever seen. How do their biomass numbers compare in that situation....if you know, sorry!
Answer: Tropical systems can have a great deal more insect biomass than is present in temperate systems. We need to look at these ratios. Some healthy mature grasslands have up to 200,000 individual microarthropods per square meter, down to 5 inch depth. Turn this into biomass, and you are dealing with an insect biomass about a tenth of that of the bacterial biomass. In tropical soils, ants can contribute about 0.2 ug biomass per gram of soil, when averaged out over the whole field. But, if you calculate on the basis of the small space they actually occupy, their biomass can be equal to that of fungi.

Consider that in a prairie soil in Kansas, the microbial biomass in the soil is equal to something like 2.5 buffalo standing on the same area. Yep, the microbes in the soil are more "important" biomass-wise than buffalo. Ah, but each kind of organism has its function, different from the others. The Great Plains would not be the Great Plains without buffalo, or the bacteria, or the fungi. It takes the WHOLE village working together to make it a village.

So let's go over the relative increase of biomass as we go from early stages (weeds) to mature prairie to old growth forest. Relatively speaking, bacterial biomass is about the same in a grasslands, and in an old growth forest. What really changes is fungal biomass. Bacteria go from 100 ug, to 300 ug, for example over that gradient, while fungi go from 5 ug, to 5000 ug, and even higher in really healthy old growth systems. OK?

18. Transmutation versus Transformation 5/6/04 8:36 PM
Hold on - let's get the definition of transmutation versus transformation differentiated. They are not the same thing!

Question: Basically, compost itself is a transmutation, a biotransformation of raw organic materials into complex humic molecules and polymers.
Answer: That is improper use of terms. Transmutation means something entirely different from transformation. They are not exchangeable terms. Mutation and formation are not the same. Transformation from one compound to another is one thing. Biology does this all the time. You transform oxygen into carbon dioxide with every breath you take. But you cannot take oxygen and

turn it into lead. Transmutation means that kind of changing of one ELEMENT into a different element. Changing oxygen into lead would require so much energy that humans would not survive in the vicinity of the transmutation. Please use the terms properly.

19. Transmutation 5/6/04 7:40 PM

Transmutation is NOT a simple electrical phenomenon. If you remove an electron from an INNER orbital shell of a molecule, but leave behind "excess" neutrons and positrons, you have a condition that results in a nuclear explosion. The molecule has to balance, and it will balance, if you can somehow supply enough energy to knock a stable electron out of an inner shell. Not simple, and somewhat difficult. And release of that much energy is not conducive to human life. So, let's not get into converting one ELEMENT from one thing to another. You are not changing boron to nitrogen, not unless you want to release so much energy that it will not be a pleasant thing.

Question: Converting nitrite to nitrate?
Answer: Organisms do it all the time, but not what is meant by transmutation. From a certain point of view, all carbon and nitrogen comes from the atmosphere. But it all has to go through quite a few intermediary steps before the plant can get those nutrients into a form they can take up. It is the biology in the soil that fixes atmospheric nutrients, and eventually cycles them into plant-available forms.

20. Beneficial Microorganisms 2/21/04 12:29 AM

a. Disease-Causing Fungi
Disease causing fungi will colonize roots and take carbohydrates, sugars, and proteins and kill the plant.

b. Mycorrhizal Fungi
Mycorrhizal fungi will EXCHANGE nutrients for sugars from the plant, but the plant controls that interaction, not the fungus.

c. Beneficial Fungi
Beneficial fungi cannot "take" anything from the plant. The beneficial fungi are fed by mostly sugars, but some proteins and carbohydrates that the plant releases. But again, the plant is in control, not the fungi.

21. Mychorrhizal fungi vs. Disease-Causing Fungi 2/15/04 12:05 PM

a. Mycorrhizal Fungi
Mycorrhizal fungi will extend hyphae into the roots, but the plant is in control of that interaction. If the fungus doesn't give the plant what the plant needs, the plant cuts off the food supply.

b. Disease-Causing Fungi
Disease causing fungi will take carbohydrates from a plant, but the whole reason we want all these beneficial fungi around the root is to protect that root from the diseases, so the crab drain doesn't happen.

22. Molds and Mildew 1/3/04 3:29 PM

The term, mold, is another name commonly applied to fungi. Many people think molds are the bad guys, while fungi are the good guys. The term is used that way in some scientific literature, but it is not actually generally accepted as having any validity.

a. White molds

White molds can include beneficial fungi that decompose plant cellulose and cell wall structures. Some white "molds" are pathogens, since they can attack plant cellulose and cell walls while the plant is still alive. Kind of a problem there, but the fungus doesn't really MEAN to cause any trouble. It just didn't know that the plant wasn't quite done with the material......

b. Mildew

Many people mean mildew when they say mold, but what they really mean is mildew. The term mold get applied to the fuzzy stuff that grows on your bread in the refrigerator (typically *Penicillium* or *Rhizopus*), or on oranges or other citrus products, again *Penicillium* is common (different species from the bread attacker), or *Trichoderma,* or a herd of brown guys, or little white guys (which we call LWG's).

c. Fungi

We mean fungi when we talk about filamentous, non-photosynthetic eukaryotes. Some fungi have the enzymatic capacity to break down really nasty, structurally complex things. Some fungi do not - and we call them the sugar fungi. They compete with bacteria ALOT, but they are not fungi you particularly want to have around.

d. Water Molds

Water molds grow in many water-logged conditions. They do not do well in open water, they need surfaces in order to grow.

e. Oomycetes – the Bad Guy

The "bad guy" *Oomycetes* generally require reduction in O2 typical of water-logged conditions in order to grow.   There is a different classification system that labels the *oomycetes* as something else, but I have never been taught that system of classification. Not sure how accepted it is in academia. Darn taxonomists keep finding out new things and re-classifying the groups of fungi. And then they find out they were wrong, and change everything back again. I can't keep up. But, in any case, *oomycetes*, or water fungi, or water molds, whatever, require temperature, and decent water films in order to grow and reproduce. The plant pathogens generally require reduce oxygen.

Question: Soil in the winter is often water-logged, but you don't get any problem with water molds then. Why not?

Answer: Temperature. Not enough bacterial growth to drop oxygen content until the soil begins to warm up, and/or roots start pumping exudates out. But when the temperature warms up, the foods arrive, then they grow, use up oxygen, and drop O2, so the water molds say, Thanks!

23. Water Mold Reproduction 1/20/04 11:35 AM

Most water molds require a true water film to reproduce. The spores produce a "swimmer" stage, and they need the water in order to disperse. Splashing from the soil surface to the leaves can be a source of these diseases on to the plant leaves. Check any mycology textbook to look at this taxonomic division. My favorite general text is Webster's Introductory Mycology.

24. Types of Fungi 5/17/04 9:38 AM

Fungi can be white, pink, yellow, green, purple, black.....Just because something is white does not necessarily mean it's fungus. Actinobacteria are white, and many people confuse that with fungi. But actinobacteria are bacteria - they used to be called actinomycetes - but they are bacteria. The white ash-like growth you get in compost, just below the surface, about 3 to 6 inches into the surface, and goes for about another 3 to 6 inches down into the pile in a nice layer, is actinobacteria. Not fungi. There are different levels of "goodness" with respect to fungi, and I've discussed some really gross-level distinctions between the major groups. It always drives my mycology buddies crazy to do that - they dislike those kinds of generalizations. "Not ALL beneficial fungi are greater than 3 um diameter!" But I didn't say that. I say, MOST beneficial fungi in general have wide diameter hyphae. As a general statement, it is true. There is one group of disease fungi that falls in the wide diameter category, as opposed to thousands of genera of smaller diameter "bad guys". And generalizations are what we need for the general public. I don't think you are going to stay awake for me to go over the diameter of the thousand species of fungi that are in your soil, much less the thousands that should be in well-made compost. But, adding fungal foods to your compost, and seeing what grows is one way for you to tell if your compost has the good guys or not. Add fungal food, and watch what happens. Then you can start fixing things where they need to be fixed, instead of spinning your wheels trying to grow fungi that aren't even present. First things first - do you have beneficial fungi in your compost? You can't get slug protection if you don't have the good guys present to do the job.

25. VAM 9/29/03 7:30 PM

In a recent post, someone wrote:

Question: Mycorrhizae is an environmental state created by the presence of mycorrhizal fungus. Mycorrhizae is a beneficial fungus not a bacteria. You need to match the mycorrhizae specie with the plant that it associates with. That is why a multiple specie mycorrhizae product is important to use. The guesswork has been taken out of the process. Plant Success is good for 99% of all the plants growing on earth because of its blend of species and types(endo and ecto). The commercial products do not work on the rhododendron or orchid plant families.

Answer: Mycorrhizae are not "an environmental state". What do you mean by "environmental state" when referring to a symbiosis? The term mycorrhizae is Latin, and translates as "fungus-root". Mycorrhizae
are an interaction of a fungus with a root, and as such a symbiosis of both organisms. There is no such thing as a mycorrhizae species, since there cannot be a fungus-root interaction, which is made up of a single species. By definition a mycorrhizae has to be two species - the fungus and the root. The singular of bacteria is bacterium. VAM rarely need to be matched with the grass or vegetable crop species, as these fungi have broad plant host range. Ectomycorrhizal fungi can be host specific, and some care is required. A good source of information about which mycorrhizal fungi

colonize different plant species can be found at www.mycorrhizae.com. Mike Allen has written several books, as well as Bob Lindeman, which can be used as resource material for this information as well.

a. Non-Mycorrhizal Plant Species

Most of the brassica plant species (mustards, cole and kale crop species) are not mycorrhizal under any circumstances, and I imagine that these species comprise more than 1% of the plant species on this planet. Most of the CROP species humans grow require mycorrhizal fungi, so perhaps that is what you meant.

b. Mycorrhizal Spores on Rhododendron

I know at least two commercial inocula of mycorrhizal spores that work on rhododendron. How do I know? We've tested them. A couple rhodies so inoculated are living in my yard. I am not aware of anyone offering commercial inocula of mycorrhizal fungi for orchids, as far as I know and I guess I missed anyone making that claim. Since I have sprayed mycorrhizal spores at up to 600 psi pressure, and had the spores germinate and grow, I have evidence that these SPORES survive pressure and passage through pumps without harm. Once the spores germinate, the story is very different. But spores? They are dormant stages of fungi, and as such, quite resistant to environmental impacts.

Question: Mycorrhizae spores can be harmed by pressure. Spraying mycorrhizae spores with pressurized equipment can harm the spores. Sure some may make it through a spraying, but why take a chance when there are other ways of delivery. Mycorrhizae is not already on the plants we buy.

Answer: The word mycorrhizae is plural. The singular is mycorrhiza. Mis-use of terminology worries me, especially from someone who apparently sells mycorrhizal inocula.

26. *Mycorrhizal* Status of Plants 10/8/03 3:26 PM

Have you looked at Harley and Harley's book (hum, maybe Harley and Waid, don't remember) where they did a world-wide assessment of *mycorrhizal* status of plants? It is quite old, but probably the only text looking at non-commercial, non-crop plants. When we started looking at Kincaid's Lupine, we didn't know if it was

mycorrhizal or not, for example. So, we had to collect roots and assess whether they were first of all capable of being *mycorrhizal*. Then we had to find spores in the field (at the surface of the soil of plant with colonized roots), and add those spores to potting soil and plant the seeds. Then once grown, we had to assess whether the roots had become *mycorrhizal*. They had. The seeds planted without the *mycorrhizal* spores germinated, but then died within three months, while the *mycorrhizal* lupine survived just fine, as I recall. Dr. Mark Wilson was involved in this study, and he's still at Oregon State University, so you could ask him about it. It has not been an easy battle to get people to accept that *mycorrhizal* fungi are important. We are lucky to know about *mycorrhizal* fungi for commercial plant species. If *mycorrhizal* researchers had been paid to do the work of assessing whether the plants you want to know about were *mycorrhizal*, they would have done the work. So, you expect scientists to work for free? Can we expect you to work for free? You are being given the best information possible, given our current state of knowledge. People don't know everything yet.

27. **Ectomycorrhizal and Endomycorrhizal Fungi** 12/22/03 8:58 PM

a. *Ectomycorrhizal fungi*
Ectomycorrhizal fungi occur on conifers and some ornamentals, not on grasses. A paper written suggesting that *ectomycorrhizal* fungi are important in rangeland soils strikes me as a bit scary. Unless the rangeland is converting to juniper, which isn't exactly what is needed, *ectomycorrhizal* fungi aren't the one doing the work.

b. *Endomycorrhizal fungi*
Endomycorrhizal fungi, and specifically VAM (*vesicular-arbuscular mycorrhizal* fungi) which are a kind of *endomyccorhizal* fungi, are what is found on grasses and a wide range of deciduous trees. Those are the ones we need on most crop species.

c. *Glomulin*
And the original report on glomulin was with VAM, not ecto, as I recall. But there are some great books and a few papers on many other glues in soil made by bacteria as well as fungi, so I don't buy the exclusivity that the USDA is pushing for fungi, and particularly *mycorrhizal* fungi, as being the sole producers of the glue that hold soil together. Important in holding soil together, yes, but not the only organism group doing that function.

28. **Mycorrhizal Requirements** 1/5/04 9:38 PM
Native versus non-native is not a way to determine mycorrhizal requirement. Grasses and row crops, most deciduous shrubs and trees, form relationships with VAM. Blueberry and SOME wetland plants are ericoid. Some deciduous shrubs will form relationships with ericoid, VAM and ectomycorrhizal fungi. Conifers tend to be ecto-mycorrhizal. But please remember that MOST of the fungi these plants form relationships are not mycorrhizal, but saprophytic, decomposer fungi. Most of the fungi in soil are not mycorrhizal fungi, but decomposers. Under trees, which need fungal dominated soil (which does not mean low bacteria, it just means LOTS of fungi as well as bacteria), it would be a good idea to have fungal dominated understory species. The same mycorrhizal fungi should colonize the plants under the trees as on the trees. So under deciduous trees, you need fungal-dominated perennial herbs that form relationships with VAM.

29. *Mycorrhizal* **Spores** 6/16/04 11:29 AM
Mycorrhizal spores nearly always come with a carrier, because the spores are microscopic and easily lost on their own. Most carriers are pretty inert - like clay or cellulose. *Mycorrhizal* Applications makes a great product, always comes out high on testing they do. They have a good research component too. Plant Health Care is more variable in the results we see from them. Other companies that take product from both of the above and re-package typically are fairly variable in results too. So, please make sure you ask for their test results - and not just one test! You need to see testing occurring over time, with good consistency. Many *mycorrhizal* products are not tested, and other than anecdotal information on their websites, you don't have any solid information on their performance. Always a bit iffy, but you can read the testimonial information and try to assess whether the information is just fluff, or some solid evidence that the product works. You should call the people in the testimonials. *Mycorrhizal* Applications makes a

consistently good product. That's what impresses me. Any product manufacturer has to first show me data that shows they can at least once make what they claim, but then they also need to show me their product consistently can perform.

30. Fungi Morphological Terminology 12/22/03 2:08 PM

Hyphae are the individual strands of the body of the fungus. A single hypha is one single strand. Hyphae is more than one strand. The body, made up of all the individual strands, is called the mycelium. The fungus is the whole mycelium, but also includes any fruiting structures, such as spores, or asci, or mushrooms, or truffles. Morphological terminology is difficult. It needs to be used correctly, or we end up with chaos in what we are saying. Precision is very important.

31. Fungi and Carbohydrates 2/13/04 11:15 PM

Question: Fungi can utilize carbohydrates, but generally more complex carbohydrates than ones in green plants. Not until the simple carbohydrates are gone will the fungi get into the act and use the more complex carbohydrates.
Answer: So, is the point of what is being asked here that fungi use things in the soil first, and then in plants? Don't know any evidence of that sequencing.

Question: Is it true that fungi feed on carbohydrates in the plant if there are none present in the soil? If so (or even if that is not true) is it beneficial to add some carbohydrates like glucose, or galactose every week after applying a tea?
Answer: Glucose and galactose would be bacterial foods more than fungal foods. Glucose is a very simple food, and thus mostly bacteria would use it, unless at high concentrations. Galactose might be a touch less strongly bacterial than glucose, but not much less bacterial food then glucose. But adding sugars every-so-often after tea would be fine, as long as you know you want the bacteria maintained in an active condition.

32. How Fungi Work in Soil 12/22/03 3:21 AM

Question: http://www.dartmouth.edu/~mpayres/pubs/abs52.htm. The above page is an Ayres Abstract about how fungi work in the soil.
Answer: Not how fungi, in general, work in soil, but how ectomycorrhizal fungi respond to some particular nutrient additions. Ectomycorrhizal fungi are unique, and very dependent on particular situations, quite often only able to grow and reproduce when in symbiosis with plant roots. Please don't take this information as typical of every day fungi in soil.

Question: http://www2.mhc.ab.ca/Users/pwallis/LabManPDF/10FUNGUS.pdf. The above page is a test procedure for fungal growth. Some interesting statements here.
Answer: Not growth in soil. This is petri plate growth, and NOT what you would expect in soil. Petri plates do not have all the other organisms, which are present in soil. Fungi are interacting with them ALL in soil.

Question: Rhizopus is not a common fungus to find growing in soil. It grows fine on bread, but how much bread is present in most agricultural soils? You can isolate this fungus from most soils, but does that mean it is GROWING in that soil?

Answer: No. May be lots of spores in soil, but not growing, not performing a function in most anyone's soils. If you want to know how fungi behave IN SOIL, you have to look at them growing IN SOIL. Please, think about things we see in the lab versus what soil is really all about.

33. *Rhizobium, Burkholderia, Bacillus* and *Pseudomonads* 11/25/03 9:45 PM

Rhizobium does infect root hairs, and the bacteria travel in an infection thread through the root hair, to the place the root hair connects to the main root, and that is where the bacteria make the plant form the nodule. *Burkholderia* is a new genus of bacteria, some of which are what I knew as *Rhizobium* when I was in grad school. So, quite likely what we used to call the non-effective *Rhizobium*. I guess it doesn't surprise me that these bacteria would be able to colonize inside plant tissues. They have a special mechanism - lecithin receptor molecules - that allow them to get into certain kinds of cells. But if you ate a zillion of these bacteria, they wouldn't be anything except extra protein. Now, the *Bacillus* and *Pseudomonads* being inside the stem.... hum, not quite sure what he meant by that. In the outer layers of stem cells? Not systemic, apparently. New things being discovered all the time.....

34. Rhizobium and Azotobacter 4/10/04 8:25 PM

Question Rhizobacter fixes N thru a mutual relationship with plants. Infections are initiated and nodules are formed; then N can be supplied to the plant. They however they cannot fix N until a suitable infection is achieved and is all to do with the protein nitrogenase. - correct me if I am wrong.

Answer: The bacteria obtain sugars from the plant, and use that sugar to form the nodule, which has to be large enough so that the active bacteria in the nodule use up the oxygen before it reaches the center of the nodule. Once the center becomes reduced in oxygen enough, then the nitrogenase enzyme (all enzymes are proteins) can do the job of converting N2 gas into NH2 (amide), attached to the carbon on a sugar molecule. Which means a protein was produced. So, yes to your question - the bacteria have to make nitrogenase, a protein, in order to fix N. They do this anaerobically.

Question: Azotobacter on the other hand can fix N directly from the air. So in the soil when does this N become available to the plant? Is it simply when they die from natural causes or does it only happen when a predator such as a protozoa or nematode feasts on it?

Answer: Azotobacter does the same process as Rhizobium, EXCEPT it does not form a nodule on the plant. These bacteria still use plant carbon - but that carbon is released as sugars, proteins and carbohydrates from the root system as exudates. Azotobacter has to grow a large enough colony so that the outer layers of bacteria use up the oxygen before reaching the center of the colony, so that the inner part of the colony lacks oxygen. That means the nitrogenase enzyme can now function and fix N2 gas in the same fashion as Rhizobium does in the nodule.

Question: My reason for asking is in relation to these two critters and compost tea. Rhizobacter is not present in compost piles as it needs a host plant to survive but I'm not sure about Azotobacter.

Answer: Azotobacter can be found in compost piles -- and worm compost too, apparently.

Question: In a situation where a plant is in need of some N in a hurry, I'm considering adding some inocula of azotobacter as a 'bomb' just before applying some tea to speed up the nutrient cycling process. With the comment below (cut from an article on AZ) is seems heaps of O2 is needed for this guy to be happy, so can we presume he will be in a well managed compost or is he only in the soil? "Azotobacter nitrogenase is oxygen-sensitive, but it is believed that the extremely high respiration rate of Azotobacter (possibly the highest of any living organism) soaks up free oxygen within the cells and protects the nitrogenase."

Answer: To have N-fixation occur, you CAN'T have oxygen, but the bacteria take care of that situation for themselves. So, both Rhizobium and Azotobacter (as well as Azospirillum) grow aerobically, but the nitrogenase gene requires reduced oxygen levels. Growing bacteria use up the oxygen, and so the center of the nodule, or the colony, is where nitrogen fixation occurs.

35. Microarthropods 4/30/04 7:22 AM

The larvae is from another group of soil critters called MICROARTHROPODS. The ones with legs may well be collembola, or prostigmatid mites, or even a mesostigmatid mite. If they truly have legs, and not just hold-fats, then you are likely OK with respect to the critters being beneficials. Soil needs microarthropods too, just like nematodes, or protozoa, or earthworms. They are all serving a similar functional role - they consume bacteria and fungi, releasing nutrients in the root zone, for plants to take up and grow. They are part of the team of critters that Mother Nature uses to make sure enough inorganic forms of nutrients become available to your plant, at the times your plant needs, in the rates the plants require. As long as the minimal foodweb is present, plant thrive. Improving the diversity of critters just means you have a healthier plant. So, if you can take a picture of the critters you see (digital camera, optical zoom of 3 or better), and e-mail the picture to me, I can do my best to ID it. May not be able to give you species, but at least get you to "good guy" versus "bad guy" distinction. In all likelihood, however, you are seeing good guys.

36. Beauveria and Microarthropods 1/5/04 7:40 AM

Bueaveria likes lots of soil microarthropods - springtails, beetle larvae, mosquito larvae (ah ha! this fungus can go after that annoying pest!), prostimatids, mesostigmatids, you name it. The more diversity of microarthropods in your soil, the more diversity in cultivar of Beauveria. Of course, it means you can't plow much, and you need a litter layer, or mulch layer on your soil surface. A cover crop helps a great deal too.

37. Microarthropods Aren't in Tea 1/16/04 1:34 PM

Now beneficial microarthropods aren't in compost tea, but their eggs can be, if you use good worm compost or well-matured thermal compost (that means it sat without disturbance for a year or two. Not a normal situation in a commercial composting operation, but is common in Biodynamic compost that requires it to be at least a year old before use. Well-matured compost is SO good because the microarthropods are most likely well and happy. Except if you sieve the compost before you put it out. Sieving destroys..... yep, you got it, the bigger critters. Lost the microarthropods again. Sigh. You have to understand the biology to really understand what is going to be in your materials.

Question: How do you know whether you lost everything, or just the bigger critters, or what?

Answer: Well, that's where doing a soil foodweb analysis is useful. Or just replace everything every time.

Question: OK, what's more expensive?
Answer: Depends on your source of compost, your AACT machine, etc. Contacting a Soil Foodweb Advisor might be the best way to approach this, so you can get a low-down on costs versus time. You can do the instant-soil improvement, or the it-takes-time approach. Instant costs more, just like anything else you try to do instantly. It-takes-time means you don't achieve the end point rapidly, but it costs less money to get the soil into a condition of health. But then you are losing money by having to water a lot, having to pour inorganic nutrients and pesticides on the soil. Talk to your local SFI Advisor, and get the costs figured out.

38. Copper 12/16/03 12:48 AM

It's the concentration of copper in the water when the tank is copper. The critical concentration is 3 ppm. In a tank of copper, that concentration can occur just by simple equilibrium with water. Copper fittings are much less likely to result in copper reaching a toxic level. But your thoughts about the biological decomposition of surfaces should be taken to heart.

39. Copper and Salts 12/16/03 12:44 AM

Quick note about copper pipes in houses. We are trying to prevent organism growth in drinking water. So copper in drinking water will reduce bacterial growth.

Question: How "good" is copper for human consumption?
Answer: Anyway, when we are trying to grow organisms, trying to keep the beneficials alive in a compost or compost tea, then copper is not a good idea. Someone e-mailed me to say someone had messed up big time by suggesting that somehow drinking water and compost tea were in the same category. Two categorically opposite purposes - drinking water should be close to sterile, tea should not.

a. Salt Problems
On to salt problems.

Question: What is it that takes sodium chloride, which is the salt we put on foods, and separate the sodium from the chloride, thus removing that salt problem?
Answer: Any organism. Fungi are really good at decomposing certain kinds of salts, while bacteria are excellent at removing other kinds of salts. A large amount of sodium is needed in cell membrane structures, while chloride plays roles in other places in the cell. Once separated, salt is no longer salt.

Question: Another example: Ammonium nitrate is a salt. But once organisms have their way with it, ammonium will be converted into what in cells? Nitrate will be converted into what in cells?
Answer: Biology converts salt, of any kind, into not-available forms. Concentration is important, as is the presence of water to help dis-associate the salt. Ammonium and nitrate are converted into protein. Not salt anymore, and will not be found as salt, unless some very specific and nasty

processes are allowed to happen. Add the foods to feed the organisms, and "salt" problems go away. Water, temperature, air, etc are also required. Stop focusing on just engineering solutions to problems. Start thinking biologically. There is no salt problem, if the organisms are allowed to be present, and they are fed properly.

40. Microbes and Salt Levels 1/27/04 7:16 PM

If someone said that microbes do not reduce salt levels, first of all, that's a very ambiguous statement -- vague and non-specific, and could be taken a number of different ways. Define salt. Salts disassociate in water. They have positive and negative components which water easily "pulls apart". Calcium phosphate is a salt, for example. Ferric citrate is a salt. Sodium hydroxide is a salt. And you better believe microorganisms can reduce those salt levels! There is quite a bit of literature on phosphate-solubilizing bacteria and fungi which take up both the phosphorus and the calcium, thus removing salt from the soil. Mycorrhizal fungi are famous for their ability to take up the various salts of phosphorus and make the P available to plants.

Nitrogen salts of various kinds are what most people commonly recognize as inorganic fertilizer. Ammonium nitrate, ammonium sulfate, and urea for example. Microbes take up those salts all the time, and convert them into protein, lipids, carbohydrates, DNA, and other cellular components. Same thing for urine, which is why, when you get the right organisms into the soil, and onto plant surfaces, urine will not cause brown spots in the lawn. The nitrogen thus released is taken up and turned into cellular constituents which are not toxic to the plants. Many people mistakenly imagine that sodium chloride is the problem in urine, but it is the high nitrogen that kills most plants. But if sodium chloride was applied, bacteria and fungi need sodium and chloride ions in their metabolic processes (big time in the ADP - ATP energy production cycle and in Krebs cycle), and so both bacteria and fungi "eat" or consume, or sequester (whatever your favorite term) "salt" and turn it into organic matter.

Now if the salt is in a place without any organic matter, no food for the microbes, then the microbes have a problem. High salt concentrations remove water, resulting in osmotic shock which can kill microbes. But just like too much water can kill a person, too much of anything is not a good thing. But you can't make the case that water is bad for people - grin! Water in too high concentration is bad - it's called drowning. Too high salt will kill anything, including people. But it doesn't make people unable to eat salt. We HAVE to have salt, in order to live.

Extreme statements of any kind are very dangerous to make, so if someone said microbes do not reduce salt levels, they were not thinking clearly. There has been some interesting work by several people at the University of California, Davis, on sodium chloride VOLATILIZING bacteria. It does happen. Microbes can turn salt into gaseous forms. Cute, huh? Let's see, the research was done by, darn, memory don't fail me. Ah, Frankenberger, as I recall. Keep those lawns green, even if you have a dog. Oh, and if you still have brown spots in your lawn after applying tea, consider that the biology is trying to tell you something..... you didn't get the biology established, growing and performing its function. Just because we dropped parrots in the Antarctic and they died does not mean that birds can't live at the South Pole. You have to drop the right birds in the right micro-habitat, that's all. It may take time to connect the two, or you may need to do something to figure out what the right habitat is to drop them into, or that you can prepare for them, so they will do their ecological function.

41. Microorganisms Deal with Salt 12/17/03 8:19 AM

Question: As far as I can tell, it is impossible to tell whether your compost has the microbes needed to deal with salt unless you specifically tailor your compost to do so and get it tested. We are not looking for salt-eating microbes anyway.
Answer: All microorganisms deal with salt. All of us "eat" salt, which means that you hydrolyze the salt into it's component parts, and turn it into something else. We ALL do that.

All you need is the food to feed the organisms, and they will do that for you. You don't have to look for special species to do that. You just need a decent amount of LIFE in your soil to get the job done. Salt build up is a message from Mother Nature - not enough life to do the job. The cycle has been broken because someone killed the critters required to do the job, or forgot to feed them. Get the organisms back into the dirt, feed them, and you are STARTED on the way. Relative to how badly the soil was harmed determines the time to clean it up.

Question: What we are looking for are microbes the plant can work with that will help the plant be more salt tolerant. What is the mechanism for making a plant more salt-tolerant? Are you suggesting a physiological change in the plant? The plant will tolerate higher salt concentration in it's phloem?
Answer: But if you do that, the fruit or seed of the plant will most likely have higher salt concentration then as well. I don't think you want that. Salty strawberries, hum, no thanks. The mechanism of biology protecting plants from salt is to mobilize the salt into microbial biomass. Simple numbers. The more biology, the more salt taken up and put into biomass instead of remaining as salt.

Question: The prospect of salt-eating microbes is interesting. If there is such a thing, I hope they never get into the oceans.
Answer: This is like saying, uh, oxygen-utilizing bacteria? How dangerous! If they get into the atmosphere, look out, we won't have oxygen left! But we have oxygen-utilizing bacteria, and fungi, and protozoa, and nematodes, and microarthropods, and people!

Question: There are herds of oxygen-using creatures on this planet, and somehow, we manage to have oxygen still in the atmosphere. Hum. How can that be?
Answer: Nutrients cycle. The fact that we are accumulating a nutrient - the nutrient in the form of a salt - is an indicator that humans are messing up the cycle at the step after the place the nutrient is accumulating. Humans have seriously disrupted normal nutrient cycling. We can pay attention and fix what we are messing up, or we'll destroy the environment that sustains us. Once humans no longer exist as a species, the cycle will return to "normal". Nature doesn't care. Biology will do its job, with or without people. We are just one of billions of species on this planet, and if we mess up, nature can do without us.

Question: Since we are salt water, they would be rather harmful to us also. There are many types of salts in our systems and we need even the trace amounts of rare salts found there.

Answer: Your body controls the environment inside your body. Your tissues are practically sterile - the only things living in you are the cells of your body. If they become invaded by any organism, you will likely die. All of the carbon in your body is food for someone else, some other organisms, big or little. So why aren't you dead? You maintain environments inside you that prevent other organisms from consuming those wonderful proteins, carbohydrates, sugars, and salts, which make up the life support system that maintains you. Thank goodness something consumes the ammonium nitrate salt that we pour on lawns. But we still have more ammonium nitrate, we keep pouring it on. How can that be, if we have nitrate consuming bacteria present in this world? Balance, cycles. Everything cycles. Humans keep trying to salt the world to death, and Nature keeps cycling that salt into something else. Thank goodness!

Question: As I understand it Lithium, as used for some psychotics, is also a salt.

Answer: Lithium is an element. In pure form, it is a metal, I believe, if I remember my chemistry correctly, we combine Li with other elements, like sulfate, or nitrate, to make the salt. In water, it dis-associates, and combines with certain reaction sites in the digestive system to be taken up and is carried to certain receptors in the nervous system. Hum, don't remember the exact mechanism of the interaction to shut down certain receptors in the nervous system from firing. But that is the mechanism by which it works, as I recall. Faulty memory sometimes. But, once across your digestive system lining, there are no other organisms present to compete with a human for that nutrient. In the digestive, there are lots of things that will make Li not-available to the human body. That's why the dose of any chemical has to be figured out, and why diet is often controlled when trying to get something into the blood stream through consumption.

Question: I would hate to think that all these people who find their symptom alleviated through Lithium are at risk by salt-fixing/eating microbes.

Answer: But we are very lucky that we DO HAVE those microbes that hydrolyze Lithium salts.

Question: What do you suppose happens to the Lithium salt in the waste coming out of a human body who is consuming lithium salts?

Answer: If we didn't already have those organisms in this world, we'd be up to our eye-balls in lithium salts. We keep the organisms that do decomposition out of our bodies by making conditions in the body completely inappropriate to grow those decomposers. But decomposers already exist. It's why we have immune systems. Think cycles. Everything cycles. There is already an organism to decompose and chew up any natural compound on this planet. (Please note I said natural compounds. Humans are making synthetic compounds that we apparently do not have any organism that will touch it, and those compounds ARE accumulating). Humans seem bent on destroying all organisms whose functions they don't understand or aren't aware of, and thus are preventing them from doing their jobs. We AREN'T getting back into dirt the organisms that are needed. Inoculation is required - but just in the right places, at the right times, with the right food. There are salt-decomposing organisms already out there. You need to get them back in your soil.

42. Residential Wastes, Biosolids and Water 6/10/04 8:29 Am

Yes, residential waste can include some less-than-wonderful food resources, but they are still food resources for critters. It is a concentration question. The microbes can take care of all the things you mentioned, if there isn't much toxic material. And in residential waste, the relative percentage of horrible stuff is negligible. The heavy metal load isn't high, the critters can sequester, tie-up, and put those toxics into not-plant available forms. But as you say, it's a dead give-away that there is something seriously not-residential waste in the waste stream if the folks giving the biosolid material away limit the amount that can be put on an area. It clearly says that a significant amount of non-residential waste is getting into the waste stream. It should be a cost on industry that they have to remove any toxics they put into the waste stream BEFORE that water leaves their property. The out-cry from industry when you say that, is horrendous, however. "We'll go out of business! We can't afford! It's too expensive!" is what is said.

Question: Wait a minute - is staying in business worth someone's life? Where are our priorities?
Answer: Water has to be cleaned up. The toxics in our water come from:

1. Some - not all, but some - businesses dumping waste into the water. That should not be allowed. If they add it to the water, they have to clean it up before it leaves the premises. Documentation must be required. Clean up has to be included in the cost of doing business. We cannot accept imports into this country if the business doing the manufacturing is polluting the water in their country. Wouldn't that as a law make a huge impact?

2. Urban lawns, gardens, parks, school yards. Leaching and run-off are the problems here. Getting biology back into these soils stops the need for inorganic fertilizers, and pesticides. We have to get working on these places.

Contact your local school system or local government office that controls parks and recreational areas. Get them on compost and compost tea. Be aware that you will run smack into self-interest, however. Be prepared to deal with it BEFORE you walk into the superintendent's office. Who has the contracts for fertilizer? Pesticide application? The superintendent's brother? Then DON'T start with the superintendent. Who is his superior? You go to that person, or to the education board, or whatever, and point out the graft. Then you tell them there's a better way......With lawns, we have to educate the public. Any and all worthwhile ideas are gratefully accepted on how we can improve getting the message out.

3. Agriculture in its many forms. Leaching and run-off is also the culprit here. Lack of decent soil structure, which means the biology has been lost through the use of pesticides, high levels of inorganic fertilizer, and excessive and inappropriate tillage. But the conversion to adding the proper biology and tilling-only-when-absolutely-needed is underway.

The nay-sayers don't know it completely or fully yet, but the old paradigm of chemical agriculture is on its way out. Theirs is a dying mode of doing business. Still, we need help in getting this revolution to continue smoothly, with the least painful consequences for people doing the transition. The organic movement started the movement, we all need to make sure it keeps going without a hitch. Get involved in an organic group. Buy organic. Add your voice to the growing chorus. Support legislation that forces people who manage their soil improperly to have no choice but improve their practices. I don't like having to live by imposed rules, but until the non-toxic way is learned, I'm afraid the limitations imposed by the Clean Water Act and by the NOP will be needed. Someday we won't need them, but for now, it seems to me, for the majority of people that don't want to learn what soil is all about, the law is the only force imposing limitations on toxics.

43. Nitrate in Water 7/7/04 7:51 PM

Question: Wow, how can any government allow nitrate at that high level in any water source? Or is this a well, or bore, and not subject to regulations, because it is not a drinking water source?
Answer: Add enough food to the tea to tie-up the nitrate by having the bacteria and fungi immobilize the N. That means adding extra food resources - and with that you will have an increased demand for oxygen. You may need to monitor oxygen carefully, and add addition aeration.

44. Mechanisms of Worms 6/4/04 11:45 PM
Contact with the outside of the earthworm also kills pathogens.

Question: What mechanism might be at work here? Muco-polysaccharides, colemic fluid?
Answer: I think competition for food resources for space, over-whelming by sheer numbers, and consumption by protozoa are all additional mechanisms, along with the foods that are added by earthworms as they move along.

Question: So it sounds like what is happening outside the worm's body is at least as important as what is happening inside. Most earthworm information I have read emphasizes the activity in their gut.
Answer: I don't think it has even crossed their minds that the outside of the worm is as important a place as the inside.

Question: Sorry about the confusion, I was including the loose use of the word antibiotic which to me means anti-life. If one type of organism inhibits the growth/proliferation of another type, this seems to me to be anti-biotic.
Answer: Right, but this mechanism just doesn't seem to be important in any natural culture condition. If it is important, it is only on a very local scale, and not likely to be of major importance in explaining why natural systems have so little disease. I didn't say no disease, I said little disease.

Question: What might this mechanism be? How does competition reduce the biomass of a particular organism unless they die and are consumed or are consumed directly by protozoa?
Answer: Competition prevents another organism from having the food needed to reproduce. If it doesn't reproduce, it doesn't produce biomass. Someone else does. So, if the pathogens never grow to begin with, we don't have to worry about reducing their biomass. We get stuck on getting rid of problems, in our culture, instead of making sure the problem never occurs. We are a reactionary culture, in the west, and we need to start thinking pro-actively, instead of re-actively.

Question: I was not thinking in terms of a natural situation. Of course, what you said makes perfect sense. I was thinking in terms of liquid biomass cultures like compost tea.

Answer: Ah - in what way is a liquid culture like compost tea not natural? The normal controls of varying temperature, food resource, huge diversity to prevent any one organism from getting way out of control are all operating. Humans can set up good replicates of natural conditions - not perfect replicates, but pretty good ones. So, all the normal controls operate in compost and compost tea.

Question: For instance if after several hours of brewing a typical ACT, one was to add a modest source of active facilitative or anaerobic bacteria (like scat), what would happen?

Answer: Depends on the set of bacteria, fungi, protozoa and nematodes that were in the compost tea. If you have lots of good, beneficial organisms, and the conditions remain aerobic, the likelihood would be that the anaerobic organisms would not be able to gain a foothold in the tea. They would be unable to grow, and so would not become a biomass consideration. The protozoa would consume them. Aerobic conditions would make them go to sleep.

Question: Would the added bacteria die from shock due to the change of environment, go to sleep, or be eaten by protozoa? Or all three?

Answer: As my husband usually says when I give him a multiple choice question: Yep.

45. Earthworms and Weeds 6/15/04 11:28 PM

a. Earthworms: The appearance of earthworms is a good indicator that you have a decent set of bacteria, most likely decent fungi, certainly protozoa in the soil. Earthworms indicate a good foodweb for the mid-successional set of plants. But maybe not a good foodweb for perennials. And if you don't have earthworms, it does not mean you automatically therefore have a poor foodweb. Other creatures can take over the role of earthworms - such as enchytraeids, springtails, other microarthropods. Earthworms can still get by - not happy, but getting by and thus present - even when soil is compacted enough to limit root growth down into the soil. Get a soil corer, or a soil penetromter, or a metal bar, and push into the soil. How far down until you hit compaction? You can have worms in that top layer, but not lower. The worms are working to help chew up the compacted areas, but it may take them awhile.

b. Weeds: Weeds are also a good indicator that your foodweb is not up to par. And you can have earthworms but lots of weeds. That means the bacterial - protozoan foodweb is alive and well enough to provide the earthworms with the food they need, but the balance of bacteria and fungi is out-of-whack to deal with the later successional species of plants. We need to deal with compaction. That means more fungi are needed.

46. Slowing Vegetative Growth 3/24/04 11:51 AM

Ah, but if you manage the soil foodweb correctly, you can slow the rapid vegetative growth of grass and not have to cut as much, but still maintain green color. Same with most any other plant. We are trialing this with a few turf people to figure out what the ratio of fungi:bacteria, AND bacteria to protozoa, fungi to FF nematodes is to control this. There's always more that we can do with the critters. We just need to understand exactly what they do, and why.

47. Chitin-utilizing Organisms 3/21/04 10:33 AM

Few fungi actually contain chitin in their cell walls - but quite nicely, the ones that do are the *oomycetes*, the particularly pathogenic species at that. So, chitin-utilizing organisms will tend to operate AGAINST the pathogen-fungi. Getting chitinase to be expressed in your compost, compost tea or soil is dependent on putting in materials that feed these organisms. Like chitin - which are high in materials like shrimp shells, and dead insects.

48. Chitin 3/18/04 11:57 PM

Chitin is a food resource for some really good fungi - which tend to also attack and consume the *oomycetes*, which is the group of fungi that has quite a few of the disease causing fungi in it. Not all the bad guys are *oomycetes*, but many are. And chitin seems to feed the beneficial fungi that protect against the diseases.

49. Chitinase 10/15/03 12:24 PM

Typically it is both bacterial and fungal species that make chitinase. Different components in the chitin molecules in crustaceans versus fungi at times, so the exact enzyme can be different. I actually think it is probably more likely that the chitin feeds a community of bacteria and fungi that are exceptional at chewing on pests. We don't have good data for the mechanism of whether it is chitinase production that selects against the pests, or just that chitin is a food that selects for the organisms that compete well with the pests.

50. Eel Worm or Nematode 5/16/04 10:32 AM

Question: Phasmarhabditis hermaphrodita (just checked) which is a bacteria feeding 'eel worm'.
Answer: Opps, not an eel worm at all. Eel worms are Enchytraeids. Phasmarhabditus is a nematode. Nematodes are microscope round worms, not eel worms at all. Phasmarhabditus is a bacterial-feeding nematode found in some soils in the US. Right species in our soils? I'm sure it's there somewhere.

51. Fungi Growth 5/15/04 8:45 AM

Fungi grow from the tip cells. They increase in biomass, the hypha grows out, the organism expands from the growing ends. Reproduction implies a sexual interaction occurring, and most of the oomycetes, the ascomycetes and many of the basidiomycetes do not undergo sexual reproduction ever. Spore production does not require sexual reproduction. Spores are just a process of the fungus budding off a hyphal extension, while putting a spore coat down to protect the hypha, and then shutting down metabolism until things are better.

Question: So, not reproduction. But multiplication?
Answer: Growth can be just simple multiplication of cells, or increase in biomass, or production of a new individual. Like a person getting fatter (accumulating more carbon) and multiplying fat cells, multiplication of cells does not necessarily imply the production of a new individual. Hypha grow outward, the cells multiply, but that does not imply production of a new individual. More biomass, yes, more cells, yes. But new individual? Not necessarily.

52. Spore Waking Up 11/28/03 8:20 AM

Think of bacterial or fungal spores as being like the seed stage of a plant. They germinate and grow when the conditions are right for them to germinate and grow. They went into dormant phase to escape conditions that were going to kill them. They won't wake up until conditions are good for them again.

Question: If I'm spraying 300,000,000 spores, should I expect a colony of microbes to start from each spore?

Answer: You could expect that, yes. That is generally the way the 300 million spores were determined in the first place. In the real world, however, many of those spores will not fall into a place where the habitat is correct for them to perceive the cues that make them wake up. Whenever the environment becomes positive for them, then they will wake up and grow.

Question: Also, are there anaerobic spores and aerobic spores? Do I need to be concerned about that?

Answer: All spores can survive anaerobic and aerobic conditions. Spores are dormant, and as such, relatively impervious to the environment. To kill a spore requires extreme measures, such as autoclaving, which is steam heat at 15 pounds per square inch pressure for 21 minutes. To determine whether the spore will be awakened when conditions are aerobic or anaerobic requires an understanding of the species of organism. Spores are dormant stages, that's all. You need to know what organism it is a dormant stage of in order to know whether it needs aerobic or anaerobic conditions in which to grow.

Question: And how long does it take for spores to wake up? Hours, weeks, a season?

Answer: This depends on the conditions the spore finds itself in. If conditions are correct, a spore generally germinates and grows within a few hours. Some spores are still capable of being brought-back-to-active after 150 years in the British Museum. Some spores are capable of returning to active stage following return to the earth's surface following 64 million years buried in deposits in the earth's surface. Classical ecological answer: It depends.

53. Successful Organic Orchard 1/8/04 11:14 PM

Question: Does this orchard rank as satisfying the successful organic orchard then?

Answer: Not if Imidan is used, I suppose. But, try to work on cutting out the chemical toxin, if you can. And you should be able to IF we get the full food web into the system. When organic matter doesn't accumulate as humus, as I think you are describing by saying the clay soil devours the organic matter quickly, you are describing a VERY bacterial situation. I'd like to have actual data, of course, but in general, when you apply OM (organic matter) and it goes "poof!" -- that's bacteria at work. If you had fungal dominated soil, then you'd develop the humus layer, and the organic matter would hang around for about 6 months (half gone in one month, but then that last half takes longer, and develops humus, which helps build soil even better).

Question: I don't have a "residual" problem. At least by "eyesight" methods. Which is obviously a simple minded method!

Answer: Yes, and simple is good. Occam's Razor applies! When the organic matter disappears, it means you have some good biology. Good! Then, we need to figure out what biology. The fast way to figure it is to do the testing with SFI, but you can observe things and come to a pretty good conclusion about what's going on. So, the decomposition being rapid is good, but now you are describing too fast. With respect to soil structure being built, if you get a metal pipe, or a solid metal rod, about a quarter to a half inch diameter, and push it into the soil, when do you first notice that it gets harder to push the rod or pipe into the soil? Sounds like it might happen at about 2 feet.

Question: So, how far down into the soil should roots of plum, or peach go?
Answer: Please don't answer that question based on current horticultural thinking, because we have done things to our soils recently that force the roots to stay shallow. Before orchards are put in these days, we compact the soil by the management that we do, and then we think it is normal that tree roots are constrained to the top 6 to 12 inches. Bad, bad news for roots.

Question: How far do roots go down on a plum tree?
Answer: Way deeper than 2 to 2.5 feet. It sounds like you have taken some really compacted soil, and gotten things started. But in 15 years, we want to build soil that roots can grow into down to 20 feet. Roots go through the water. They reach below the water table. Water has to have good aeration too, or the anaerobic conditions in the water will kill the plant roots. You've gotten things started in your tough clay soil, but don't stop now!

Question: I live in Michigan, Zone 5, and have rich clay soil left by the receding glaciers. Problem is, no organic matter to speak of after the builders left us with the classic clay subsoil after grading the lot, etc. It's rich soil but devoid of organic matter as you know.
Answer: Your soil is very young, and all the nutrients you want should be in that soil. But you could have lost the calcium you need. That is very common in compacted soil. Nitrates, and those nutrients that move relatively rapidly with water will be lost too. Have to get them back. So when making your lasagna compost, add eggshells. Use your soft rock in the composting too. Not straight onto the soil, because any rock, lime, gypsum, N fertilizer, P fertilizer, whatever, is a salt. And salts kill organisms, pushing you backwards on the holding-nutrients scale of success.

Question: I love adding the organic amendments and it is going to be hard to stop adding so much as you suggest. It's just plain fun for me, it's not work.
Answer: I DID NOT SAY TO STOP ADDING ORGANIC MATTER. I said STOP ADDING SO MUCH N! Big difference. Add organic matter to your heart's content. Well, ok, in some soils it can be overdone, but in a clay soil of your description, you will not have to worry about that in your lifetime, most likely. But please, differentiate between inorganic forms of N, and organic forms of N. I have to laugh at chemical salespeople, who like to say, "N is N! It doesn't matter where N comes from, or what form it is." Such ignorance revealed when they say that! Think about yourself – is the form of N important? If I handed you a glass of nitrate, what would happen to you if you drank it? Is the source of N important? Just try consuming your N as ammonia…

Question: What is the form of N that people need?
Answer: Protein. Comes as meat, dairy products, eggs, or plant material, including seeds, grains, nuts, etc. The form of N, and the source of that N are very important. Plants need N as nitrate or

ammonium, perhaps as protein. But nitrate is the most water-mobile form of N, nitrate is second, and ammonium is third. Organic N tied up in the bodies of bacteria and fungi are not leachable to speak of. Well, unless you mess up the soil seriously by adding so much salt…So, cool it on the excess nitrogen. Keep adding organic matter.

Question: I can't make compost piles on my lot as there is really no room.
Answer: You can't manage a pile that is 4 ft high and 6 foot wide in a corner someplace? Or several piles in several places? That you turn twice, maybe three times? OK, takes 4 months to be mature, but if you start with the right mix of organic matter, it almost composts itself.

Question: And I don't want to turn the neighbors off.
Answer: Why would compost turn the neighbors off? Are you sure you are talking compost? Or are you are thinking of making putrefying organic matter, not compost? Real compost DOES NOT STINK, EVER. Real compost does not have leachate coming out of it. Soggy, water-logged organic matter piles are just horrible, and are not compost. Don't put that material on a plant you care about.

Question: Why do so many people think compost stinks, draws flies, and has dangerous leachates?
Answer: Because you have never been taught how to make compost, that's what. Read the information by the Luebkes. Then read my information on compost. The SFI website is finally getting up, and if you go look, I think all the stuff on compost will be up!

Question: That's why I use the mulch mower and lasagna compost to decompose organic material. I wish I had a spot to make a compost pile but I don't.
Answer: You compost-in-place, and there's nothing wrong with that. Just DON'T add so much excess N! You have enough already.

Question: Finally, I didn't want to give you the wrong impression about my trees and plants. They are growing extremely well IMHO. The fruit is delicious, dense and healthy. Same for veggies. Flower beds grow good flowers and I don't appear to have any excessive leaf growth that you would expect with too much N application.
Answer: Phew! Good. But you know what? It can be better. You are still doing something to attract PC. So AACT is working for you, and if you keep working at the AACT, you'll probably deal with the PC.

Question: I buy most of my compost from a store that sells Forest Floor compost that has wood chips and manure as the ingredients. I definitely see fungal strands in that compost. Mushrooms grow from it when applied to the soil occasionally. Is that a good sign?
Answer: I want to see a diversity of mushrooms, not just one kind. Every time you are out walking in the forest, and see good fungi growing in the forest humus, take some home with you. Good fungi can be pink, yellow, gold, lemon, brick color, red, mustard, and of course, white.

Question: The dogs have a favorite spot to pee and do leave a brown spot.

73

Answer: Hum, work on getting the food web right in there. Needs help, or the organisms would take care of the excess inorganic N. Add EXTRA tea to that area. The paths that develop because of the dogs is really a result of running on the soil when it is wet. And not having truly great soil structure. I've pounded 500 pounds weights on really good soil, and seen no compaction develop, because the biology was really in good shape, good chemistry was in place. Amazing – the soil squishes, but then springs back. OM level of around 8%, of course. Structural integrity requires the building materials to be in the soil, and the foods to feed the organisms. OM does both jobs.

Question: "Exit the bloodmeal" no please don't say that, I love how a little bloodmeal helps growth. Anyways I'll do what you say and stay away from bloodmeal for now.
Answer: Why don't you try a few experiments? See whether bloodmeal is really needed, if you get the full foodweb in place. Do the bloodmeal, no bloodmeal, and then a full foodweb treatment. Full foodweb - compost in the spring, tea drench of the soil in the spring, core to the bottom of the root zone, drench cores with straight tea, fill cores with sand (70%) and compost (30%), the foliar applications each week, or as needed to deal with diseases and pests.

Question: I'll also try to limit the alfalfa and feeds I put in the yard but that soil of mine devours any organic matter I place on it. That stuff is gone within two weeks in mid-summer applications. Do I really have to reduce those applications? It's just so much fun for me to add these things. I know that sounds weird but I do enjoy it.
Answer: Limit the alfalfa meal. You just don't need it. Put on a bit more carbon, to feed the fungi better. You should see litter decomposition slow down compared to what you have right now. Too bacterial! Use some feathermeal, or corn gluten instead of anything with high N levels.

Question: I use bonemeal a lot to add calcium. Is that a bad thing. I get very good flowering, etc., with bonemeal. Why do you say I have an iron problem? All plants seem to be deep green, healthy and growing densely. No chlorosis is seen.
Answer: I think I was talking to people who have compaction problems, and addressing a possible situation that is common when compaction occurs. Sorry, I stopped concentrating on you, and started doing general teaching. You can take the professor out of the University, but you can't stop the professor from teaching.

Question: I always grind up the leaves with the mulching mower and never leave them whole to decompose. I don't see fungal strands in the leaves as they are decomposing but they do decompose quickly.
Answer: Yep, strongly bacterial decomposition, which is good step one and two, but now, to move beyond that and get humus you need steps 3 through 12. Need to get the fungi going, you want to start seeing those strands. In the lawn, ok, no, it needs to be bacterial, but you want more fungi present so the OM you add doesn't go "poof!". But not too great fungal. Yes, you are right, balance is important. But under the trees, help the fungi to the best you can. The beneficial fungi, right? Don't want to have the disease fungi, and that's where creating the habitat is so important. Foods to feed the good guys, homes for them to live in. AIR! Water, food, comfort.

Question: The soil devours the leaves. I mean it Elaine - the soil devours the leaves. In fact, you can't visibly see most of the leaves I mulched last October. I have a lot of worms, so maybe they're mixing up the organic matter and soil?

Answer: Exactly! You have a lot of Lumbricus, or night crawler types of worms. These guys like to take litter material and take it into their burrows, and grow herds of bacteria and some fungi. The leaf material is important – I think. Well, pretty sure. We need more work on this but green grass clippings will grow mostly bacteria, while oak, conifer needles, will grow mostly fungi. So, the kind of carbon determines whether the soil where the worms are will be fungal or bacterial. But the presence of the worms is a good indicator you don't have pesticide residues. I didn't catch you saying this before, but you did say it. So where you have worms, the soil food web has good bacteria, protozoa and nematodes, but you still lack fungi for your trees.

Question: My objective with adding feeds is to provide organic matter and fertilizer. That's all. I hear you when you say I'm overdoing it. I'll limit those applications. However, it's so much fun for me to add those things. They decompose quickly IMHO, but I'll try to limit those feeds.

Answer: Limit just the nitrogen, ok? Keep the organic matter additions.

Question: I use molasses to hasten decomposition of the organic material I'm adding to the soil. Didn't that help in getting 2.5 feet of clay loam from clay subsoil in 15 years? I'll limit this to grassy areas mainly in the future.

Answer: The molasses helps the bacteria, and so would be ok in the grass areas, and in the veggie garden, BUT NOT the trees. OK?

Question: I mainly add cornmeal or oatmeal to the ACT along with kelp, rock powder and 1 Tablespoon of molasses. That's about it for the majority of my brews. I generally see some fungal threads in the tea, they're small but they're there. I don't know the percentage however.

Answer: So, a test might be a good idea. I expect you could drop the molasses in the tea, you have enough bacteria, you need to let the fungi have their day.

Question: I definitely see fungal growth in the ACT dregs. Mushroom growth sometimes happens from the areas I drop the dregs. Not always, just sometimes. Remember though, I've only used ACT for two years now. Is that enough time to expect permanent soil changes?

Answer: Yes, that's enough time. Example: We put one application of fungal compost on a soil that had been at pH 4.5 for as long as anyone knows, and the conventional approach said to add 8 tons of lime per hectare, to fix pH. Every year, pH shifted upwards for a few weeks, and crash! back to 4.5. One application of fungal compost, and the pH rose to 6.8, and has stayed there for the last 12 months. Ah, soil chemistry folks, tell me again that soil biology doesn't control soil pH? Mushrooms are good signs. But over-apply N in the tree area, and that will set up a stressful situation for the trees.

Question: Lasagna compost - I would say about 1/3 manure and 2/3 leaves. Generally, I see that "white" fungus growing on the manure chunks. Is that good?

Answer: Yep, good. Add those handfuls of fungi that you collect on walks in the forest to the lasagna compost. Take a handful of your lasagna compost next spring – see all those little critters just barely visible? The little white guys? The little reddish ones? You don't see them? Well, I have to admit my eyes are no longer able to focus on them without some help, so get a magnifying glass. If you see them, they are even better indicators that life is fungal in that soil. You should see at least 10 to 20 per handful of the compost. If not, you don't have enough fungal life, and you know then what you need to work on.

Question: Spreading the dregs from my juicing is just to use the organic matter. Much like a lasagna compost. That's all. I sometimes see that "white" fungus growing on the pulp but I usually water the pulp into the soil and don't see much of that fungal growth. I water it in because it attracts too many flies.
Answer: What does attracting flies mean? Putrefaction is happening right, but what exactly draws flies? Any kind of alcohol. and the anaerobic products such as hydrogen sulfide produced only in anaerobic conditions. Which means your S, or N, or P has gone where? Can you put the juices into the lasagna compost areas instead? You aren't helping the trees with the juice. In the veggie garden – ok, as long as you do water it in. Bacteria grow so fast in juice material, and if there is poor aeration, you have anaerobic conditions no time flat.

Question: There you go again Elaine. Telling me to limit the application of the meals, etc. LOL. I'll try Elaine but I just love to apply those meals. It's fun. (I know - I'm wacko.) But you have a great point - the birds are pooping and fertilizing the yard.
Answer: You just like to be out enjoying all the great things you have done in your yard. I know the syndrome. I have the same problem (grin!) But, to not attract PC, and so avoid the insecticide you are applying, do just this little bit more. Limit the NITROGEN. Don't confuse Nitrogen with organic matter though, ok?

Question: Mulch mowing dead veggie material. Just more "lasagna" type composting. I can't make a compost pile where I live. Too unsightly for the neighbors, etc. I wish I had more room!!! I helped make huge compost piles when I was young and worked for a landscape company. I know how to do it but just don't have the room here.
Answer: Ah, what did those compost piles smell like? Were you really making compost, or just reducing waste?

Question: Boiling leaf tea. Just more of my wacko gardening practices. I learned this from my grandfather and he swore by it. He felt it gave a good dose of tannic acids, etc., to the soil where it helped "feed the soil". Mainly maple and oak leaves are what I collect. Of that, most are oak leaves. There are some beech, birch, hickory and other hardwood leaves in the mix because some of the leaves I collect come from a nearby forest where I walk the dogs.
Answer: OK, good fungal foods. Keep doing that under the trees.

Question: Coffee grinds, just another organic amendment this wacko adds to his yard. Evergreen shrubs get the majority of this stuff.
Answer: Dig in what you have put down. See any fungi? Then ok. If no fungi, get some really fungal material (Alaska humus? Check the SFI website for fungal products, fungal compost and get some as an inoculum. Or put your boiling oak and maple leaf tea on the coffee grounds. Keep it fungal under the evergreens.

Question: Freshly ground corn and crimped oats. Just adding more organic matter. More wacko behavior - LOL. The materials seem to decompose very quickly.
Answer: At the risk of sounding just as "wacko" as you (big grin!), you want to slow that decomposition just a bit, then, by getting fungi in there.

Question: Human urine - wacko behavior again. Just adding organic material. It doesn't "burn" the grass and the grass is mainly where I apply it.
Answer: This is different from what you said in the previous post, I think. As long as you aren't seeing burning, you probably have the biology to deal with this high N addition. And in the grass, no problem. Under the trees – make sure it would go on top of an area with good lasagna compost, or wood chips. It does help the bacteria much more than the fungi.

Question: Ok, I get it Elaine LOL. I'm adding too much fertilizer. It's going to be so hard for me to stop doing these things. I love doing it so much!! What advice can you give to limit the habits of an obvious wacko? I probably should have a some tissue analysis, but my plants grow so well that I never saw the need for one. Isn't it possible that PC is migrating to my area from adjacent forests and neighbors trees?
Answer: Yes, but all insects "migrate". We protect plants from white flies, spider mites, scale, and other insects, so why not PC? The insects are attracted to your trees, coming to investigate what looks and even more, smells like a good site, but something is encouraging them to then to stay. Make it less inviting for them, and more inviting for the organisms that would like to make a meal of any PC that come to visit. So, again, check your microarthropod community. Get the magnifying glass out and go on safari looking for big game. Well, it's big game from my point of view. Remember, I'm a microbiologist! Those springtails, mesostigmatids, prostimatids, etc are lions and tigers and bears (oh my!) to the critters I usually look at!

Question: Btw, I don't have any weeds to speak of. When one pops up I just yank it out by hand.
Answer: Excellent! That's as it should be. But consider the fungal cover crop plants under the trees. Maintain the fungi, the mycorrhizal fungi and the higher level predators and shade and block out the weeds at the same time. I really enjoy getting into the specifics, but you can see that I can't often do this. For folks that want this kind of one-on-one interaction about what to do for problems, please check the SFI website, and contact an SFI adviser, and get them to help you do what I've started to do here.

54. Prions 1/8/04 10:28 PM
Whether it is copper that causes the prion to go rouge, or something else, we still have to deal with the material once it is present. And if we can be assured that normal decomposition processes remove the copper, or chew up the carbon backbone, it's a relief to think there is a way to exit prions, or rouge prions.

55. Keritinase 1/7/04 4:28 PM
Keratinase is indicated as the enzyme that decomposes prions! Good old Bacillus licheniformis! This is good news, because guess what compost abounds in? If you use hair, feathers, fungal hyphae and other similar materials in the compost, you are enhancing keratinase! So, compost is a good way to deal with suspect materials.

Question: So, what concentrations are needed to make sure 100% reduction?
Answer: Well, that needs to be figured out.

56. Biological Control Methods 1/5/04 6:15 AM

Question: Why don't the biological control methods work?
Answer: Just like a person, if you don't set up the habitat so the person can work, then amazingly, the person isn't productive. If you don't feed a person, they don't get anything done. If you don't give them air, they don't get anything done, because they are dead. If you don't give them a way to write down their findings, they don't produce any written reports. Worthless person!

Question: So, if you have not fed Beauveria, how can you expect this fungus to work?
Answer: You dump the fungus in the soil, but still see the insect, you say, "see, it doesn't work", when in fact, it is you not doing your job of feeding the fungus. When you sanitize your orchard by raking up the leaves each fall, that's fungal food you are taking away. And you wonder why biological approaches don't work. Food. Water. Air. Comfort.

Question: Did you make the soil habitat right for plum curculio, or did you make the soil habitat right for the fungi that parasitize the larval stages of the insect? Or for the nematode that can spread the bacterial inoculum that will kill the insect? If you'd like to answer my question - have you measured compaction in your soil? Have you made any effort to make the soil a suitable home for beneficial biology, or have you just assumed that you have done this?
Answer: There can be light years between what you think and what actually is. And if you are going to come back at me and say you don't have the money, or interest, or whatever, to test with SFI, that is NOT what I'm telling you to do here. I have, over and over, explained how to assess compaction in your soil without ever sending a test into SFI.

Question: So, what is the situation with compaction in your soil? Have you given the biology you so easily dismiss a chance to work? Can we not feed you for the next three months? Can we put you in a water-filled room with no aeration and see how long you continue to function? Can we then say "See, he can't do the tasks we give him, he's worthless." Is turn-about fair play?

57. When Organic Approaches Don't Work 1/4/04 8:39 AM
When we run into problems, it is often because there is pesticide residue in the soil that is keeping the biology that combats, inhibits, or consumes the larval stages from being able to return and thrive. Just because you add organisms doesn't mean they will survive, or grow. You have to make the habitat right for them to be able to do their thing. If your soil is compacted, and you add *Heterorhabditus* expecting him to do the job, think again. Won't happen until you fix your soil. So when organic approaches "don't work", it's often because you haven't done your work of figuring the whole habitat problem. So, tell me, how do you figure out if your soil is compacted? Have you done that examination?

58. Reduced Organism Activity Conditions 11/8/03 4:37 AM

Good points. To fully sterilize something requires nothing living left, including spores and dormant stages. Cooking certainly moves us in that direction, but fully sterile? Not if there are dormant stages such as spores left in the meat. But the cooking process is done in part to reduce microbial life on the surfaces of meat, grains, veggies, etc. Drying is another process that moves materials in the direction of reduced activity of the organisms in the material, but may not actually result in sterile conditions. As long as we do not provide the conditions to allow growth of the remaining organisms after sanitizing the surfaces then decomposition will not occur.

59. Ways of Achieving Sterilization 11/7/03 6:58 AM

I think you need to re-think what you are considering as sterilization. You might be requiring a big autoclave in your mind, in order for something to be sterilized, when in fact there are many other ways of achieving sterilization.

Question: When we boil something, what does that do? When we steam heat each day for three days, does that rate in your mind as a kind of sterilization?
Answer: You sterilize your food all the time. It's called cooking. Don't tell me Coors doesn't sterilize their grains. I have worked with Coors on their production methods. All culture media are sterilized, some is even sterilized in an autoclave.

a. Plating in a Sterile Medium

I am NOT against "plating(enumerating) in a sterile medium". I have clearly said, over and over, that plate counts cannot be used to determine diversity. Plate count approaches cannot be used to determine diversity. It is a flat-out, total mis-use of methodology to represent plate counts methods as being able to give reliable, useful answers about diversity. As I have pointed out over and over, plate count methods are useful if you already know the precise growing conditions for a bacterial, and sometimes even for a fungal, culture.

Approximately 99.9% or more of the bacterial or fungal species we know exist in soil, compost, or compost tea do not grow on any medium, in any condition that we can produce in the lab. When you do select to grow a particular species, or set of species in the lab, the medium has to be sterilized in order to grow those particular desired strains of organisms.

b. Mushroom Facilities

All commercial mushroom facilities sterilize the media they use. Just because you do not recognize the sterilization part of the process does not mean that they do not use sterilization procedures.

c. Commercial Beer Production

Commercial beer production centers treat their grains to prevent contamination of their products. While you may have worked in a part of the beer production process, the grain may have been treated before it ever arrived at that facility. All sterilization does not require an autoclave.

60. Sterilization Required for Culturing Specific Species 11/6/03 7:34 AM

Any time you culture microorganisms in order to grow a specific species, or set of organisms, sterilization has to be performed. The set of microorganisms that are normal inhabitants of any surface have to be killed if you want to be 100% successful at growing the desired set of organisms. To be assured that a pure culture of *Agaricus bisporus* (the white mushroom we all love to eat) will grow on a desired substrate, all the other organisms on the substrate (food resource) have to be killed, or a significant percentage of the time, some other organisms will out-compete the *Agaricus*, and the grower will lose money.

a. Sterilizing Grains -- it's done all the time. Typically grains used to make beer are at least pasteurized, and usually sterilized, especially in large production facilities where they can't allow contamination to destroy the product they are trying to sell. Does the heat treatment affect the quality of the final product? Sure it does.

b. Wine Production

Wine production uses high sugar content, inoculation of HIGH levels of yeast, and low pH to control the fermentation instead of sterilizing the initial starting materials. If you use high heat on sugars and proteins - which is what grape juice is all about - you denature the sugars and proteins, and the yeasts you want for the fermentation, won't grow. Some folks use sulfur compounds to try to control yeast populations, but many of us are sensitive to that sulfur in the wine.

Question: Why don't we sterilize or pasteurize the substrates gong into compost tea brews?
Answer: You could do that, except it is usually not necessary. You do want to be careful though. We recently had a person sending in tea where tea had an unpleasant microbe growing in it. The person got upset at me (they still aren't speaking to me), because we showed them their tea was contaminated. We asked them to send in all the starting materials for the tea, and proved that the contamination was in the molasses. They wanted to sue the company making the molasses (sigh), except they were using a molasses container that they had been using for years. Probably that container became contaminated by various people making tea. Not the fault of the company providing the molasses.

c. Take Home Story Number One: If you put compost tea onto things you will eat without washing them, make certain the material you put into the tea are food-grade.

d. Take Home Story Number Two: If you live in high human density areas, wash your food before you eat it. What was on the hands of the person who handled that food before you? Did that deer that wandered through your garden pee as it walked through? Wash fruit before you eat it. Haven't had time to go look for USDA peat pasteurization regulations. Will try to do that soon.

61. Bindweed and Nutsedge 8/21/03 5:42 Am

Bindweed and nutsedge both tend to be helped by high nitrate levels. So, you have to drop the nitrate. You do this by tying up nitrate in the bacterial and fungal biomass. And that requires foods to feed bacteria and fungi. If the tea adds the inoculum of bacteria and fungi but your soil does not have foods to grow bacteria and fungi, you won't get the reduction in the nitrate, and may have little effect on the weeds. Weeds that are present because of lack of Ca require that you get Ca back in the soil, but not just Ca in the soil for a few days, but high Ca in the soil during the germination period, OK? Weeds requiring low iron to out-compete your grasses (foxglove, for example, or moss), need low iron in the spring period. If your grasses have plenty of AVAILABLE iron, then the moss will not typically be a problem.

62. *Sclerotinia, Trichoderma* and Crop Rotation 8/19/03 1:15 PM

Question: It has been at least 15 years since this work was done. It did not work on other peanut diseases because they unlike *Sclerotinia* would also grow on Cornmeal. *Sclerotinia* does not grow much on cornmeal and thus allows the *Trichoderma* to get ahead.

Answer: The thing you have to pay attention to is the limited species that were used in the testing on peanut diseases. There was little to no organic matter in the peanut soil. They added one kind of food resource - cornmeal. What did the Trichodrema have to grow on? A little corn meal, which is not Trichoderma's favorite food. What else did it have to grow on? What about the herd of other fungi that should be there to suppress the disease? They don't count? When you limit your vision to just one species interacting with one other species, you are going to miss the boat. Think whole system here.

a. Crop Rotation

There are lots of reasons for crop rotation. Disease is a major one. Take away the host for the disease, and the disease will lessen. The real trick is, however, to out-compete, inhibit and consume the disease as well. That's what the proper microbial foodweb will do. It lessens the need for crop rotation, but does not remove it, unless you are putting compost back into the system. You need to have a diversity of food resources to feed the diversity of organisms in the soil that are needed. Crop rotation can help. Compost helps. Tea helps. Tillage helps at certain times. Weeds can be a benefit, if you pay attention to what they are trying to tell you. All these things together, in a whole system, help you build a healthy soil.

63. Organisms and pH 8/12/03 6:42 Am

The chart of availability of nutrients relates strictly to pH. Takes no account of organic matter, salts, biology, roots, or anything else. It is strictly true, based on just pH, but biology is always changing pH around each individual. Roots change pH -- Bacteria, fungi, protozoa, nematodes, water-logging, and all kinds of other things. Take a soil pH, but that is just a sum of the pH in all the microsites, and mixed together, it ignores the fact that pH was one thing next to the root, something else next to the mycorrhizal fungus, something different yet again next to the bacterium. So, it is correct, once you add the organisms, pH is less important. And we have data on a nearly 2 unit pH shift with addition of the biology to soil within a few weeks, and maintaining that pH shift for 6 months now over a large acreage here in OZ. And soil scientists will tell you that's impossible. They need to pay attention to the biology.

64. Moss 3/22/04 10:52 PM

No truth to the grass clippings causing moss. Typically, moss means a couple things, compaction, lack of air into your soil, water puddling on the surface. The soil goes anaerobic. Moss is now more competitive than grass in this soil condition. A major factor is that iron has been put into a plant unavailable form when it is reduced. If air returns to the soil as the soil dries, then the iron just becomes even more plant-unavailable. Your soil chemistry test will tell you there is plenty of iron. But because harsh extractants were used to pull that plant unavailable iron out of the soil, that test means nothing. You have to get the biology back into the soil in order to make that plant unavailable form of Fe into a plant available form. In general, phosphate is too high, and calcium (Ca) too low in soil where moss is rampant. So, lots is wrong. You have to add Ca, since it is flat out lost when things go anaerobic. You have to get fungi back into the soil, since they are what holds onto added Ca. Otherwise you are wasting your money, you lose so much of the Ca you add. You have to tie up the excess phosphate too, and getting the biology to grow and take up that PO4 is about the only way to do this in an economic manner. You need to get the organisms back into the soil to convert plant not-available Fe into plant available. So, tea! Compost! Get the good critters back into the soil, and feed them! But you need QUALITY compost, not any stinky, smelly organic matter! There are standards.

65. Moss and Lawn 3/24/04 12:31 PM
To deal with moss, you need to be adding plant-available iron. So add a kelp high in iron in your tea. Just a little kelp - look at some of the recipes that have been posted in previous threads. Kevin Richardson's post on kelp was an excellent one recently that dealt with amounts. Add some fish hydrolysate, if you need to green up the lawn, and some calcium in the form of rock dust, to help de-flocculate your clays. That relates to getting rid of the compaction. Check your roots to see how deep they go, and if your tea is doing a good job, you'll see the roots going down deeper in just a few weeks. Then do a soil chemistry and a soil biology test, to see where you need to go from there.

66. Moss Control 1/5/04 9:48 PM

Question: How's the tea brewing going? Is the sludge on the bottom of the brewer getting dealt with?
Answer: For moss control, what you need to do is provide the nutrient that is lacking in the soil, and that is why the moss can out-compete the grass.

Question: So, what is that nutrient?
Answer: I believe there is some good evidence from the turf folks at Oregon State to indicate that iron is the limitation. But if you test your soil, the soil chemistry report will come back and say that iron is in excess. So, I'll explain what's going on. The extracting chemicals that most soil chemistry labs use are quite harsh, and extract iron that is not available to the plant. If the soil has become compacted and anaerobic, or will be reduced, but the instant any air enters the picture, the iron will precipitate as hydride. Not plant available. It takes the proper biology to mineralize that hydride material back into a plant available form. But the proper biology will not survive anaerobic conditions. So, the recommendation from the turf folk is to add ferric sulfate. Which kills the fungi, which are the organisms which are responsible for mineralizing hydride material. It means you keep applying more iron, and keep killing the fungi. Is it that the turf folk don't understand what they are really doing, or are they just trying to keep you buying the product that is sold by the company that provides funding to their society?

Question: Anyway, how do you get off the treadmill?
Answer: You need iron in a plant available form, that does not kill the fungi, and may in fact allow fungi to grow better.

Question: The form of iron?
Answer: Ferric citrate. So, same dosage as the ferric sulfate, just make it ferric citrate. Encourages some good bacteria, as well as some fungi. Probably still want to follow up with some better fungal foods, and possibly an inoculum of beneficial fungi, if you need to improve diversity of the fungi.

67. Weeds 11/16/03 8:31 AM

Question: I have heard somewhere (probably at the one-and-only bio-dynamics workshop I went to many years ago) that the predominant weed is able to supply the needs of the soil. I took that to mean that the major minerals, and trace elements could be added back to the soil by applying these plant teas. Someone in this group probably knows which weeds have a predominance of which minerals, and which weeds are telling us something about our soil.
Answer: The problem there is that sometimes weeds seem to concentrate nutrients, sometimes they don't. You need to do plant tissue analysis to know that the weed is higher in concentration in a particular element before trusting to this approach. OK, I'm a scientist and require data before I will back anything. Other people don't need that level of quantification, and I'll give you that just because we haven't quantified something, does not mean it isn't true. Grin.

Question: Classical scientist, huh? How do we reconcile this?
Answer: We need data. Show that all comfrey in all parts of the US, in all soils, concentrates N, K, etc. I suspect that in fact, comfrey in Oregon concentrates different nutrients than comfrey in Georgia. Some work is needed.

Question: I have lots of huge thistles (supplies copper, I think), Cobblers Pegs, plantain, and a host of other weeds and I reckon these could make a very "nutritious" soil additive once they've fermented.
Answer: Could be. Any chance you could test that anaerobic/fermentation tea after it is done, and show the nutrient level? Or even better, do a plot of just adding water, a lot of the just AACT, and a plot of the AACT plus plant tea, and in a week, pull plant tissue, and have an analysis done of each of the three areas. SHOW US THE DATA, if you would. That way you

68. Shift in Weed Species 8/3/03 8:53 PM

We see shifts in the weed species with use of tea. Don't get rid of all of the weeds (because to some extent, a weed is in the eye of the beholder. If the habitat for the "weed" is the same as the crop plant, tea is going to be hard pressed to exit the weed). Typically tea gets rid of weeds that indicate high nitrate, nitrite or mineral N presence. If you don't get rid of these weed species (thistle, many composites, chickweed, horsetail) then your tea isn't right, or something is causing nitrate to be present. Imbalance of predator - prey relationships? Proximity to a highway and fuel/air pollution? Fertilizer drift?

69. Stop Spraying Chemicals and Weeds Exit the System 1/5/04 7:40 AM

Anyway, in succeeding years, if you stop chemical spraying (and that includes herbicides - no more Round-Up!), then you maintain and improve soil life. Weeds exit the system, because you get rid of the excess nitrate that helps so many of the weed species germinate and out-compete the crop you are trying to grow.   But remember, nature abhors bare soil, and Mother Nature will send weeds into a place that you are disturbing. Tillage and use of toxic chemicals kills the organisms that help trees grow, so the less tillage and toxic chemicals you use, the less weed you have. But you have to avoid bare soil. Plant that perennial cover-crop under the trees. Grass in the driving row. For more information on the details of these interactions, more how and why and mechanism for why these things work, please come take a SFI course. The best part is, this Biological Agriculture works. It is less expensive, getting you back to using your own resources to make your orchard productive. Doesn't mean you throw out the pesticides (copper sulfate is a pesticide, but it is allowed on organic farms).   Sometimes plagues happen, and then you need the toxics. But if you use a toxic chemical you have to then use compost or compost tea to put back the beneficial biology you just killed. And you have to then give them time to recover and get back to work. Sort of like recovering from Christmas, and now trying to get back to work. I don't wanna! Feel free to ask more questions if this isn't clear.

70. N Available Over Three Months 4/2/04 1:18 PM

The N will become available over the next three months, if the biology is maintained.

71. Giant Cabbages in Alaska 5/17/04

Growing giant cabbages in Alaska long before ACT bobbed up. The soil is the important difference.

Question: What is the soil, in Alaska where they grow the giant veggies?
Answer: Alaska Humus. Doesn't matter how you get your microorganisms to protect and help your plant, and build soil structure. They just have to be there, and be balanced correctly for the plant's needs. People have destroyed the soil there too, by over-applying pesticides, fertilizers, etc. and then no more giant veggies. Long day-length is NOT the sole answer to larger veggies in Alaska, although it can help, if the soil is great, too. Many places with long day length in this world, and they don't grow giant veggies. So, long day length is not the key. It can help, but is not the explanation. So clearly, ACT is not the sole reason plants grow well. No one has claimed that, and it would be nice if people wouldn't attempt to tweak others for things they never said. ACT is an easy way for lots of people to move the right microbes to the right places. They still have to pay attention to many factors, but it's less expensive than most alternatives.

Question: Ah, but not all alternatives in all cases, right?
Answer: Compost can be less expensive (it you grow your own starting materials), and make your own compost. A single compost addition has a longer positive effect on your soil than a single tea application. So....... what suits your purpose, your situation and your time best?

a. Sulfate Effects on Soil Biology

When we (I am speaking in the sense of the whole soil ecology community here, not as SFI alone, ok?) start looking at direct effects of sulfate on soil biology. We're seeing impacts at levels lower than 35 ppm. Especially if we are looking at specifically beneficial species. Couple interesting caveats in this - when you have been using copper sulfate for a few years, the diseases start to become resistant to the sulfur, and it takes higher concentrations to have an effect on the pathogens. The more you use the sulfur, the faster you get resistance.

Question: Why is it that the same thing does not select for sulfur tolerant species of beneficials?
Answer: It probably does, but then we neglect to feed those good guys, and they don't survive both a lack of food, and the sulfur stress.

Question: Why do pathogens manage to survive?
Answer: Ah, but we do put in food for them - it's the plant. So, the things we do in agriculture select for the problem organisms, and select against the beneficials.

Chapter III

EFFECTS
ON
DISEASES

COMPOST TEA EFFECTS ON DISEASES AND PESTS

1. Tea is Not a Bio-Pesticide 5/6/04 8:44 PM

If you occupy the leaf surfaces with bacteria and fungi that do not cause disease, then the diseases, when they arrive, cannot get to the leaf surface to cause disease. Not a pesticidal interaction, but it does serve to reduce and prevent disease. There is no death of the pest involved. There is lack of germination of the disease spores, but this is not death. Therefore, not a bio-pesticide.

2. Compost Tea is Not a Fungicide 12/9/03 4:22 AM

It might be possible to protect parts of the plant not already infected with the fungus by applying compost tea at this point. But compost tea is not a fungicide, and cannot be claimed to kill, or prevent an already existing infection. You need to apply compost tea when the plant starts growing, so the surfaces of the plant are protected from the diseases.

3. Fungicide vs. Compost Tea 8/25/03 11:14 PM

A fungicide is a chemical that kills a fungus using a specific mode of killing action, such as solubilizing the cell membrane, or interfering with cell elongation, or disrupting a metabolic function.

a. Compost Tea Protects Leaf Surfaces

Compost tea does not function in these ways. Or at least we do not have any evidence that tea has these modes of function. Compost tea results in protection of the leaf surface by using the food resources that the mildew would otherwise have and be able to grow on (the beneficial fungi in the tea use the foods; the beneficials are better adapted to use the foods than mildew under the conditions on the leaf surfaces, specifically good aeration, specific foods made by the plant to select for the beneficials and not the mildew).

b. Root Coverage of Beneficial Organisms

Another mechanism is that the leaf or root surface is now covered by rapidly growing fungi and bacteria which prevent the disease fungus from getting to the leaf surface. All the infection sites are occupied by the beneficials, so there is no way the disease can get to the plant cells.

c. Protozoa and Nematodes Consume Disease-Causing Fungi.

If the EPA wants to make us register this interaction, then they will have to register cats as biocides to control mice. Predation is generally considered a physical control method, and not something that is under EPA jurisdiction. We are not growing ONE specific species to CONTROL a different species, unlike biological pesticides.

d. Antibiotics is not a Potential Mechanism

Antibiotics may be produced in tea, but there is no evidence that this is a mechanism by which tea works. So no one should use that as a potential mechanism by which tea performs it's function.

e. Nothing Toxic about Compost Tea

There is nothing toxic about tea. There is a great amount of protection, competition, competitive exclusion, and consumption. But no specific one-on-one control. Compost tea is not a fungicide. DO NOT MAKE ANY CLAIMS THAT IT IS.

4. Undefended Plants 11/25/03 7:20 AM

Check the growth conditions of the plants in those fields where the E. coli entrance into the plant tissue was found. The plants were not healthy, in anyone's estimation. Root surfaces, or leaf surfaces, absolutely devoid of any microbial growth is not normal. The plants were undefended. If you were left without any protection, no clothes, no coat or boots, stressed for water, in the hot sun during the day, but chilly temperatures once the sun went down, the only thing to eat basically potato chips (that would be your C, N, and P, and salt inputs), routinely doused with chemical cocktails, how long would you remain un-colonized by pathogens? Now that you are in that condition, someone applies water contaminated with ten to 100 times the normal levels of pathogens.

5. Disease Occurrence 11/25/03 7:01 Am

Disease occurs when a plant or animal's tissues are invaded by an organism that enters into the plant or animal, grows and is spread, system-wide and therefore systemically, through the host. Typically the result of this is death of the host. I hope you don't consider that a normal, healthy occurrence. That was what I was talking about. Normally, you do not get the growth of other organisms in what should be a sterile condition inside the tissues of a living organism. When a bacterium or fungus that will kill the plant or animal enters, the host is not going to be around for long. Not a sustainable situation.

Question: The original question was, are there bacteria that live inside plants?
Answer: My response was that this is not a normal or healthy condition. In food plants, you notice that the plant material you are about to eat is not consumable. The pathogen has begun to decompose the leaf, and the taste will be un-desirable, and the metabolites of the pathogen as it decomposes the plant material will often produce highly undesirable symptoms in the person eating the contaminated plant material. The work suggesting that E. coli can move into and colonize plant leaves comes from an experiment where an unusual condition resulted in the bacterium being taken up into the plant tissue. Colonization of plant tissues by any bacterium is an unusual condition - or at least let us try to keep it that way.

a. Benefit of a Healthy Foodweb

A major benefit of a healthy foodweb is protection of plant surfaces. The pathogens cannot find the plant surface, and that great layer of bacteria, fungi, protozoa and nematodes growing on the exudates the plant puts out keep the pathogens from being able to reach infection sites, so that the pathogen can never access either the cell wall or the cell membrane. Could you please give me the reference to the work the bacterium you were talking about? The one that enters with the *mycorrhizal* fungus and systemically colonizes the plant. I have not heard of this, and in all my years of looking at *mycorrhizal* colonization of roots with VAM or *ectomycorrhizal* fungi, have never observed systemic infection of a plant with beneficial bacteria. What I do see is reduction in systemic infection by either bacteria or fungi once the root system becomes colonized by *mycorrhizal* fungi. We see many associates of *mycorrhizal* fungi on the root surface, but never anything in the root along with the *mycorrhizal* fungus.

6. Toxic vs. Non-Toxic Materials 8/12/03 5;25 AM

Toxic materials are bio-causal. Which biology they kill depends on the material. AACT - actively aerated compost tea - does not result in toxic materials, and thus the mechanism for protection is not a biocide one. Protection is because the organisms use up the food resources that would be used by non-beneficial organisms. Plant surfaces are protected by the fact they are covered by the layer of organisms that result in disease, or toxins, from reaching the plant surface. Protozoa and nematodes on the plant surfaces, drawn there because bacteria and fungi are in high biomass levels, consume the diseases and pests. All the infection sites for the disease causing organisms are occupied. No toxic interactions. If you are going to use anaerobic materials, then you have toxic effects, some of which are toxic to human beings. The EPA will get involved in controlling that material, because you are dealing with toxins.

7. Altering Outbreak Capacity 1/2/04 8:13 AM

Question: To understand how to alter the outbreak capacity of any insect pest, you need to look at the pest's life history cycle. Where in that life cycle could you put in a competitor, or a consumer, that would effectively keep that pest in balance? Does *curculio* have a soil stage? If it does, one part of the strategy would be to make sure you have fungi in the soil that will parasitize the larval stages of the curculio?

Answer: Make sure you have bacteria and fungi in the soil that will consume the eggs of the *curculio* as it overwinters in the soil. Or if *curculio* is one of those insects that lays eggs on the leaves, when those leaves fall to the ground in the autumn, get the diversity of bacteria and fungi on those leaf surfaces. Soil applications of compost or compost tea are called for.

a. If You Have Good Healthy Soil

If you have good, healthy soil, with the microarthropods that will "taxi-cab" the bacteria and fungi from the soil onto the fallen leaves (but you have to have a goodly number so the job gets done fast enough), then you don't have to be out there applying compost or compost tea. If the biology that spreads the beneficials around has been killed, then you get to perform the function of the critter you killed, or you will suffer the consequences of that function not being performed. Diseases and pests will get out of hand.

b. Disease is a Message From Mother Nature

So, a disease or pest is just a message from mother nature telling you that the biology in your soil isn't what it should be. Don't blame compost or compost tea as "not working" because you don't instantly get the biology back to balance. Look again at your soil. You have a chemical residue, most likely, that the added organisms can't deal with. They need some help.

Question: Oh yeah, and for the folks that keep applying round-up despite the facts that are coming out about the break-down products from glyphosate?

Answer: That's why compost tea "doesn't work so well" in your situations. Until the herbicide is done away with, you are going to have to use compost twice a year, or compost tea weekly through the disease-intensive part of the year. Your choice.

c. Using Toxic Chemicals on Weeds
Weed using toxic chemicals, and you will have weeds forever. Weed by undercutting, or flaming, along with getting the beneficial biology into the soil, and using a cover crop, establishing normal nutrient cycles and you will, after a few years, not have weed problems.

d. Using Toxic Chemicals on Insect Pests
Same with insect pests. For immediate, you-have-to-deal-with-it-now control of foliar pests, try an biopesticide such as *Beauveria bassiana*. *Entomophagus* is another fungus that will likely also help. Some of the *entomophagous* nematodes like *Heterorhabditus* can do the job, too.

e. Isolating a Fungus
If you want SFI to help you isolate a fungus that will work in your specific system, we can do that. Send in a specimen of the insect which has been attacked by a fungus (it's a white fuzz ball), and SFI can work on culturing that fungus for you. We'll send you a plate culture of the fungus, and you add that fungus back into your compost or compost tea. Now, please realize that there's an assumption being made here, that there will be no adverse side effects on other things by multiplying that fungus in this way. Thus, it is better to put the fungal inoculum into the compost, and let normal microbial interactions have their way before putting it into your garden.

f. Commercially Available Beauveria
But something like commercially available *Beauveria*, if *Beauveria* actually attack *curculio*, can be added as spores into the compost tea. *Beauveria* will germinate and grow in the compost tea during the 24 hour brew cycle, IF YOU HAVE FUNGAL FOODS IN THE TEA RECIPE. When you spray the tea with the actively growing *Beauveria* onto the soil, the fungus will colonize the soil, IF YOU HAVE FUNGAL ORGANIC MATTER IN THE SOIL. Active *Beauveria* fungi will colonize any curculio it comes in contact with, and as long as you don't have something that will kill the fungus in the soil, or on the leaves, then you should see the adult curculio turning into fuzz-balls.

g. Fungus-Killing Factor
If you have a fungus-killing factor on your plants, or in the soil, you won't see this happen. So, do not spray round-up or other fungal-killing or not-fungal-friendly herbicides or pesticides after using Beauveria or using compost tea, if you want the tea to work. Copper sulfate is a serious no-no if you want to keep these biological control measures functioning in your soil and on your leaf surfaces. Anything with sulfur in it is a no-no. Sulfur in most any form except a protein will harm fungi.

h. Pathogenic Fungi
OK, if all you have is pathogenic fungi, then have fun with sulfur compounds. But you will never get out of disease mode until you let the beneficial fungi grow. And that means leaving the toxics

behind, making your soil a habitat that allows the good guys to live and grow, removing the habitat that lets the bad guys have a place to hang-out.

8. Insect Problems and Walnuts 12/30/03 10:52 AM

Question: I have insect problems in my walnut plantings: Butternut curculio, husk maggots, and maybe apple maggots. I believe you mentioned the use of some bacteria, fungi, nematode, etc. as a soil treatment to interrupt the life cycle. Can you help me with that information again, please? Any suggestions on organic sprays to help protect the crop from adult insects would be appreciated.

Answer: Last fall, you needed to get the beneficial organisms that consume the over-wintering forms of the pests you asked about back into your litter material and into your soil. You want to leave the litter on the soil in the fall, not rake it up, or burn it or something like that. Litter, or leaf debris from your trees, is supposed to remain on the soil. The dead leaves are food to feed the beneficial fungi and bacteria, which you need to form structure in the soil (so roots can grow down to the depth they are meant to grow down to, not be arrested by anaerobic conditions that develop as a result of compaction at 12 to 18 inches).

a. Inoculate the Right Aerobic Biology
You also then need to inoculate the right aerobic biology to process nutrients and return them to your plants at the rate, time and form the plant requires. You need the beneficial organisms to combat disease-causing organisms in the soil, and on that leaf litter. If the good guys are not present, then the bad guys rule. And you have the pests and pathogens you asked about reigning supreme. So, you have to get the good guys back. The good guys DO NOT return fast enough on their own. You CANNOT assay for the good guys by using plate counts or microbial biomass as assessed by chloroform fumigation. Do not be mis-lead by "soils" that people try to use as these methods of assessment to negate a true understanding of what is going on in soil, and with soil life.

b. Chloroform Fumigation to Assess Microbial Biomass
The papers presented at meetings this last fall concluded that soil life doesn't change when you plow, or when you add an inoculum of organisms. But they used methods that couldn't possibly tell them about these things. I just shake my head when someone uses chloroform fumigation to assess microbial biomass in soil. They are measuring soil organic matter, and really, not much else. I think plate methods are idiotic for trying to assess species diversity of bacteria or fungi. Imagine what I think about something that tries to make statements about biology based on the CO_2 being produced from the microbial biomass killed by the chloroform. Especially since the fungal hyphae are usually not even touched by the organism that survive fumigation - and thus the fungal biomass is almost completely ignored by this particular method.

Question: So you didn't get compost or compost tea, or an inoculum of bacterial beneficials on the litter last fall? Or maybe you have tried tea, but it "didn't work".

Answer: Well, you didn't get enough on, the tea wasn't good quality - didn't have the proper biology to displace the disease organisms or begin the process of decomposition - or you have toxic chemicals in the soil that killed the added biology.   In any case, the presence of the diseases tell you that you DON'T have the proper biology present to protect the trees. So, start this spring

ASAP. As soon as the ground temperature is about 45 F, apply about 20 gal/ac of good tea to the litter and the soil. If it's really good tea, you can put 15 gal/ac. There is some benefit in testing the tea then, to know what amount you need to put on....and it would be good to know where you are starting from, in the soil, to know if addition of the tea or compost improved anything, and whether you have a toxic chemical present in your soil that has to get dealt with before you can get the biology to do their improvements for the soil and your plants.

9. Fungi Could be *Chitinase* Producers 4/1/04 10:31 PM

These fungi could be *chitinase* producers. Put the dead bees in a container with other insects, and see if the fungi attack and kill those other insects.

10. *Sclerotinia* 5/6/04 8:15 PM

There have been scientific papers showing reduction in *sclerotinia* following compost use. Other papers show no control with compost - and I THINK it is because they didn't really use compost in those studies, they use what I like to call "Putrefying Organic Matter". No studies on compost tea controlling *sclerotina*, just anecdotal observations by several onion growers.

11. Fairy Ring Fungi in Lawns 6/2/04 10:07 PM

Aerate the lawn, spray tea that is high in fungal biomass before filling the aeration holes, then rake 70% sand mixed with 30% GOOD compost (please, NOT municipal waste reduction mulch), and use compost tea at weekly intervals for the next 3 to 4 weeks, and then tea monthly. Typically, the reason the fairy ring fungi can do what they are doing is that very little is competing with them for that source of wood down in the soil. If you add some good diversity of fungi, and some good fungal-feeding nematodes, you should be able to solve the problem pretty rapidly.

12. Protozoa and Ants 3/24/04 12:23 PM

The protozoa involved with the ants are a specific set of - hum, flagellates, I think - of the genera *Nosema*. What you need to do is find an ant mound that has died from such an infection, and get those dead ants into the compost pile, so you have that particular set of genera of protozoan species. So, as you go through your yard, or take walks in the woods, keep your eyes open for insects that have died. The fuzzy ones were killed by fungi, and if you put these guys in your compost piles, you enhance that insect-attacking set of organisms. Add a little chitin into your compost (shrimp shells, dead insects) and you can enhance those species even more. If you find dead grasshoppers, that seem to have died for no apparent reason, you are probably looking at a *Nosema* infection. Get those critters into your compost ASAP. ant colonies that suddenly die out, for no apparent reason (sorry, insecticides don't count here, that is a clear cause-effect), same story. From now on, when you take a hike in the woods, you are on a business trip, right? You are in search of beneficial organisms to put in your compost......

13. Asian Rust 2/8/04 1:30 AM

Hum, Asian rust -- don't recall talking about it specifically, just in general. Here on the list serve, we have people who have been able to protect their plant surfaces from rust.

14. Pear Blister Mite 2/7/04 12:00 PM

Question: What is the treatment for the pear blister mite?
Answer: I would want to get compost tea on the trees - after dormant oil if you have used that, because the dormant oil treatment seems to be compatible with the use of compost tea. The oil is just an additional, albeit not outstanding, food resource for the fungi in the tea. It would be interesting to observe the foliar surfaces after dormant oil, then after compost tea. I'd like to know if you see the fungal component begin to grow in thick enough strands that you can see. What biology does the oil select?

15. Apple Scab 1/22/04 8:33 AM

Question: Would use of the vinegar - peroxide treatment, with compost tea, work?
Answer: If you do the vinegar treatments, could you run a pre-vinegar leaf assessment of organisms, followed by post-vinegar assessment of the leaf organisms? Then we would know what happens with the vinegar, and how much of the scab inoculum is taken out. Then, apply the compost tea, and see how much of the leaf surface can be re-occupied, but not with scab. Can the vinegar be used as a food resource by the compost tea organisms?

16. Banana, Avocado and Mac Nut Diseases 1/7/04 11:58 AM
In Australia, we've had success with diseases of banana (borers, for example), avocado, and mac nuts. You need to e-mail the Australia SFI for their info on these. The contact person is Effie.

17. *Plum Curculio* 1/7/04 9:37 AM

Question: Plum Curculio (PC) can be reduced by 90%, but still have 50% damage.
Answer: I just don't buy that statement at face value. When any pest is in plague mode, or an outbreak condition, there is no approach that will control it at that point. This condition is brought on by making the habitat perfect for PC, while making the habitat horrible for the things that keep the pest in check.

Question: How about an example using a different situation?
Answer: When grasshoppers are in swarm phase, reducing their populations by 50% does not make any difference to the destruction of the wheat crop. When in outbreak mode, reducing 2 billion pests by 90% still leaves you with 200 million pests, and no wheat crop. When in that mode, the take-home message is not to say that biological approaches don't work. The take-home message is that the pest situation was ignored until it got out of hand. Next time, don't ignore it.

a. Gypsy Moth, Pine Bark Beetle and Codling Moth
We've been through this with gypsy moth. We've been through this with pine bark beetle. We've been through this with codling moth. Learn the lesson. Learning does not occur when every approach offered is rejected as not being capable of dealing with the situation. When in outbreak mode, there is nothing that will work except the weather. Fumigating everything to nuke the pest

just leaves the few pests that do survive without any competition what-so-ever. Hello pest outbreak again next summer.

b. Winter Dormant Stages

But now that winter is here, the adult pests have been frozen to death. Great, the pest is gone - NOT! Eggs and dormant stages are still present. You have until those eggs hatch, until the larvae molts, to knock out next summer's problem.

Question: So, plum curculio, where does it go over-winter?
Answer: Send in the armies of consumers to eat the eggs through the winter. Send in the armies that will take the food resource away from the larval stages of the insect. Send in consumers. Send in some parasites of the eggs and the larval stages.

c. PC in Outbreak Mode

PC is in outbreak mode, which means they are in such high numbers in your neighbor's yard that they are looking for someplace to move into that offers food. Sort of like Europeans moving into the New World (emptied of native populations because the natives had never encountered the diseases of over-crowded human conditions) from over-crowded Europe. Empty space looks really inviting when too many individuals are trying to divide up a limited food resource. So, you have to make your food resource look un-inviting. Or you have to have predators, parasites and diseases lying in wait for the colonists. It's what we do with white fly, mites, Colorado potato beetle, and pine bark beetle -- 100% protected pine trees from bark beetle infestation -- trees treated with compost tea, even AFTER the beetle attacked and the tree was dying, have been brought back to health (green needles, new growth).

Question: Mechanism?
Answer: Spray the surface of the tree - bark, needles, everything, with an ADEQUATE SET OF BIOLOGY. The beetles themselves carry the inoculum of beneficials into the tree. The other microarthropods that use the beetle tunnels (called galleries) bring the inoculum of good guys into the galleries. The fungus that normally causes the gumming up of the tree's water up-take channels is not a good competitor, and thus does not grow, does not kill the tree. But you have to make sure that the biology needed is in the tea. The folks making the machine which can make this tea have figured out EXACTLY what you need to make a good tea with their machine.

They get adamant that you don't play games with the recipe. Try a different set of foods, or use a compost that doesn't have the right biology in the compost, isn't known to be good, fungal dominated compost, then sorry, all bets are off. They will not accept that they are responsible for your "tea" not working. Which is as it should be. If you take a microwave oven, and change it, the manufacturer of the machine is not responsible for you burning down your house because the machine explodes. If you buy a recipe for bread, and then add something not in the recipe, the seller of the recipe is not responsible when your bread doesn't rise. Play game with the ingredients for the tea, and sorry, don't complain when the tea doesn't do what it should do, could do.

18. *Penicillium oxalicum* 12/9/03 10:37 PM

Penicillium oxalicum is commonly present in many soils, typically as a spore. Waking up this spore and getting it to grow can be tricky. As I recall (memory could be faulty), this fungus requires fairly high levels of carbohydrate in order to become active. Thus only in certain conditions would it begin to grow on a plant surface, but those conditions would likely be when something like *Verticillium* attacks the plant. So, it seems a perfect control organism, since it is triggered by the disease it controls. *Penicillium oxalicum* would have little effect on most other foodweb organisms, as it isn't typically growing except in specific conditions.

19. Insect Attacking Fungus 11/15/03 2:16 PM

Typically a fungus that attacks soft-bodied insects and larval stages of insects is useful. *Beauveria* and *Steinernema* are possible additions to your compost or your tea. *Steinernema* and a couple species of *Beauveria* are available from Peaceful Valley Farm Supply catalogue. Also Soils Alive carries several types of these fungal parasites of insects. Add to your tea, or your compost. They grow and spread into the soil when you put the compost or tea out.

Chapter IV

APPLICATIONS

for
Actively Aerated
Compost Tea

APPLICATIONS FOR ACTIVELY AERATED COMPOST TEA

1. Conditions for Tea for Survive in the Field 6/10/04 9:04 PM

Yes, working out the definitions took years. Because you have to quantify the organisms in the tea, and follow the effect of those organisms on plants. We do organism assessment of the tea, then spray out and determine what actually gives protection, or improves nutrient cycling, and builds soil structure. It's the organisms. But at what concentration? That takes time to figure out. Some of the data are on the SARE website. Please look at the reports there. And you have to remember that just because the tea is excellent does not mean that conditions in the soil might not result in organism death. Great tea, but killing heat, or drought, or freeze, or pesticide drift, or.....no food. Any one of those conditions may kill the critters in a good tea. Just because you apply tea and don't see a positive effect cannot be put down to "tea doesn't work". The organisms can be killed once they are put out. Over and over, when we hear of people applying tea, but not having any benefit, and we investigate what happened, we can explain to the grower what they did that resulted in organism death. The tea was likely great, but if you spray out 2,4-D three days after applying tea......People continue to use sulfur sprays, not understanding that even though sulfur may be organically certified, sulfur sprays still kill the beneficial fungi....So, lots of years of work to see the correlations. Now you can check EVERY batch of your own tea, and discover that it is, or isn't, good compost tea. If compost has beneficial bacteria, fungi, protozoa, and nematodes in it, then does compost tea not have to have the same critters? No beneficial fungi, protozoa or nematodes.....how can it be compost tea?

2. Dormant Spores 11/25/03 9:10 PM

Dormant spores don't stay on the leaf surface. They have to be active in order to stay on the leaf. As part of a soil drench, spores are fine. But if you are trying to understand soil processes, including spores as part of a PROCESS assessment, such as occurs when using plate media, this just isn't kosher.

3. Soil Drench 5/7/04 9:00 PM

Soil drench refers to wetting the soil with significant amounts of liquid. A soil drench for a compost tea means applying 20 gal of tea per acre, but in enough water to adequately wet the soil. Water is just the carrier for tea. You apply the amount of water you need to evenly spread, or drench in, the tea.

4. Air Dropped Tea 8/14/03 6:19 AM

There is no problem applying tea via air drop. The organisms aren't harmed by the joy-ride. We get good coverage applying tea to bananas, avocado and grapes.

5. Application of Organisms if Ground Not Frozen 12/30/03 11:20 PM

As long as the ground is not frozen, you will get some benefit from the organism addition. The colder it is, the more likely the critters will go to sleep, and not do much. But then they are there to get started ASAP next spring.

6. Transporting and Applying Tea 5/17/04 76:54 AM

You don't want to run the critters out of food completely, but if you have to transport the tea, you want just enough food left after the 24 hours to hold the critters in an active state, but not have high O2 demand. If you are concerned that there won't be food on the leaves, then mix foods into the tea AS THE TEA GOES OUT. Add food to the spray line as you are spraying. As you spray, everything goes flying through the air. You don't have to worry about oxygen. The tea is in small droplets, surrounded by air. On the leaf surface, the tea is a thin film on the plant surfaces, and thus fully aerobic. Consider monitoring leaf bacterial and fungal activity to see if the leaves are covered, and if the organisms are present and active. That tells you if the critters needed food added with them, or whether the leaves were not putting out the food the critters need to stay alive.

7. Soil Injection 3/27/04 12:55 PM

In the work done in banana in Australia, injection into soil did not work at all to bring the plants back to health. The banana started out with no roots to speak of, except immediately at the soil surface. Injection into the soil
needed to pay attention to where the existing roots were and to inject around the roots. Injection was in fact placed at 10 cm into the soil, but the roots weren't there, so little benefit was observed. Makes sense, doesn't it? If using soil injection, you should find out where your roots are before deciding on depth.

8. Tea Under Vines 3/24/04 11:42 AM

Mow the grass down, so you enhance the decomposition of the grass. I like to direct the tea under the vines, and also plant in a perennial cover crop under the vines, so you make the soil in the root zone of the vine fungal
dominated. You get better flavor in the grapes when you allow them to stop fighting the grass for bacterial versus fungal dominance. Of course, if you have deep root systems on the vines, then this isn't so important.

9. Softening the Soil with Microbes 3/21/04 11:32 AM

Softening the soil comes down to having the microbes in the soil that do that work for you - AND - feeding them. If toxic chemicals, which kill bad guys as well as good guys are used continuously, you are going to go backwards on the productivity scale. If you allow the microbes to colonize, and give them food to flourish, then you go forward on the scale of productivity.

Question: With grass growing and staying green, what was going on?
Answer: No toxic chemicals being applied - so the organisms were no longer being killed. The grass was growing, so the plant itself was delivering foods to the microbes around their root systems. And thus, normal soil softening processes were occurring. The biology builds soil structure. It can be that easy. In commercial AG, the results need to come along a bit faster than we tolerate in our lawns, however. So we get more aggressive about returning fertility in commercial enterprises. WE have to make money from commercial AG, and so crops have to succeed. In your lawn, we are less demanding, so often, just letting nature take it's own time and do things slowly is just fine.

10. Plant Responses 3/17/04 11:31 PM

Use the plant responses to tell you if things are really bad. Then use the smell, immediately at 24 hours, and after 4 hours in a sealed container, to tell you about quality. The microscope will help a great deal too, in that you can monitor every single batch of tea.

11. Measuring Plant Responses 5/15/04 8:56 AM

Question: Is there a more general test that goes a step beyond the measure of soil content? Can we measure the plants reaction? I can't. I don't know how. Some of you can?
Answer: Plant responses that have been measured are things like yield, biomass of the plant, biomass of fruit, BRIX, nutrient content (vitamins, minerals, calcium, boron, etc), height, runners, and so forth.

Question: When you measure the protein in your hay does that tell you how the ACT worked?
Answer: Measuring protein in the plant is not enough as a stand alone measure. You have to have an area where you did NOT apply the tea, and an area where you DID apply tea. Comparison of the protein, or brix, or plant biomass; then can tell you if the tea improved plant response or not. But you always have to have the comparison with the control, not-tea treated area. Your toxic chemical neighbor's lawn, or vegetable garden, or agricultural field works as a comparison point.

Question: Is it possible to tell whether the activation made your hay a better feed for your animals?
Answer: You would need to make a tea with not-activated compost, and tea with activated compost, spray them out, and then compare plant response. SFI has done that (on the website, in the CTBM, on the WSARE website) and shown that if you do not have more than 5% coverage, you cannot achieve disease suppression. So, activation may be needed to get the fungal component you need. If you apply to soil, then you need a threshold level of fungal biomass in the tea, or you don't get the soil building that is possible from getting the organisms out there. Again, lots of anecdotal information, but also data in the CTBM, on our website.

Question: I think Elaine suggested that when they tested TEA with certain microbe content they were able to relate that to plant quality in the field. Is this measured quality? I think so.
Answer: Yes. Three applications of tea to a pasture in Texas, compared to a conventional pasture next to it (actually, the rest of the ranch). Conventional pasture had 0.5 lb weight gain per animal per day; the tea treated had 2.5 lbs weight gain per animal per day -- Protein AND a shift in species of dominant grasses.

12. Rapid Response 8/8/03 9:50 PM

If a foliar application of tea can improve foliar nutrient uptake, it is through a series of specific occurrences, which are not "everyday" in nature. If you are getting the beneficial organisms growing on the leaf surfaces, you can get a within-hours response, but it is not seen that often, because of what I just said.

Question: What conditions are needed to get that rapid response?
Answer: Stressed plants lacking the nutrient you add to the tea in a chelated, or biologically activated form. The plant ALSO has to be putting out foods to feed bacteria and fungi. Then, the

biology you just added have to be able to grow and elevate carbon dioxide on the leaf surface, and that can cause the stomates to open. The biologically activated forms of nutrients move into the plant. It is not a "works every time" response, as you can see. You have to meet the proper conditions. You are doomed to failure unless you know why you are doing what you are doing. Think things through. Understand the system before you start messing with it. Why would you not put tea on a stressed plant? Tea may be the only thing that would have a chance to bring a plant back if it is too stressed.

13. How To Help You Fix The Biology 11/17/03 7:38 AM

Question: Soil food web testing and recommendations: Soil food web tests done on strawberry soils and grapes have come back with a recommendation of 2 to 4 liters per ha humic acid and 150 liters per ha compost tea (sample no 3080 and 3081). Does this mean that after applying this we can expect to see active fungal biomass and total fungal biomass in the correct range (other things being equal) or put it another way, do you have data showing that a once off application such as this will bring the fungal numbers into the correct range?

Answer: When we say that you just need to add fungal foods, and we give an amount of food, I am alluding to research and practical experience that shows that other folks, SFI included, have had biomass levels in the range you had on your SFI report, added foods in the amounts we give on the SFI report, and ended up with excellent fungal biomass as a result. Time frame for the improvement was within several weeks.

a. Outside The Normal Range

Question: What is "outside the normal range"?

Answer: Winter, for example, is outside the normal range for normal plant growth. Addition of humics will Not fix the lack of fungal activity in a couple weeks in the winter. If you add humic acids in the winter, it will take until next spring for the fungi to chew away at those foods, and for you to see an increase. If your soil has a toxic residue, the growth won't occur. So, if you had a test taken last year, and you take another one this year, and no improvement has occurred in fungal biomass, start thinking about toxic residues. Or think about your practices over the year - something impacted the fungi, or their biomass would be higher.

Question: We have MANY examples, and believe me, it's examples in the plural, of people doing control versus tea-treated areas. Fungal biomass increasing wonderfully in the tea treated areas, plants responding with improved health, increased blossoms, healthier foliage, much better water infiltration, etc. Then the next samples come in and there's no difference in biology between the control and treatment. The client says, "why the *&^# are we paying for all this biology stuff, when it isn't making any difference?" Shocked me the first couple of times, because, of course, the plants were doing better. But the organisms had crashed, back to the same levels in the tea treated as the control. Can you see the reason?

Answer: The answer is obvious - they applied a chemical that killed the biology. They swear up and down they added nothing that would harm the biology. You have to get them to tell you precisely what they did. You eventually get the "oh, do you mean to say that applying an herbicide killed fungi?" I ask them, "why did you put an herbicide on? You didn't have weeds in the tea-treated plot", and their response is something along the lines that they always apply herbicide at that time. It's a preventative. Have to get them off that kind of thinking!

Question: My view of this is that multiple applications will be required to restore the soil food web. Note this is intensive horticulture so regular applications of AACT and Humic acid etc are not a problem.

Answer: It may indeed take multiple applications, because you don't stop doing other practices that kill the fungi - things like tillage, fertilizer applications, herbicide applications, etc. Sometimes you have to do things that harm the foodweb, for reasons that are necessary given the system. You now need to rescue the organisms that were harmed. The SFI recommendation on the report cannot cover a practice that will harm the organisms, UNLESS YOU TELL US what you are going to do. SFI has advisors that can help you work through the WHOLE program. But you have to let us know what you plan to do, so we can help you figure out how to nurture the biology in the soil, even if you have to do something that will harm the biology. So, the SFI recommendation can't cover how to help you fix the biology if you don't tell us what you are doing. OK?

Now, the caveats. The data reported on your report show you have at least the minimum levels of total fungal biomass, and therefore the diversity of fungi desired that could reasonably be woken up by feeding the indicated foods. The data indicate fungal activity to be present, but not as great as desired to achieve the crop production you probably desire (SFI assumes the reason you are doing this testing is because plant growth isn't as you desire). Addition of the foods should result in resolution of the biomass situation, given that everything is "normal" in your soil. Normal being temperature, moisture, pesticide residues, heavy metal loads, diseases, insects, etc. in normal or reasonable ranges for plant growth.

14. Diluting Tea and Adding Food 5/31/04 5:47 AM
The dilution of finished tea with well-aerated water is critical to the situation here. If you started with, say, 100 liters of FINISHED tea (beyond the highest oxygen demand and growth period), and added 100 liters of well-aerated water, you will have about at least a 10 to 12 hour time frame before the organisms use up the oxygen in that water. If the organisms were still in rapid growth phase in the tea, and you stop the brewing too early, you may have only a 4 to 5 hour time frame, even with the addition of all that extra air when you add additional water. Addition of more food to this 200 liter mix at the rate of 1 to 2 liters, will reduce the time you have to spray the tea out. I don't want to hazard a guess whether the organisms will suck up all the oxygen immediately or not - it depends on whether the organisms were to the stable point before the tea was taken out of the brewer. If they were, a two hour spray time is probably safe enough. But ONLY if tea was diluted with good clean, well-aerated water first. But notice that I am using hedging words on this. I don't have solid data on this point.

Question: There are many interacting factors here that would need to be tested to have a solid answer.
1. What is the oxygen demand of the tea?
2. How much oxygen is in the water added to the tea?
3. What kinds of foods were actually added to the tea plus water?

4. How much did those foods (now also well-diluted, 1 to 2 liters in 200 liters is getting nicely dilute) activate microbial growth?

Answer: So, a bit waffle on the answer since I have to use logic based on different things we've tested to be able to answer. Some testing of oxygen in mixes where you add increasing amounts of water to the same amount of tea from a tea brew, and then add the additional food resources would be useful.

15. Adding Food to Finished Tea 10/6/03 9:21 PM

Question: What happens if you use the tea straight for foliar coverage with a very low amount of hydrolysate for food/activation (say a teaspoon per 5 gallons or less)?

Answer: Once you add food to a "finished tea", the organisms can start using that food very quickly. You have to spray that tea out quickly, or aerate the tea in the sprayer. The food and organisms on the leaf surface help keep the organisms active and growing. So, this is a good thing for improving coverage.

Question: Does this compensate for tea in which the numbers are not optimal?

Answer: It can compensate, just please make sure that you get the coverage that you need.

Question: Are there problems or considerations for this approach? Cost is not a significant factor, since in small applications I don't brew less than 15 gallons anyhow.

Answer: The consideration is the growth of the organisms while still in the sprayer. Aeration is important.

16. Effect of UV 5/17/04

Now, the 1 mm DROP size comes from some of the observations we've made about the effect of UV on organisms in the droplets flying through the air. When we first started working with pivots and compost tea, the concern was that UV would kill the organisms in the tea during the sunlight-intense hours. Based on all the microbiologists I talked to about this problem, they all agreed that UV would kill the organisms in the tea droplets if the tea was applied between 10 am and 3 pm. We thought we'd see "pie-wedges" in the pivots where the organism were killed. Never saw it. Leaf analysis in day-time applied areas of the pivot, versus night-time applied areas showed variation in the areas, but not significantly lower coverage in the daytime areas. Data - ok.

Pivot Quarter	%Bacteria	%Fungi
1	54	13
2	66	5
3	71	14
4	70	3

Pivot Quarter	%Bacteria	%Fungi
1	89	10
2	78	12

| 3 | 91 | 12 | (both bacterial and fungal coverage |
| 4 | 84 | 7 | of the same area sometimes) |

So, which of the quarters were the ones to which tea was applied during the day? Then take a look at these data-

Pivot Quarter	%Bacteria	%Fungi
1	21	2
2	18	1
3	22	7
4	59	15

Do you want to tell me what went on here? Quarter four was the mid-day tea applied area, but you need to also know that a fish hydrolysate was applied here too. Adding foods to the tea as it is sprayed out can really pick things up. But bottom line - as long as the droplet size is large enough, the organisms will be protected from UV. Air bubble size is important only if there are significant amounts of stationary bubbles in the water column, which occurs only when air bubble size is very small.

17. Droplet Size May Be Important 11/17/03 8:20 AM

We've done a fair amount of work with pivot application of tea, where tea is applied, from the same batch, for 18 to 35 hours. It takes a minimum of 18 hours, usually, for the pivot to get all the way around a 130-something circle. We do not see an area in the field where the tea was not effective because it was put out between 10 am and 3 pm. Sunlight, even in bright sunny places like Idaho, eastern Washington, or Oregon, where the tea is applied to potato, does not have an impact on the critters. So, is the UV concern about sunlight bogus? A little more data needed, I think. What we see is if the droplet size being applied is fairly large - 1 mm drop size, or the drops coalesce after spraying - then sunlight does not impact the organisms. They are safe from UV, because the droplet size attenuates the UV. Soil versus foliar spraying isn't the concern with time-to-time spray, because it's a UV thing that was the concern. When applying to the soil, if the droplets go through the air, UV is something to consider. If the tea is applied via dripline, then a whole different set of concerns, not UV concerns, apply. Anyone else have observations to support or not-support these observations?

18. Maximize Benefits 8/8/03 9:50 PM

Question: Finally, it seems that the whole process includes: make good tea, activate inactive organisms, mix and add spreader and/or sticker, use a microbeast-friendly means of applying tea to foliage or ground (avoid UV, allow at least 30 minutes to dry on leaves before it rains), and FEED THE FOODWEB.
Answer: Yep.

Question: This brings us back to a recent post about what compost ingredients provide for which parts of the food web. To maximize the benefit of the application, should I be simultaneously applying the K-rations for the food web members I am applying? How does one identify the useful rate at which to apply web food?

Answer: Standard ecological answer. It depends. Why are you applying tea? What is your purpose? If you apply tea to a plant, the plant should provide the foods that will grow the critters. If you add tea to a soil with nasty chemicals still in it, the critters are going to need help for a bit to chew up the nasties. If you add critters to soil to get decomposition going, you may want to add an enzyme, like Vitazyme for example, that will help start the process of break-down of the plant material, and get the organisms really chewing fast. If you add organisms to soil to have them build structure, exit compaction ASAP, then addition of fish, or molasses will give them the foods to do their work. Get the plants growing ASAP, then, so you give the critters the plant foods they need to keep working.

19. Healthy Soil 7/27/04 11:04 AM

Question: My goal is to develop a healthy soil for vegetable production in a 60 x 60 area, that is mainly sand loam. I understand tea is not a substitute for organic matter, but I want to put healthy bacteria into the soil to aid in the digestive process of turning the organic matter into plant foods.

Answer: Exactly right! You can't turn plant debris into soil if you don't have the organisms to do the job. Hence the idea of sour milk. OK, but..... sour milk isn't going to grow the beneficial organisms that you
need. At least, I have seen no data to suggest that it selects for beneficial organisms, and I have seen some work showing some really negative impacts on leaf surface organisms. Sour milk seems to work if you want to kill some of the leaf surface disease-causing fungi. But then you have to put the beneficial organisms back out on
those leaves - or the bad guys come back. Competition is all important.

a. Kelp
The Kelp is for the macro / micro plant nutrients as well to build in some cold tolerances, about a 1/2 c per. gal. OK, there are data to show all of the above. Excellent.

b. Greensand
The Greensand and egg shells for calcium and macro / micro nutrients .But in the compost tea? My experience is that they are better in the compost. But maybe I just got that wrong, and you meant the compost. How much? Consider that if you make your compost with the right set of starting materials, the final C:N ratio of the compost is 10:1. That means a minimum of 5% N. There should be no need to add greensand for N. But maybe for other micronutrients.

c. Egg Shells
Egg shells are a great source of calcium, but you need about 100 pounds, MAXIMUM, per ton.

d. Compost
…and Compost for bacterial and nutrient support. Yep, compost for foods to feed the beneficial organisms, BUT ALSO for the inoculum of the organisms themselves.

Question: What plants are you trying to grow, and what is the biology that they need? What ratio of bacteria and fungi are needed?
Answer: You should match your tea to improve what the plant needs in the soil.

20. Chelates 5/5/04 7:41 AM

Question: International Ag Labs notes that our soils are deficient in copper and manganese. Recommendation: 10# copper sulfate and 10# manganese sulfate applied to soil, ideally in fall.
Answer: It is 100 times worse to add the sulfate-containing compounds, than the chelated variety. The sulfates are very hard on fungi, and applied at 10 pounds per ac, will have detrimental effects on the organisms, both bacterial and fungi. If you are dealing with a strictly chemical system, then these recommendations would be acceptable, but if you need beneficial biology, then these recommendations take you half a light backwards. So, the chelated forms of these nutrients are the much better choice. Most of the time, when someone says chelation, it means they have bound the metal to a protein (any protein will do), or a protein analogue, like EDTA. That helps the plant take up the metal, without harming the active transport molecules in the meantime. Generally, if just the metal is hanging around, the damage to the root when it tries to take up the non-chelated molecule means more damage than benefit to the plant. So, chelation is important.

Question: Chelates (for instance Baicor products, I gather, are much more plant friendly and more quickly assimiable as they have already been processed by plant enzymes, etc. (I'm a little fuzzy on the science, can you tell?)
Answer: So, processed by plant enzymes just means the metal ions were tied to an organic molecule, typically a protein. Organically certified chelates are even better, since then the protein is protein, and not a protein analogue. Who knows what a protein analogue really does to the organisms in the soil. Probably not good, and indeed there is some data to show that EDTA, for example, is bad news for many soil beneficials.

Question: One Scientist says flat out that he does not know the effect of the chelates on microbes in tea but suspects that any antagonistic effects might be concentration dependent.
Answer: Absolutely right there. Testing is the only way to know for certain. So, IF you want to know, take a sample of your tea before you add the chelate, then add the chelate, let mix for a bit (an hour?), and test again. Then you know for sure.

Question: He does not feel that the chelates will have a negative effect on the metabolites that are in the tea, but is unsure about organisms themselves. He says the chelates will internalize quickly into the plant and not remain on the leaf.
Answer: Actually, the organisms in the tea will take up the chelates, and improve plant uptake of the nutrients, IF you have protozoa in the tea. Nutrient cycling occurs on leaf surfaces just like anywhere else. The bacteria and fungi glue the nutrients to the leaf surface, the protozoa and nematodes consume the bacteria and fungi, and release the nutrients in a plant-available form.

Question: The recommendation is for 1 - 2 gallons of Manganese chelate and 0.5 to 1 gallon of copper chelate. In our case that would be mixed with approximately 200 gallons of water and 20 gallons of tea for our foliar program (four 50 gallon tanks per acre with chelate, tea, kelp, fish, molasses, minerals and spreader/sticker). It's our hope that the copper chelate and the tea will be helpful with apple scab (Venturia sp.)and help make up plant tissue and soil deficiencies through translocation.

Answer: Those levels of chelates will not be a problem (I am assuming you mean 1 - 2 gallons per ac, right?) The tea itself will provide a barrier layer of organisms on the leaf surfaces so pathogens cannot reach the leaf surface. Just make sure that your leaves are covered by at least 70%. Try putting a red food dye into the tea at the end of the tea spray, and make sure the leaf surfaces are being covered at least 70%. I'd love to have people try this approach, and then let me know if it worked for you. I've tried it myself, with pretty good results, although the red color is hard to see sometimes. I put 1 of the red food coloring bottles in 5 gallons of tea. If the color isn't enough for your eyes, try putting two bottles in. At least it is a cheap, and immediate way to tell if you are getting coverage. The color should then disappear if the organisms are active on your leaf surfaces. Remember, active organisms stick to the leaf surfaces, and consume the exudates the plant puts out. They should consume the red food coloring. The red color should disappear if you have active organisms sticking to the leaf surfaces. OK? Let me know your experiences, please! I've given away some good (I hope) information here. Please do your part for the world by letting me know how this works for you.

21. Organic Approaches 1/6/04 12:09 PM

Whenever I get someone saying, "none of the organic approaches work", it is always that they are doing something to un-balance the biology. Organic methods work, but you have to pay attention to what mother nature is saying back to you about what you are doing. When you still have pests, that means you are doing something out-of-whack still.

The fact that you are doing all this work, and you still have brown areas when your dog applies N to the grass says you don't have the right biology in that soil. A few curculio are to be expected if your neighbors have them, but for you to have serious damage tells you that mother nature is sending you a message. Something is seriously out-of-whack.

Question: How can you possibly have a seriously out-of-whack system when you are working so hard?
Answer: You need to understand what you are doing when you add each of the different things you say you are adding.

Question: How can you not have the right biology, when you are doing all the great things you are doing?
Answer: Let's go through what you are doing. If soil probes go easily through the soil, then this says good soil structure to the depth you drive the probes. Kudos to you!

Question: But, what about below that? When you dig a hole, what happens at 4 feet? 6 feet? 8 feet? - and - Are you really going through soil? Or are you just going through organic matter that you have built up over the years?
Answer: I ask because you say you have a problem, despite all your efforts, you still have a problem. So we have to figure out why. That means I'm in detective-mode to figure out what it

could be. I'll be asking you to supply more information, because you haven't told us the whole story here.

Question: No tillage
Answer: Ok, you aren't destroying what you have worked so hard to build. Excellent.

Question: Laid drainage tiles around all the fruit trees to drain water to French wells I constructed in two central areas of the yard.
Answer: How rapidly does the soil dry out? I put in French drains in my yard as well, because my yard is solid clay – a pottery used to be where my house is. Good clay for making pots, but growing plants? Nope. The drains worked (until they clogged up with clay). While they were working, the soil dried out in the summer. So now, I'm building soil structure with the organisms, and that's doing a better job of draining the soil, without the Army Corps of Engineers operation. Still building though. I need to do a core aeration on the soil, and fill with sand. Sometimes, you have to do engineering. Need decent structure so water will be held in the soil all summer, no matter what the heat load is. So, just a question back to you – what have you observed about water during the year? Too much, too little? When?

Question: Spread compost over the entire yard once a year. Spread a second application of compost around the fruit trees, to the drip line in the fall. In areas where there is dog damage I spread compost about once a month.
Answer: Have you looked at the compost to see if it is fungal? Can you see fungal strands? If not, you might not want to put the compost around the trees so deeply. The fact that you have dog damage – I am assuming you mean brown spots, not dogs digging – says the biology is lacking. It says you have bacteria that convert the N in the urine to nitrate. But that is the form of N which means browning on the plants. Not good. You have to convert that nitrate into protein, microbial biomass and organic N. You need to improve diversity of bacteria in the soil, so you have some organisms that take up the nitrate and move it into biomass, instead of nitrate. You need fungi, with species that also utilize urea to make biomass, not nitrate. You need protozoa to work in the root systems of the plants to make nutrients available to the plants. But not just N, but Ca, Mg, B, Si, whatever.......

Question: Mulch the grass clippings. Mulch around the trees with hardwood mulch. Core fertilize with organic fertilizer and/or bonemeal, bloodmeal, alfalfa pellets, compost, rock phosphate, greensand, sul-po-mag, rock flour, peanut and ground kelp.
Answer: Exit the bloodmeal. Too much N, way too much benefit to pests and diseases, especially when not balanced with enough carbon.

Question: Why alfalfa pellets?
Answer: You are putting too much N in the system.

Question: Do you have weed problems?
Answer: Pests really like this much N. Put on just mulch and compost, nothing else. Especially if you have been doing this regime for some time, you are overloading your system with N, N, N, and not enough Ca. Too much P, K, Na.

Question: How much N, P, K is added with compost? With the mulch? Why do you think that level of N is not enough? What to you think happens to all the N, N, N, that you are adding? If it all stayed in the system, what would your N levels be after 5 years of your fertilizing practices? What is the amount of N you remove with the produce and eat? Why do you need to put back more N than you removed last year? So, where is the excess going?

Answer: Balance is the ticket here. Instead of spending so much money on these amendments, spend some money on a soil chemistry analysis so you know what is out-of-balance chemistry-wise. With all these inputs, you are driving your soil seriously bacterial, and harming the fungi. Think about what sul-po-mag actually is. What is the impact going to be on the fungi?

Question: Mow in the leaves from the trees. Collect copious amounts of raked up leaves from the neighbors and mulch them onto the lawn and fruit tree areas EVERY fall. Thickness of leaves mulched is at least 3 inches before mulching.

Answer: What kind of trees do you have? What's in the leaf material? What kinds of tannins and terpenes? Leaving the leaves under the trees would be fine, but on your grass? Maybe not the best idea. Perhaps you should compost them, not apply directly to the grass. I have described how to compost in the backyard system, where you turn once after the pile is made and mixed, and in 4 months, you have great compost. Do that instead. Add calcium into the compost process. Add any lacking nutrient element into the compost process. I bet you have a problem with iron, and you need to add ferric citrate to the composting process. Soil chemistry will say you have plenty of iron, but the plants are telling you they don't have iron. What's going on there?

Question: Keep a number of collected leaf bags over the winter and mulch mow them into the entire yard and fruit tree areas each spring. So now the yard is getting two feedings of leaves. One more than nature provides.

Answer: And is this a good thing? Are you building soil, or building a thick thatch layer in your grass area (which may be why your soil probe goes in happily, but is it really soil? Just a suggestion, you need to go out and assess whether this IS the situation)

Question: Under the trees, are you just building layer on layer of leaf material? Is this truly soil? Or just compacting leaf material which can give your trees fits? Do you have fungi to decompose the leaves?

Answer: If not, the trees are stressed and that would explain the curculio. Especially with all the N you add. But, you need to be the eyes in this detective investigation. I've suggested a simple explanation, but maybe the simple explanation isn't the actual explanation. More observation is needed. Please go look and assess what is happening in the grass, the veggies, and under your trees.

Question: Are you really dealing with soil? Which means sand, silt , clay in the organic matter, not just pure organic matter.

Answer: You should have no more than 1 inch to maybe – no more! – 2 inches of leaf material happily decomposing under your plants. The depth of litter this time of year depends greatly on where you live, and the depth of litter I would say is right varies through the country and with time of year. Add more mulch when the mulch begins to get down to a half to 1 inch deep. Please look at litter decomposition rate – how fast is something you put on the soil last October disappearing?

Question: Every two months broadcast one of the following: Alfalfa pellets, cornmeal, chicken layer feed, turkey growers feed. Sometimes I fertilize more than once every two months.
Answer: Can your plants possibly need this much N? Are you feeding your soil the right things? What biology does alfalfa feed? Is it fungal or bacterial food? What biology will be selected by the presence of layer or grower's feed? What biology does corn meal enhance? What are you doing to the organisms in your soil? Part of that answer lies in observing how fast these materials are decomposing. When you add these materials on the soil surface, what happens to them?

Question: Spray the entire yard with blackstrap molasses solution at a rate of 2 Tablespoons per gallon. Spray about every two weeks. In the fall I increase the rate to 3 Tablespoons per gallon and spray once a week from October 15 to November 15.
Answer: What is the purpose of this? Who are you feeding? What organisms are you setting up a habitat for by putting on small, but constant amounts of molasses? Molasses might be ok on the grass, but under the trees? You are asking for diseases. In the fall, you should not put molasses on a soil that should be fungal dominated, unless you lack all biology and need to start the process of bringing soil back. Hopefully, you are way beyond that, so application of molasses to the soil under the trees is not going to help move things in the direction the trees need.

Question: Apply soil drenches of compost tea every two weeks to the fruit tree roots. I've now used ACT for two years and soil drench at the same rate and spray everything about once a week during the growing season. Add kelp to the ACT during brewing along with many other foods. I brew about two 5 gallon buckets of ACT per week during the growing season (i.e., April through November).
Answer: What foods do you use in your tea? Who is growing in your compost tea? Do you have any idea of what organisms are in your compost? Are you helping the grass, or the trees with the tea you are making?

Question: Spread the dregs from the ACT around all trees, veggie and flower beds and shrubs."
Answer: This should be helping. Are you seeing fungal growth in this material? Once the compost dregs go on the soil, it should absolutely bloom with good fungi. If you see that, great. If you see no fungal growth in the material you are putting down, you have a problem. The compost is not conducive to fungal growth, and you need to change sources of compost, or do something to activate the fungi in the compost before you use the compost in your tea. If you see no fungal growth in the compost dregs, please check EC in the compost.

Question: Water with a dechlorinating filter attached to the hose.
Answer: Good.

Question: Lasagna compost all the raised beds with organic matter. Mainly raw horse manure and leaves in the fall.
Answer: What is the ratio of manure to leaves? Do you see fungal hyphae growing? Temperature the compost reaches?

Question: Spread the pulp leftover from juicing my home grown produce around bushes, trees, raised beds and, of course, the fruit trees.
Answer: Please compost this material. What biology are you selecting for when you apply this material? Is this helping or hindering your fungal-requiring plants?

Question: Have two birdfeeders that are constantly frequented by birds. Bird droppings all over the place decompose into the yard. Birds eat many of the pest insects. Hummingbirds are always in my yard, bats frequent the yard at night and I oftentimes see them at dusk and dawn. Spiders live everywhere!! Worms are everywhere!!
Answer: This is great news. But then, why do you need to be fertilizing over and over and over again? Too much of a good thing is not a good thing. The birds are providing fertilizer. Your dogs are providing fertilizer, you are putting on alfalfa meal, bloodmeal, manure, chicken feed, and more and more N, P, K. All the critters you are trying to get in your soil should be doing the nutrient cycling processes for you. You are working so hard to get your labor force in place, but you are over-doing it! Please, let your critters do their jobs. Stop over-loading the N, P, K, sit back, and just enjoy life more! Which worms do you have? The little red wrigglers? Night crawlers? Who is home? This can tell us much about the foodweb.

Question: Mulch mow all dead veggie plant material into the lawn each fall.
Answer: Doing a compost pile would be better. If you have any disease on the veggies, and you don't compost it, you can be setting yourself up for a problem. On the other hand, how fast does the dead veggie material disappear on your lawn?

Question: Every month I boil a bunch of leftover leaves I collected in the fall and make about two gallons of leaf tea. Sprinkle a diluted solution of this leaf tea around the fruit trees during the growing season. So now the fruit trees are getting "leaf" food many more times per year than nature provides.
Answer: Do you know that you are making things better with this constant input of certain kinds of foods? There's a reason nature provides foods when and where she does. Balance is the key. Are you pushing things bacterial, or fungal with the constant management?

Question: Save coffee grinds from work and spread this around all plants every year."
Answer: Who are you feeding? Coffee grounds are foods for ...who?

Question: I can get whole corn and crimped oats very cheaply where I live. I always have these on hand and freshly grind up these feeds into a meal and spread them around all plants. I do this periodically during the growing season. Each week some plant is getting a feeding of these freshly ground meals. Of course the fruit tree areas are a major recipient of these meals. These freshly ground meals are in addition to the large amounts of alfalfa pellets, etc., I buy and use in the garden. I also have whole soybeans that I grind up in small quantities and add to the corn and crimped oats meals. (Same for flax seeds.)
Answer: Great bird food -- these materials feed which kind of soil critters? How fast do these materials decompose, once you put them down?

Question: I know this might sound disgusting but periodically I dilute human urine and sprinkle that solution around all plants during the growing season."

Answer: Great, more N. More K. More nutrients …. Do you need them? Who are you feeding by putting on this much N? What is the effect of this on the soil biology? What happens to urine when it is applied to soil?

Question: I use fish emulsion, liquid rabbit fertilizer, Bill's Perfect Fertilizer and other purchased organic liquid fertilizers I've had good results from over the years."

Answer: Oh boy. When you over-apply N, what biology do you select? You have plum curculio and what other pests? Weeds? Fungal diseases? Please, compost everything. Reduce the N additions, you don't need them, really. Get a soil chemistry done, so we can see what it is that is really limiting plant production. It's not N, I can tell you that! And if perchance you do a plant tissue analysis, and N is low, it is not because your soil lacks N, it is because uptake of N is limited by the lack of some other nutrient. You have to track down what the lacking nutrient is, you need to get the RIGHT biology for your trees going, so they will provide the nutrients needed at the rates the trees need. What other management do you do to deal with the weeds?

22. Molasses in Irrigation Water 7/10/04 8:19 PM

Question: Should we add molasses to the irrigation water? Will the soil organisms act as a filter for Nitrates reducing the leaching and in turn feeding the plant as per her needs? Do we run the risk of lack of oxygen in the soil?

Answer: If you add too high levels of food, and oxygen is limited, anaerobic conditions will result. You would have to decide if, and how, the anaerobic conditions could be alleviated rapidly once the nitrate was tied up.

23. What is Out-of-Whack? 5/17/04 7:31 AM

Question: The molasses should move the critters in the right direction. How much molasses did you spray out? What did the plants do? Color? Healthiness?

Answer: A check of your soil might be a good idea, then you'd know for certain what was out-of-whack, but I understand that homeowners often don't like to spend money testing their lawn. So, then you get to do trial and error instead. Your choice. So, trial and error - Make a compost tea with kelp as a source of micronutrients. Then split that tea into several parts. The first of those parts; spray the tea as is in one area. Add a fish hydrolysate that has high calcium concentration, like Organic Gem, or Geofish, to another part of the tea. Spray in another section. Add ferric citrate to another part of the tea, and spray in another section. Watch plant response for a couple weeks. If one section is clearly going the way you want, then you know what to add. If you aren't seeing any of the sections respond, then the problem is either a different nutrient that you didn't try, or a biological one. Both would indicate that you really need to do the soil chemistry and soil biology testing, or you will likely spend many, many more dollars without getting any closer to figuring out what's up.

24. Sugar Beets 7/10/04 8:19 PM

At present sugar beet producers are having big problems as they are producing a lot of tonnage but with little sugar, with the added problems of the pest attacks also due to high Nitrates. This is similar to what I understand from sugar beet growers in the US. We have some areas here in Portugal with 200 ppm of Nitrate in bore hole

water, if we apply CT and keep irrigating with this water. You need to add both bacteria and fungi, and foods to feed both, but I would probably add corn gluten, or low N fish oil, as possible food resources, before adding molasses. Try each to see which will grow the organisms best, so the increased organism growth ties up nitrogen in the microbial biomass.

25. Lime 6/24/04 2:54 PM

Albrecht test says you need 8 tons of lime per ac. Don't do that, you are wasting money, and harming surface and ground water. A ton is about 2000 pounds, so the recommendation is to put 1600 pounds of lime per acre. That's a chunk of change, plus think about trying to actually spread 1600 pounds. That's a chunk of change too. So, instead, of putting the 16,000 pounds of lime ON THE SOIL, you add 1/60th of that in the compost, and apply a half ton of the compost. So, if the recommendation was 16,000 pounds of lime, then divide by 60 to get the amount you put, per ton, in the compost. 16,000/60 = 267 pounds in 2000 pounds of compost. That goes out as a half ton of compost. Or, if you want to put a ton of compost out, then you would only add 133 pounds of lime in a ton.

26. Bacterial Mulch or Fungal Mulch 5/17/04 9:44 Am

Question: So what mulch materials could I use that would encourage bacteria that are good for the brassicas? Mulch tends to be C material, and what they need is N. Or can I drench my straw mulches with bacteria-rich tea and somehow alter the balance that way?

Answer: Use the tea to push bacterial biomass. But I would bet your soil is already very bacterial, and the broccoli likes the fact it is getting some fungal improvement with the straw. Remember, bacterial-dominated does not mean there are no fungi. It's balance. Your soils in Israel are VERY bacterial. Use the mulch to help the fungi that broccoli need. For comfrey - that is a plant that requires much more organic matter in the soil, and needs a more fungal condition. Build the soil for comfrey production by adding LOTS more plant material, and use a tea that pushes fungi a great deal.

27. Inocula for Compost 3/27/04 11:25 AM

Question: I would like to spread the chips/compost in our orchard and am wondering if anyone can suggest what I might add to the pile to encourage the right biology before I put it on the orchard.

Answer: Add inocula of different local leaf and soil and humus materials with the fungi evident would be good additions to your pile in order to enhance and improve diversity.

28. Mold and Nematodes 5/16/04

Question: What about spoiled hay that was rained on. Lots of mould... is it still okay to mulch or will it upset the balance?
Answer: That mold can be a problem, as it could be a disease fungus. Any observation on "fuzzy-wuzzy-ness"? Color? Smell? Mildew has a distinctive smell, color and fuzzy-ness. If present, you need to compost the spoiled hay before using around any plant. You need to take a bio-dynamic hands-on training course where they will teach you what the smells are and what they mean.

Question: We use a Brillion seeder that scatters seed so plants are everywhere with no need for herbicides. We use compost at planting at 2.5 tons/acre and same at each harvest or at the beginning of a grazing rest and have little weevil damage (we do plant weevil resistant variety).
Answer: Add a few Steinernema into your next compost. This nematode is available at most garden stores. They like moist soil, so the compost you are adding each fall and spring will make sure that they will survive! Those nematodes take out most soil weevils at the larval stage.

29. Beneficial Nematodes 5/1/04 10:07 AM
The beneficial nematodes should be able to take the pressure just fine. The concern would be opening sizes on the drip nozzles.

Question: What is the opening size?
Answer: We need them to be in the range of 400 micrometers, or larger, so the big good guys can get through.

a. Predatory Nematodes
Buying the predatory nematodes from the US doesn't make any sense, since the sub-species you have in OZ are adapted to your soil types, and climates. We do not have the same conditions in the US, so US-imports don't survive well in your conditions. The exception is the conditions that you describe - where the soil has been fumigated. There is no decent life left in that soil, so addition of ANY kind of beneficials, OZ-adapted or not - will help immensely. But, for long term survival, you want OZ-critters. So, keep looking for that compost made in OZ that has the predatory nematodes present. Otherwise, stockpile some compost, and add predatory nematodes that you extract (you may want to talk to the Lismore lab and get them to save the predatory nematodes they find from all over OZ for you), into that stockpile. They should grow and increase in numbers, but it will take 6 months to a year for that to happen. They are slow-growers.

30. Slugs and Tea 5/15/04 8:25 AM
My experience tells me that tea is perfectly capable of dealing with slugs IF you have the organisms in the tea to deal with the slugs. Mother Nature acts with multiple mechanisms of control all the time. That's normal. Addition of yucca feeds the organisms that attack and decompose slugs. Certain nematodes attack and consume slugs.

31. Slug Control and Tea 5/16/04 9:55 AM
Some people manage to control slugs just fine with compost tea. Mechanism for control? Adequate fungi, and probably the right set of fungi. Possibly yucca needs to be used to get those

fungi to grow. Possibly certain sets of nematodes are present. I gave examples of where compost tea was clearly the cause of the slugs no longer being present.

32. Slugs and Yucca 5/11/04 11:10 AM
Have you tried yucca at all for the slugs? I, of course, think that it is the organisms (fungi in particular), since yucca is a fungal food, that do the trick. But that requires showing that yucca directly impacts the slugs, with or without the fungi being present. I think fungal growth, enhanced by yucca being there to feed those specific fungi, is the bottom line. But note I said think - I don't know for certain that the mechanism for yucca working is the growth of fungal species inimical to slugs.

33. Slugs in the Garden 5/10/04 5:13 AM
I historically had slug problems in my garden, and when I used compost tea with adequate levels of bacteria, fungi, protozoa and nematodes in it, I no longer had slugs in my garden. When others used good tea, defined as good by the fact it has great biomass of bacteria, fungi, and protozoa, they too see no slugs. Most of us who used to have slug problems and no longer do, live in places where slugs are much more rampant. The critical factor is having the proper sets of organisms in the tea.

34. Slugs Attracted by Alcohol 5/9/04 6:14 PM
Slugs are typically attracted by alcohol production. An inability to control slugs with ACT may suggest that your ACT isn't as aerobic as you think.

35. Lilies 5/10/04 4:49 AM
The data I have seen suggests that most lilies are on the bacterial side, about 0.5 to 0.75 ratio fungi to bacteria.

36. Solarization with Black Plastic 5/10/04 4:14 AM
Solarization is the term for what you are asking about, and there are a couple scientific papers on the topic that answer the questions you are asking. As long as you don't seal the black plastic around the bed's edges, and as long as you cut slits in the black plastic, air will get into the bed just fine. If the temperature in the bed gets too high, and you have moist conditions in the bed, the steam heat can kill organisms in soil. If you live in a sunny part of the country, this could happen quite rapidly as temperatures, and sunlight, warm things up in the spring. Please note that moisture is needed. If the soil is dry, then the killing effect is less likely. In cool, cloudy parts of the country, the temperature never gets high enough to kill anything. Black plastic, or clear plastic, don't work particularly well as a solarization method here in the Pacific Northwest. With clear plastic, you don't even get the weed barrier effect.

37. Microbes and pH 2/28/04
You select from a population of microbes that tolerate and grow in that pH. Extreme pH usually means growth is slow, limited and you probably did not add the right foods to get those organisms to grow. You likely limit microorganisms too much to have decent coverage on the leaf surfaces to give proper coverage of plant surfaces with their protective ability. They may work quite nicely if

you are putting your tea into soil that has the same pH, and thus the same limitation for microbial growth. Do some testing to figure out what microbial foods those soil bacteria and fungi like best.

38. Spraying Livestock with Compost Tea 2/1/04 6:08 PM

We need more data (there speaks the academic scientist, I know!) on this before we can go recommending it to people. All results on skin microflora and compost tea are anecdotal so far. People, just like plants, have layers of bacteria, a few fungi, and protozoaon their skin. We feed very particular sets of microbes with our exudates and select for our own "good guys". There are a couple of books on this.

39. Compost Tea for Deicing? 1/26/04 1:44 PM

Would have to have high concentrations of sugar in the mix, to keep the bacteria growing fast enough to generate the heat, and when they got spread out on the pavement, there isn't enough food to keep them cooking, I imagine.

40. Profits vs. Continued Application of Inoculums 1/24/04 8:29 AM

Once a bacterial inoculum has been applied, and the bacteria survive and grow in that soil, addition of more of that inoculum will not be beneficial. Survival and growth of inoculated organisms will occur as long as toxic applications (pesticides and high levels of inorganic fertilizers are prime examples of these toxic applications) are not made.

Question: If added organisms have survived and are growing, why do you have to keep applying those organisms?
Answer: If you have to keep applying those bacteria, it means something is going on, which the grower should recognize. One possibility is that the inoculum cannot survive in those climatic conditions. A second possibility is that toxic applications are continuing. A third possibility is that disturbances which kill soil organisms are being used. In the case that the organisms cannot survive in that soil, it would be wiser to find bacteria that can and do survive. A different inoculum is required. Try some indigenous organisms. Make your own compost. Add EM, but then also add some other inocula, and get them all growing in your compost. In the second case, where toxic materials are being applied that kill the biology, assessment of benefit must be made.

Question: Is it more expensive to keep adding back the organisms that are killed, or more expensive to keep using the toxics?
Answer: It gets down to plant production here. More profit from which set of practices? At the very least, try getting the whole food web back into the soil and see if that doesn't allow you to completely remove pesticides and inorganic fertilizers. Same line of reasoning with the disturbances that kill the organisms.

Question: Are profits higher when you disturb and add the organisms back, or higher profit when you get the organisms established and have healthy soil?
Answer: Many of the EM bacteria survive for a period of time, but at a certain point, about 2 years after first application, the species that can survive, have survived and are doing fine. At 2 years, those bacteria that are not appropriate for the climate will not survive and will not grow, no matter how many times you add them to the soil. So, why keep adding them? Therefore, I said that

addition of more inoculum is not beneficial. I DID NOT say addition would result in "two steps back". No such conclusion can be made from my statements.

Question: Does saying "addition is not beneficial" lead to the automatic conclusion that it will be detrimental?
Answer: No. If there is no benefit to the addition, it may well be that the application is neutral. And that leads directly to the question, "Why keep spending money to add organisms that will not survive?" Different story if the grower is killing off the organisms, but gets benefit from adding them back. Fine, that's up to the grower and they have to pencil out cost versus benefit. To continue getting improvement, the rest of the food web needs to be put into place. That means also getting the fungi, protozoa, nematodes, and microarthropods into the soil, letting them establish, grow and give benefit to the plant. EM has it's place, an important place, but it is not the end-all of getting soil into a healthy condition. The rest of the food web is required.

41. Urine on Lawns 1/8/04 1;11 AM
Urine isn't per se bad, as long as it is not in high concentration. Of course something peeing on the lawn, it is in high concentration. But the problem is that certain bacterial species convert the nitrogen in urine to nitrate rather rapidly, or to ammonia, if the soil is anaerobic. Either form of N can cause the burning or browning effect that you see. Excess nitrite, nitrate or ammonia kills plant cells. There's a salt effect with urine too. To prevent browning, you need to have microorganisms which will "pull apart" or dis-associate the salt, consume and retain the nitrogen in their biomass instead of releasing nitrate, or ammonia. So, you need to get the organisms in the soil, get them established and growing on the plant surfaces and the roots, and then urine is just another food resource, stimulating the biology, not killing your plants.

Of course, you have to have adequate water or the salt effect of the urine can do a job on the plants and organisms as well. Talk to the people reporting on the benefits of compost tea in turf, or golf courses or sports field about this. The places where dogs pee, or other critters as well, no longer turned brown. Frank Rossi from Cornell University has reported, just in the last few days, of 65% reduction in turf disease using compost tea this summer at BethPage. If I understand correctly, this was better reduction than any other treatment that was used, including the toxic chemicals. Given that this is dollar spot, a HUGE problem out east, compost tea is going to TAKE OFF in the golf industry.

42. Animal Urine 1/28/04 1:00 AM
It would be nice to get something solid on dog urine differences - must be a study done somewhere about it…..the important point is that AACT does a great deal to reduce the problem. Male dogs, female dogs, probably doesn't matter, even if male dogs do less damage than females. Don't know about deer.

43. Calcium 1/3/04 3:46 PM
In my opinion, you choose the form of calcium you want depending on the other nutrient needs your soil might have. Extension folks tend to choose the form of calcium to play games with pH, but as Arden Anderson points out, there is no hydrogen in calcium carbonate. I know that it is the biology that determines soil pH, so I don't play pH games by messing with inorganic anything.

a. Nasty Acid

If you add nasty acid, yes, you will change soil pH, but you also wipe out your biology, and then you are stuck using inorganic salts to try to grow things.

b. Eggshells for Calcium Carbonate

I add calcium to my soil as eggshells (calcium carbonate), since eggshells come with the protein your biology needs to deal with the shock of having that form of calcium dumped on them.

c. Add Calcium to Compost

I add calcium to my compost as the cheapest form I can find, except not gypsum (calcium sulfate) unless I want to kill my fungi. Or if I need a small amount of sulfur, then I'll use a little gypsum.

d. Soil Biology and Soil Chemistry Interaction

Arden Anderson and I have been working on the interaction of soil biology and soil chemistry for the last 4 years. I've changed what he recommends, and he has altered my take on soil chemistry as well. Arden has logical and well-thought through reason for everything he does. I enjoy interacting with him immensely. Arden and I don't always see eye-to-eye, but we always agree to go collect more data if we don't agree. No use in arguing about something we don't have enough data to make a clear case. A couple times, he has come back with more data in a year or so, and I with more data, and we discover that we were both right, given the circumstances we were working in. There is no one right way to grow things, that can be stated categorically around the globe. It is all relative. Use whatever form of calcium you want, especially if you are putting it into your compost. Just don't use high concentrations. OK?

44. Oyster Shells 7/29/04 11:36 PM

Crushed oyster shell is great for adding to soil - it's calcium carbonate, but much is chelated, and so easier for the bacteria and fungi to use than purely inorganic calcium carbonate.

45. Calcium Sulfate or Calcium Nitrate 1/3/04 12:08 PM

Yes, you could add calcium sulfate, but I prefer calcium nitrate, if you need N, or calcium carbonate if you need to chew up some hydrogen ions, or eggshells (calcium carbonate with protein), or calcium hydroxide, if you need to mess more with the chemistry of hydrogen. But please make sure to not add more than 100 pounds of any of these salts per 900 pounds of compost (think of it as a 1:10 dilution if you need to). More than that and you get too many things dying from the salt effect.

46. Sulfur in the Form of Biology 1/2/04 8:15 PM

You add sulfur in the form of the biology. The proteins in bacteria, fungi, protozoa, nematodes, and organic matter. In rare instances, maybe addition of a low concentration of sulfur (no more than, hum, 1 pound per acre as I recall) in combination with carbon to feed the fungi harmed by the sulfur.

48. Elevated CO2 and Plant Growth 12/22/03 3:10 AM

Please note that the elevated CO2 being talked about in this paper is an effect ON THE TREE, not the fungus. One piece of mythology out in the scientific world is that elevated CO2 will increase plant growth. The logic goes like this: If plants fix more CO2, they will increase sugar production, then there will be more sugars released from the roots, and thus more food for the fungi growing on the roots.

Question: But, what is the limiting factor for most plant growth? What keeps your plants from growing more fruit, right now? Is it a lack of CO2?
Answer: No, it's a lack of nitrogen, or calcium, or iron, or some other micronutrient. Elevating CO2 doesn't increase plant production. UNLESS...... you add excess nitrogen to the experimental units, as was done in the research cited here, I believe.

Question: So, if we continue to over-fertilize the world, as we are doing right now, and continue to destroy water-quality, as we are doing right now, then elevated CO2, as we are doing right now, will result in increased plant production. Except, how many of you are seeing this? Do you realize that you are paying more per gallon of drinking water, since the stuff coming out of the tap is no longer drinkable in most places, than you pay for gasoline? People go nuts when the price of gas goes up by ten cents. But you are paying what per gallon of drinking water? When did this one slip by?
Answer: Given the logic of more CO2, more foods in the roots, then more O2 in the atmosphere means less CO2 getting to the plant surface, so less sugar for the fungi. Except, it just doesn't work like that. Plants only use 20 minutes of sunlight out of each hour of sunlight they receive, based on some work by the folks at the Duke Phytotron (sorry, don't have the reference at hand). So, if plants don't get "enough" CO2 in the first 20 minutes, they can accumulate for the next few minutes and get what they need to make sugar, protein, etc. The limiting factor in plant production is N, or some other nutrient, not CO2. This is the reference being considered in the contributor's post: http://www.co2science.org/journal/1999/v2n11b5.htm. The above article seems to state that elevated CO2 rates promote fungal growth and elevated O2 rates inhibit fungal spread.

48. Hydrogen Peroxide is a Sterilant 12/17/03 8:41 AM

H2O2 is hydrogen peroxide. When added to anything containing catalase (which means the biology to make catalase must be present and functioning, i.e., active, not just present), H2O2 breaks down to water and an oxygen radical (O-). That oxygen radical is EXTREMELY reactive, and will destroy membrane integrity of any organism that does not have a mechanism to deal with that reactive compound. So, H2O2 can be a great sterilant, which is why we use it on cut, scrapes, wounds, etc. It kills a lot of organisms.

Question: So using it for soil remediation to GROW organisms?
Answer: I don't think so. But H2O2 does supply oxygen.

Question: So if you have anaerobic conditions in soil, and you therefore have a whole bunch of anaerobic organisms growing there, why not kill that biology that makes things that cause plant root to die?

Answer: So, aerate by adding H2O2, but then you HAVE TO inoculate aerobic, beneficial organisms after that, so they then rule, instead of the anaerobic organisms recovering and taking over again. So, hydrogen peroxide can help you move in the right direction, but PLEASE, understand why it works, or you will mess up sometime, thinking you are doing the right thing, when in fact you could be harming the very things you need to encourage.

49. Soil Compaction 11/25/03 9:36 PM

Question: First, how compacted is the soil?
Answer: Take a metal rod and push into the soil. How far can you push the rod easily? Can you push with some force and get deeper? How deep, and how much force? A slight lean, concentrated effort, or grunting? When do you get to the "can't push it in any further" depth? To what depth are you going to till?

a. Clay Soil
When you pick up the clay soil and play with it in your hands, does it ball up easily? Please make sure the soil is at least 50% moisture. Put the ball between your hands, and roll the ball into a long worm. How long does the worm get before it finally breaks of it's own accord? This will tell me Ca:Mg ratio.

b. Sheep Manure
The sheep manure - composted? Aged? Mixed with anything? What have the sheep been fed?

50. Clays 6/14/04 10:25 Am

Question: With bentonite added (a montmorillonite clay, which BTW has disease suppression properties of its own) to my teas, the clay blends very well into the tea, unlike the results of mixing calcium carbonate with water which tends to clump. I also apply the bentonite as a skin to my compost piles, a biodynamic practice. Or should we be inoculating our compost with dolomite and let the critters digest the minerals first for use later in the compost tea?
Answer: Any clay adsorbs water, and available nutrients to a limited extent. That means, the clay reduces the availability of water and nutrients to the organisms in the compost, or in tea. Those are the most likely ways that the clay influences the growth of the biology. But it is non-selective. Good guys and bad guys are affected. Sure would like to know if the bad guys are more affected than the good guys - and what the dose response actually is there. One part clay selects against bad guys, while two parts will take out both good and bad? I sure would love to have that kind of knowledge. But we don't, as far as I can tell. But I was in the library checking out literature, and there are now three new pubs on actively aerated compost tea having good to excellent beneficial effects in reducing foliar and root disease. Oh, a last note - DON'T use dolomite!!!!!! There is more magnesium than calcium in the material, and the point of using these calcium-containing materials is to improve the ratio of calcium to magnesium. Can't do it, if the material you are putting on has more magnesium than calcium......Use lime, eggshells, ground oyster shell, ground fish bones, calcium nitrate... there are other sources, just not pulling them into active brain space, but I think you get the idea. Avoid gypsum, unless you need the sulfur. And then make sure to add the biology back - the sulfur in gypsum seems to negatively impact the fungi.

51. Flocculation of Clays 12/17/03 8:32 AM

Flocculation of clays by adding calcium will soften soil, but it won't last, unless you get the biology back into the soil ASAP, so the fungi can hold the calcium.

Question: Why is it that your Kinsey soil report, or the IAL, or an A&L, or Plant and Soil report will come back each year, forever, and say between 3 and 8 TONS of lime is needed? When do you ever stop having to add lime, lime and more lime?

Answer: When you get the biology back into the soil. It is the organisms, using the organic matter to grow and do their jobs, that hold calcium, N, iron, B, PO4, etc in the soil. Lose the biology, and your soil compacts. No structure. It is the right set of organisms that is required to keep the nutrients in soil, and the reason you have lost the nutrients is that you no longer have the appropriate set of organisms present to keep those nutrients in the soil. The good guys don't hang around where you are adding things that will kill them. Guess what 3 tons of lime does to your biology?

52. Inorganic Nutrients 12/15/03 9:14 PM

The problem with adding inorganic nutrients is that they are all, pretty much, salts. That is, they dis-associate in water, and thus hold water away from the organisms, thus resulting in organism death, if the salt impact is great enough.

Question: So, if you know that addition of more than 100 pounds per acre of salt will kill many desirable organisms, then how can you get biology going, so you can hold your inorganic elements in the biology?

Answer: Unless you do that, these nutrients will be mobile in water, and leave the rooting zone very rapidly.

Question: And please don't tell me that Ca, or NH4, or other nutrients aren't all that mobile in water. Relative to what?

Answer: Inorganic nutrients are quite leachable.

Question: If they weren't, how come they end up in your drinking water? Why do they cause toxic blooms of bacteria and algae in surface rivers and lakes? What garbage information is being listened to when the information is in front of people's faces, but they keep believing that ammonium isn't very leachable? Or phosphate?

Answer: Phew! There are herds of folks that need to wake up and smell the roses - or is that purification?

OK, tirade over. The point is that we need to learn how to add inorganic nutrients to replace the nutrients lost once the biology was pretty much killed off. Once there were no organisms to hold the nutrients as chelated or biology-bound forms, those nutrients leached, rapidly.

Question: Or why do you have to keep adding tons of gypsum each year?

Answer: I know people who have added 8 tons of lime each year for the last 8 years, and they still have to add that much again this year - or at least that's what the chemistry tests tell them.

Question: Or take the case of researchers in New York, or New Jersey, or California, where they have added the inorganic nutrients every year for the last 10 to 14 years ,just as the soil chemistry tests says they have to, and they never have gotten improved soil levels. When does this farce end? How do we add the inorganic nutrients in a way they won't leach, so you don't have to add those nutrients in an inorganic form ever again?

Answer: You have to add them with the organisms, and the foods to feed the organisms, so the nutrients are converted to biological forms, and do not further leach from the soil.

Question: Why is it that bacteria and fungi do not leach from the soil?

Answer: Well, unless you kill them, of course...I hope to work with Arden Anderson to develop the exact programs needed for different situations so we can minimize the inorganic additions, make them in conjunction with the biology, so nutrients going in are held, and not lost. Then all you have to add back into the soil is the nutrients removed in the crop yield. No more loss of nutrients to groundwater, or drinking water, or surface waters......

53. *Pseudomonas* Inoculum 10/18/03 9:25 AM

What is your recipe? If the fruit is having problems, then we aren't using up the sugars on the fruit surface properly. So, a *Pseudomonas* inoculum would be what you need.

54. Fish Hydrolysate Balances N 10/6/03 9:29 PM

Question: How much does number of organisms per square foot added affect competition for food, and how much does amount of food added or present affect this? The effect of combination of adding microorganisms and adding food for them, and adding food intended for the plant, is what I want to understand.

Answer: Typically, competition is for food. Bacteria win, usually, if they have close sources of N, S, C, P, etc. Otherwise, fungi win. The plant doesn't get much chance at N, P, S, etc, unless there are predators around. Protozoa, beneficial nematodes and microarthropod presence are critical.

Question: Specifically, is it possible to induce a bloom of microorganisms that can show up as symptoms of out competing the plant (e.g. chlorosis)?

Answer: Yes. I have killed plants by getting bacteria and fungi to grow on sugars and woody materials that had no N. Straight sugar has no N in it, and by adding pure sugar, you can immobilize a large quantity of N, P, S, etc. in the bacterial and fungal biomass, thus killing a plant, or at least severely stressing it.

Question: Is food available or food added at time of application related to what happens with the plants?

Answer: If you add plenty of N along with the sugars and proteins, then the impact of stressing the plant for N does not occur. If you get the bacteria and fungi growing too fast, and they use up the oxygen, you lose your N because under anaerobic conditions, N is volatilized as ammonia, sulfur us volatilized as hydrogen sulfide. Bad news for the fertility of your soil.

Question: In a drench, how important is the amount of water carrier?

Answer: Don't over water and water-log the soil. Oxygen problems can therefore occur.

Question: I'm thinking of manual applications and the challenge of evenly applying tea as a drench, and the possibility of localized higher rates of critters interacting with plant food and outcompeting the plant.

Answer: I don't usually manage to evenly apply my tea (I use a sprinkler can usually), and somehow, my plant manages to muddle through and look happy. I usually use fish hydrolysate, and thus am balancing the N for the sugars I'm adding.

55. Alternative Sources of Copper 1/8/04 12:38 AM

About alternative sources of copper -- I think most cold-water kelps come with adequate amounts so you don't need to be adding more. But I haven't done much looking into alternative sources for copper, so maybe someone else knows?

56. Spreaders and Organisms 10/3/03 5;49 AM

Soap neutralizes charges, and results in water being able to spread more evenly. Think about why we add soap to dishwater - you solubilize the fats and lipids (grease) clinging to your dishes. That's what any spreader does.

You wash your hands with soap to neutralize the charged bacterial surfaces that result in them clinging to the cells on your hands, and wash them off you. It works well. Putting your hands on the surface of a petri plate with rich medium before washing your hands, and then after washing your hands is a great way to demonstrate this. Lots of bacteria growing on the petri plate medium on the plate before you wash, much fewer after you wash. The danger with a spreader is that you will wash the organisms you want to have stick to the surface, off the surface. The only way to know if it is working properly is to test. A leaf organism test is required so you know what the effects actually are.

57. Ripping Under the Roots 10/1/03 7:22 AM

Plugging up the irrigation system is of concern, that the spores are not delivered to the roots. There is an easier way to deliver spores to the roots, if the coring is too laborious (as I recall, my recommendation for coring was for someone who wanted to save a few oak trees. Coring is fine for a few oak trees - depending on what you mean by "a few"). Angle a four foot bar from the drip line at about 30% angle (angle depends on your plants root distribution as well, so take that into account please), and rip under the roots of the plants while spraying the tea just behind the bar as it passes through the soil. The tea organisms, the spores, and foods get into the soil, presumably getting the spores to the roots as required. I know people who have done this and their roots are coming back with higher colonization. I know people who have done this, and have not had success in getting the roots colonized. What are the critical factors in getting this to work? Getting the spores to the roots. You need to check that as you under-cut, you are catching some of the roots. You'll lose some roots. Don't rip off too many.....The angle on the ripper is critical. Getting the sprayer to get the tea down the cut is critical too. Working with a consultant on this might be a good idea.

58. *Mycorrhizal* Fungi 10/11/03 6:20 AM

When there is no data, people should say that there is no data. Isn't it also correct to point out to people that even though research may not have been done on a specific species of native plant, that similar plant species, which happen to be commercially important plants, are colonized by *mycorrhizal* fungi? The expectation would be that the same *mycorrhizal* fungi would colonize the native plant. That's the best that can be done, with the current data. I like another one of your suggestions very much, which is to post information about success or non-success with colonization attempts on some public forum. Any ideas on what list-serve already does that, or where might be useful to start doing this? Other *mycorrhizal* folk, any directions for where this is happening? Or could happen?

59. *Mycorrhizal* Fungi Require Roots 12/22/03 2:44 AM
Mycorrhizal fungi require roots in order to produce a large amount of biomass. *Mycorrhizal* fungal spores can germinate in tea, mostly when there is humic acid present in high enough concentration. That is often the cue *mycorrhizal* fungi need in order to germinate. But without the root, *mycorrhizal* fungi will not continue to grow. Any *mycorrhizal* expert will tell you that. *Mycorrhizal* fungi are VERY sensitive to any disturbance, and once they are germinated, agitation will typically destroy them. That's why *mycorrhizal* spores are added at the end of a tea brew, so they WON'T germinate while they are still in the tea. You want them next to a root before they germinate. Want data on this? Come to SFI and germinate some VAM spores, and then move them. Broken hyphae everywhere. Shake them in a tea, and you just have dead hyphae. Very sensitive to mixed.

a. Fungi Use Molasses
Many fungi use molasses just fine. Most bacteria are better at using molasses than fungi, however, if other conditions allow bacterial growth. Quite often, bacteria use molasses so rapidly that oxygen concentration drops, and then the beneficial fungi are out-of-luck. So the bacteria win. But, add enough concentration of molasses, and the bacteria will be shut down. No growth. Osmotic pressure keeps the bacteria from growing. At high molasses concentration - or high concentration of any sugar - the ONLY organisms growing will be fungi.

Question; Practical observation - what organisms grow in a container of molasses? Or syrup? Or jam? Jelly?
Answer: Fungi, and only fungi. If you spill water in your jelly, then bacteria will have a grand time, but only after you dilute the sugar, so the osmotic concentration is dropped. There are a number of textbooks that speak about these interactions - try Webster's book on Introductory Mycology as a good beginning text. I believe Paul Stametz's website would be good place to go looking as well. North Carolina State University has a good biologically based website. *Mycorrhizal* Applications website explains *mycorrhizal* factors.

60. *Mycorrhizal* Colonization 10/2/03 6:52 AM
Spores are rugged, that is true. Most dormant stages of organisms are rugged. They have to be able to survive adverse conditions, so tough outer layers are the order of the day when dormant. So, as you suggest, banding should work. I believe there are several scientific papers in the literature where spores were placed below where the seed or seedlings were placed, and *mycorrhizal* colonization was improved significantly. Dry *mycorrhizal* products would probably work best for this approach, although drenching the soil below the seed, or seedling roots, works as well. Before *mycorrhizal* inocula were available, I told people over and over about collecting

spores from their own land or from existing plants and applying them to their new plantings or planting rows. Collecting spores from the habitat in the environment that matches the habitat you are trying to develop is not new by any means. The concept of having landscape plantings partly for the purpose of being a source of non-lab-culturable organisms was probably first suggested by Lady Eve Balforth. Not a new concept at all. Still, showing people how to do things is important, and updates on the "how-to" generates new interest in the methods. I just would like less hype, or perhaps recognition that there is a long line of scientific development behind all of this.

61. Mycorrhizal Sample Analyzed 11/25/03 9:31 PM

Question: Dry weight of sample 0.79g, AB 153.2, TB 476, AB 29.2, TF 78, HD 2.5, Flagellates 7,269 (high), Amoebae 35,024 (high), Ciliates 1,751 (high, which makes sense to me because of all the rain), Total Nematode #/g 2 (low), and % *Mycorrhizal* Colonization 16 (low). Any suggestions on how to further biologically optimize this field?
Answer: Add fungal inoculum to improve the fungal component quickly, feed fungal foods. Use a good fungal inoculum on the compost pile to activate the decomposition process.

Question: And I have a related question (trying to stay on one subject here..:-): How is that 16% mychorrhizal colonization is "low?" Or is that a typo (meant 16 spores/gram... I also assume 2nd "AB" is "AF")?
Answer: We measure the length of the root colonized by *mycorrhizal* fungi, as compared to the total root length that we observe. We know that VAM colonization should be at least 40% to be able to have all of the benefits from VAM that you can get. Anything over 85 to 90% is probably a bit too high. We don't ever see that happen in healthy soil. Someone consumes some of the hyphae and keeps things in balance. So, 16% colonization is low. In general, there is enough colonization there that you have the inoculum, but you need to help colonization expand, so feed humic acids to give the VAM a bit more jump-start, a kick in the butt, to get the colonization improving.

139. *Mychorrhizae* and Crop Rotation 10/1/03 6:00 PM
Of course it would be best if you did not need to inoculate with *mycorrhizae* in the first place. One of the best things that people can do to help out the native *mycorrhizae* that they already have in their fields is to plant a winter hardy cover crop, like rye. By having the living roots for the *mycorrhizae* to live on over the winter greatly increases the rate and amount of colonization in the following spring on the desired cash crop. Using a plant species like rye will enhance VAM, and will maintain *mycorrhizal* fungi that typically colonize row crops or vegetable crops. Most deciduous tree and shrub species will also usually be able to tap into the same VAM network. But conifers need *ectomycorrhizal* fungi, and a perennial understory is needed. Just a point of clarification. The take-home that Matt was trying to express remains correct - living plants maintain the *mycorrhizal* fungus. But extra-matrical spores and hyphae in the dead and dying roots of the previous crop also maintain the *mycorrhizal* fungi through the winter. There should be no need to inoculate a soil again, if the plants from the last year had good colonization.

Question: What about crop rotations? This theory is very similar to Japan's Natural Farming. In Natural Farming they use the same field for the same crops year after year. The idea is that the soil will start to "like" or "appreciate" the plant that is continually grown in it, and the soil will then accommodate for this plant. My question is how does what you said about different soils for different plants fit into the concept of crop rotations?

Answer: Crop rotation is not needed, if you are maintaining the diversity of the organisms in the soil. But if the only food going into a soil is from a monoculture of a single crop, year after year, diversity is lost. The species of early spring and summer microbes aren't maintained. The diversity of food that is added by having other crops helps maintain the diversity of microbes to compete with the pathogens. So, if you don't want to rotate crops, but maintain soil health, you have to add something that adds back the diversity of food resources for the full foodweb. And that is.......? Compost. Well made, aerobic, compost. No loss of N, P, or S if it stays aerobic.

63. *Mycorrhizal* Applications 9/29/03 8:40 PM

Yes, this is the one I'm talking about. Thank you for reminding me which species they are using, I couldn't remember. If there are no *mycorrhizal* fungi on the roots of the strawberry, I'd suggest going to an existing strawberry field that has good VAM colonization, and using roots from those plants as an inoculum. I'm leery of VAM inoculum that has only one species in it. The reference offered on growing your own inoculum sounds pretty good. The Australia company selling the "grown in" Australia *mycorrhizal* inoculum works in conjunction with *Mycorrhizal* Applications.

64. *Mycorrhizal* Fungi Spores 9/27/03 10:34 PM

Question: Why would *mycorrhizal* fungi not be meant to be sprayed?

Answer: *Mycorrhizal* fungi should be present as spores in the material you buy. If they aren't spores, then the shelf life is very short. The hyphae in roots probably died while they were sitting around getting ready to be shipped. If they are present as spores, then addition to tea is not a problem. Spraying them is not a problem, as long as they don't germinate and start to grow in the tea. Germinated spores are very sensitive to any pressure, and they will likely not make it through the pump. Just make sure to add the spores to the tea, and spray within 4 hours or so. It generally takes that long for even a few spores to wake up and start to germinate. Now, spraying spores on the soil surface may not do much good - the spores stick to organic matter, and then don't move further in the soil. But you can spray the spores onto seed surfaces, or root surfaces without any problem. Spraying into planting holes and aeration holes in turf, into potting mix, should work just fine.

65. Organic Matter Retains Spores 9/29/03 8:40 PM

Question: What about putting the *mycorrrhrizae* spores through an irrigation system? Spores added to the AACT at end of brewing time then through the irrigation system so is delivered direct to the roots.

Answer: Only if the irrigation actually applies the spores to the roots. So, an irrigation system in the ground, where the spores are applied right to the roots? Then ok. But if the irrigation is above ground, and the spores have to pass through the soil or through organic matter, they probably will have problems getting the spores to the root. SOMETIMES, if using a sand medium, the spores will pass through the sand. I recall Bob Ames telling me that spores would wash through sand with low or little organic matter. Maybe? Could always try and see. It is organic matter that retains spores. No organic matter -- the spores should move into the soil.

66. Spores in Different Soil Types 8/11/03 6:07 AM

I'd say that the reply you got back from that company would suggest finding someone more reputable would be a good idea. In my experience, *Mycorrhizal* Applications (www.*mycorrhizae*.com) is a good place to start. They do research, they talk to most of the other researchers in the biz, and they are connected to both Oregon State University ecto- and endo-*mycorrhizal* people. They usually provide me with good data, test results and published scientific data where such data exist. There is a difference between sand and clay soils in regard to watering in. When we've looked for spores (sorry, not published data) in sand, the spores move downward quite rapidly. But in loam, or clay, very different story. If there is organic matter in the soil, the spores hang-up on the OM. I recall seeing published papers on this, but I couldn't track them for you easily. Do a CD-ROM search on Agricola, or see if *Mycorrhizal* Applications has references for you. Or perhaps ATTRA (www.ATTRA.org). Steve Diver often has already researched this information and will share his references with folks.

67. Spores vs. Hyphae 7/28/03 12:19 PM

Ecto and VAM come as spores, and thus, you can beat them up any way your like, until they germinate. Inject as spores, no problem. Inject as hyphae - not going to make it.

68. Fish Hydrolosate, Aloe, Pine Sap & Molasses 9/27/03 10:16

Question: Hi, here is sunny South Africa we cannot buy fish hydrolase's. Will fish emulsion also work and do I use the same amount? Can I substitute yucca with aloe? I can buy a cubic meter of aloe leaves (which the sap(bitters) has been drained from) for about fifty dollars. I just have to figure out how to grind it to a paste. What is the saponin content of yucca?
Answer: Fish emulsion has had the fish oil removed, and thus much of the fungal food has been lost. It is a bacterial food then. If you don't have fish hydrolysate, then try oatmeal. Aloe leaves have a highly toxic material in them, and thus aren't really useful for making something for the tea. The saponin component is in the sap material that you describe as having been removed already. Each method of preparation of yucca determines the saponin content. You need to go to the company which makes the preparation and ask them for that information on saponin content of their material. Pine sap is a good sticker, fruit juices often get the bacteria to make glue-like materials that help things stick to leaves. Molasses can work well for this, but you probably want to find a microbial inoculum that includes good amounts of Pseudomonas and Bacillus species. They will help make the sticky materials when you use molasses. Most well made, aerobic composts contain these bacterial species.

69. Rototilling is Not Evil 11/23/03 1:28 PM

Question: Someone apologized to me about using a rototiller, and intimated that I thought rototillers are evil.
Answer: No. I have never said that. Please, stop trying to put words into my mouth. Tillage intensity is important to understand. The greater the destruction of aggregates, the greater the

impact on the soil foodweb, especially on fungi, the larger protozoa, the beneficial nematodes and the microarthropods. If you WANT to get rid of these organisms, as in you want to grow early successional plants, then rototilling, which is a very intensive tillage method and nearly completely destroys the macroaggregates - but not microaggregates - is a good idea. I just want people to understand what they are doing. I don't think rototillers are evil. Any tillage method has some impact on the soil biology. Not tilling results in greater growth of fungi, in general. Maybe more fungi isn't a good idea, sometimes. Depends on what you are trying to grow, huh?

Question: So, if you brought good forest duff, highly fungal, into your garden, and rototilled it into the soil, what is it that you have left in your garden? What's the fungal to bacterial biomass ratio after you rototill? And therefore, why would you expect that your broccoli would not be very happy to have all that wonderful bacterial biomass humming around it's roots? But, are ALL the fungi gone because you rototilled?

70. Strip Tillage 8/12/03 5:26 Am
I like strip tillage a great deal. It leaves most of the soil intact, so you have a close source of the critters from which to allow colonization. Sometimes tillage is needed - as when the soil gets to fungal to grow the
plant you want to grow. Often, the soil is too bacterial, and tillage is not a good idea. Often, compaction is so severe that the organisms will have to have a great deal of help in order to work the soil and open up the air passages to allow air back in. Tillage, followed by getting the biology going again, is more rapid in this condition than adding the organisms without tillage and hoping they can break up the hardpan, or compaction, without disturbance.

71. Herbicides and Tillage 8/2/03 5:52 AM

Question: Should/can ACT be applied with the tillage, such as being incorporated, or after the tillage? Of course, the idea is that tillage become unnecessary with enough ACT applications, but this mostly applies to the first couple of years or so.
Answer: If there is a compaction zone that needs to be broken open, and there is little biology in your soil to be damaged by tilling, then add the AACT with the tillage event. Often tillage works because it allows oxygen to move into the soil, lets roots start to grow again, deeper into the soil. To maintain soil structure, the organisms need to be added into the soil, so use the AACT to get the organisms into the soil.

Question: What specific herbicides are detrimental to aerobic microbes?
Answer: Not all have been tested.

Question: Atrazine?
Answer: That's a better bactericide than herbicide

Question: Alachlor?
Answer: The little data I've seen, and as I recall, this is affects protozoa more than anything else.

Question: Are soil-based herbicides worse than post application herbicides?

Answer: Can't generalize that way.

Question: And, I'm guessing that mixing the ACT and the herbicides together would not be a good thing?

Answer: That's correct. Add the AACT AFTER the herbicides, so you can resuscitate any organisms killed by the herbicide. Try to figure out why you have the weeds growing, and do what is needed to change conditions in the soil so that the weeds aren't helped, and no longer can out-compete the plants you want growing.

72. Most Weeds Indicate Soil Information 9/24/03 11:06 PM

Most weeds indicate information about the soil. Thistle always indicates high nitrate levels, especially at seed germination. If thistle doesn't have high nitrate at that time, the seed may not germinate. If it does germinate without high nitrate, it will be outcompeted by other plants. Composites often outcompete other plants when Ca is low. So, composites indicate low Ca. Add back Ca - but how much is enough to get over the low? If the dandelions keep winning, you aren't adding enough Ca yet.....So, your weeds mean what? Get rid of the condition that is selecting for them to be more successful than your crop plant, and make the conditions right for your crop plant to win the competition. You'll have fewer weeds.

73. Weed Suppression and Animal Weight Gain 7/27/04 9:06 Am

Betsy has put her data on the list already. I think what most people find most exciting is the weed suppression, increase in animal weight gain with the transition to improved forage quality. So, if you could share the forage quality data as well, that would be great.

74. Discing in Weeds 9/27/03 10:16 PM

Question: Dr E., being that we're talking about discing weeds (green) wouldn't that make the bacteria the most important consumer over the fungi? As the fungi go for the brown stuff, bacteria the green. I realize that given plants require specific B:F ratios - but for this purpose a B dominant brew seems best?

Answer: When discing in weeds, green means the bacteria will be the first bloom of organisms growing on the simple sugars, proteins, fats, lipids, etc in the green material. The finer you disc, the bigger the bloom, or greater the bacterial increase. But after the bacteria finish their first bloom, then the fungi start doing their thing. Bacteria and fungi seem to compete, and bacteria will beat fungi to the foods when the foods are simple, sugary, juicy material. Once the bacteria are done, however, the fungi use the cellulose, the structurally complex sugars, proteins, lipids, fats, waxes, hormones, phenols, humics, etc.

a. Green Material Recapitulates Succession

So, use of green material recapitulates succession, and the steps we talk about in SFI about building soil structure. Bacteria first, to build microaggregates, fungi second to build macroaggregates. Protozoa and nematodes, and if you are lucky, microarthropods, wake up in the spring and build the next layer of soil structure.

Question: So, which brew to put down in the fall?

Answer: You need a balanced brew - and as fungi are difficult to get to do their thing in the tea, try to make the tea as fungal as possible. Use a compost that has at least good-range fungal biomass. Use kelp or rock powder to give the fungi a place to attach while in the brew so they feel comfortable and will grow for you. (Sounds like I talk to fungi, doesn't it? Not really, we just note that time and again, the fungi do not germinate and grow unless they have a surface to attach to). If you use good moist worm compost, it seems like there's enough soluble bacterial food in the worm compost that you don't need to add molasses. So, maybe we can drop using that component, unless you use thermal compost. Thermal composts seem to need some bacterial food to let them grow.

75. Survival of Organisms – Temperature and Discing 9/25/03 1:00 PM

Question: Applying AACT this fall over the disced soil and residue will bring down nitrate levels next spring cause the microbes and fungi will have it tied up right? Or perhaps it's possible?
Answer: AACT adds the organisms that will decompose the plant residue during the winter. The organisms tie up the excess nitrate in their bodies, and the nitrate does not leach as snow melts. This happens. No perhaps.

Question: Or do the bacteria chew up the food before winter sets in, die and the nitrogen from all the green weeds disced in is lost before Christmas.
Answer: Bacteria are not the main chewers of plant residue, unless the plants are green when they are disced in. Most plant residue is not green when disced in. They have translocated most of their sugar, protein and carbohydrates to the seeds, to the fruit, or to their roots. Thus fungi are the most important at decomposing plant residues. Both bacteria and fungi survive winter just fine, frozen soil or not. But the nitrogen in bacteria and fungi is not available to your plant as bacteria and fungi. The predators have to be present. But they don't wake up until temperatures warm in the soil in the spring. The same temps that get the seed to germinate get the protozoa, beneficial nematodes and microarthropods to wake up. And they start making nitrogen available to the plant.

Question: What temp range do protozoa thrive/survive?
Answer: Many protozoa prefer soil temp above 45 F. Growth and feeding rates are higher as temp rises, but max out around 155 to 160 F. Temps above that are detrimental, and the protozoa get too hot, and go to sleep. Note, they go to sleep, they don't die. There is of course species ranges, so some protozoa go to sleep at lower temps, but others wake up at the warmer temps. Species vary, the community of species always has someone functioning until beyond the temp range for the critters to survive.

Question: Did I disc too soon? Soil temp is probably above 60F currently. What happens with bacteria and fungi at spring discing prior to planting as soil hits perhaps 60 F?
Answer: As fungi decompose plant residue, they release foods for other organisms. They release humic acids, fulvic acids, and other slow release foods for other fungi and bacteria. When you disc, some of the foods are opened up to bacterial attack, and bacteria go through a bloom. Fungi also find new surfaces to chew on, but aren't as fast as bacteria, so their bloom happens later.

Question: Bacteria flourish again? Or how can they, as food supply should be low, unless I disc in more weeds this spring. Believe me they like to grow with spring rains and after first discing.
Answer: It's the foods, the organic matter incorporated into the soil from the last fall's plant residues that the bacteria and fungi use. Lots still there, but thankfully not as foods that pathogens can use, especially if you have a healthy set of beneficials!

Question: Do you cover some of this info in your crop prod cd's for specific crops? So I need to get a soil test for Ca in the watermelon patch for starters.. Or do I need Cu, Mn,Mg,Zn,K,P,N,NO3, Boron,SO4, as well? Or all the minerals?
Answer: You want to do a full soil chemistry test. Choose a test that will tell you what will actually be available to the plant, not "extractable-using-this-nasty-extractant" sort of test. So, Reams testing is good (International Ag Labs, MN for example. Environmental Analysis Lab at SCU, Lismore, Australia, Agri-Energy Lab in Illinois as a US example). Albrecht labs are a back-up to that (Perry Labs, for example). You don't need yearly sampling, however. If you did a soil test in the last couple years, it's good enough. If you added anything since then, I just need to know. Send your soil chemical analysis in with the Foodweb sample, and I'll try to integrate what you need to do chem-wise with what you need to do foodweb wise. Choose the set of minerals that are known to be a problem in your area. Ca, Mg, Na, K, for example. If S gets limiting, run that analysis. Or any other limiting nutrient that could be a problem. Bo, Cd, Si, etc.

76. Feeding Fungal Biomass in Strawberries 9/17/03 11:02 PM
We've always tried to go straight for the fungal biomass in strawberry. The bacteria will take care of themselves, but the molasses is the way to go. Use the SFI report to tell you how much is needed. I expect that you will have about nothing in the soil, given the chemical abuse visited on that soil. So, max bacteria, fungi, protozoa level in the compost is needed. Both molasses and fungal foods - fish hydrolysate? Humic acid? Something else to feed fungi. But amounts to start with ..... we need the data.

77. Rotation is a Good Idea, Eventually 9/2/03 4:06 AM
In my experience, use of compost or compost tea applied in amounts to maintain the diversity and biomass of bacteria, fungi and protozoa allows for planting the same plants in the same place for quite some time. Not forever, rotation is a good idea eventually.

78. Giant Veggies 11/1/03 6:04 PM
We grow giant size veggies too, here, where we don't have midnight sun. A combination of the right biology, good soil, good light, and the right seeds can garner most anybody giant veggies.

79. Copper Sprayer 12/15/03 9:28 PM
Please, not a sprayer made of copper. It only takes 3 ppm, or 3 micrograms of copper per ml of tea to kill a bunch of the beneficial bacteria. Or if copper is used, it must be carefully lined and you must be careful to not scratch or damage that lining. You wouldn't drink from a cup made of copper, don't make your beneficials do it either.

80. Copper Alternatives 1/8/04 12:38 AM

I'd like to ask Arden Anderson about alternative sources of copper. I think most cold-water kelps come with adequate amounts so you don't need to be adding more. But I haven't done much looking into alternative sources for copper, so maybe someone else knows?

81. Pyrethrum Effect on Organisms 11/25/03 9:00 PM

I haven't studied the effect of Pyrethrum on organisms. I expect it will be mostly a food resource for a set of microbes. Try it and tell all of us what it does!

82. Hot Pepper and Garlic Treatments 11/23/03 5:50 PM

I think the way to deal with the hot pepper and garlic question would be to repeat the experiment that Jeff described with soybean meal. Part of the lawn, or part of the vineyard gets AACT alone, AACT with garlic, AACT with hot pepper extract, garlic alone, hot pepper alone, compared to the conventional management. If you wanted to assess the microbial response, SFI could run the teas, although, since I have to pay the technical folks for their time, some payment plan would be needed.

83. Antimicrobials 3/30/04 5:51 PM

I would use the antimicrobials only in places where you need sterile conditions. So, in the areas where you aren't using the biology, and that water from that area won't come in contact with the tea.

84. Test for Chemical Residues May Be Necessary 11/16/03 1:55 PM

There's a chemistry lab in Santa Maria, CA that does pesticide residue testing. Name of Pro-Chem or something like that. When biology is low in the soil, and addition of compost or tea can't seem to pull the numbers up, then you need to test for chemical residues. Just going out and testing is too expensive, and why do a bunch of testing when most of the time the biology and foods you add in the tea or compost will decompose residues, or sequester the heavy metal so it is plant unavailable? So, only when you have added the biology and foods, and they don't improve, then worry about toxic levels. Then do the testing. First step there is to try to determine what pesticides were used in high concentration or for years and years. DDT, 2,4-D, dieldrin, benomyl, bromine (from methyl bromide), coppers from any copper base pesticide, sulfur from any sulfur-based pesticide or from gypsum or potassium sulfate additions are the ones we have run into. But not that often. Biology is amazing!

85. Turf Questions 3/27/04 7:22 PM

What you need for your turf depends on what is in the soil. Generally, to know for certain, you need to assess the biology in the soil, so you know what needs adding. When you are doing commercial work, it is safest to do the baseline assessment, so you can demonstrate to your client where the soil biology was when you started, and the improvement you have made with time. If you don't need that kind of documentation, then you can pretty well bet that your turf lacks fungi, and that you need to improve that component most of all. If pesticides, such as fungicides, insecticides, nemacides or herbicides have been applied, you might just add the maximum set of beneficial fungi that you can, since we can be pretty well assured that the fungi, protozoa and beneficial nematodes are no longer present.

86. Eastern Red Cedar, Osage Orange, Chinese Elm 7/13/04 7:32 AM

Question: How about eastern red cedar, Osage orange and Chinese elm trees? They seem to grow real well here in KS in pastures and almost like weeds in untilled fields. Would they grow in either fungal or bacterial dominant soil?
Answer: Cedar - most likely VERY fungal. Osage orange - shrub or tree? What is it's natural habitat? Where does it grow in nature? Chinese elm? Same questions - you need to understand the natural habitat it grows in order to figure out what it needs, OR you need to do some testing to figure out what the plant makes it's root system. Whenever we disturb the ecosystem, we alter what the plant is trying to maintain in the root system, so if you want to know what is normal for the plant, test a plant that has not been obviously disturbed - which includes herbicides, fertilizers, etc - for some time. I would guess that all three species you ask about are fungal dominated, but the usage would be more slightly fungal, the elm about 10:1, and the cedar 50:1

87. Blackberry and Raspberry 7/13/04 7:27 Am
To the best of our knowledge (i.e., reviewing the database), healthy blackberry and raspberry are in the shrub category, and like the soil on the fungal side. Somewhere between 5:1 to 2:1 fungal to bacterial ratios. Which suggests a couple approaches to making the soil not-good places for these plants. Push the biology much more bacterial, or MUCH more fungal. Your choice. With perennial plants, you may want to cut the aboveground part of the plant off, so the plant has no energy to respond to your soil treatments by altering the foodweb back in the direction the plant wants/needs.

88. Brambles 7/10/04 8:46 PM
What kind of brambles are you asking about? In general, early successional plant species are very bacterial,
mid-successional grasses are somewhat bacterial dominated, late successional grasses and row crops are balanced fungal to bacterial, shrubs are slightly fungal, deciduous trees are fairly fungal, and conifer old growth extremely fungal.

89. Peat Moss and Fungi 11/3/03 8:21 PM
Many fungi produce mushrooms when they undergo sexual reproduction. Could have been in the wood chips, but much more likely the fungi came from the compost tea. Peat moss is usually pasteurized by law. Any peat moss from a foreign country has to be at least pasteurized as I understand USDA regulations. So the peat moss you buy is mainly just a fungal food, maybe a few spores of some fungi survive pasteurization.

90. Did the Tea Not Work? 6/14/04 9:43 Am
Ah, but you can't say that tea didn't work. You didn't apply tea, so it neither did nor did not work. The Compost Tea Brewing Manual pretty clearly states that other things besides tea can bring healthy biology back into your lawn. No one has ever said that the ONLY way to get the good guys back in your soil is through addition of tea. Compost works just as well. And waiting for Mother Nature to get around to it works too - if you can wait that long. Compost and compost tea are for people who need to get back to a healthy condition ASAP. Your choice to wait for natural

processes, or instigate a natural process and get it going faster. OK? I think what they was asking for were examples of where tea was applied, but did not have the beneficial effect we expect. When there's a situation where tea is applied, but nothing good happens, that's when I suspect the tea isn't what the person thinks.

Chapter V

APPLICATION RATES

For
Actively Aerated
Compost Tea

APPLICATION RATES FOR ACTIVELY AERATED COMPOST TEA

1. Spring and Fall and Foliar 2/21/04 5:02 AM
Each spring and fall (after harvest) the soil needs 20 gal/ac to cover plant residues so disease does not grow on the residue material. Weeds will be reduced after each application. It may take a year before weeds are really so low and wimpy that the grower feels safe not herbiciding, so reduced herbicides are needed, but won't be completely gone, usually. Foliar applications at 5 gal/ac three times through the growing season in systems where disease is under control.

2. Application Rate to Soil
So, apply 15 to 20 gal/ac to the soil. Then, check the VAM colonization of the roots of your plants. If you need to improve the mycorrhizal colonization of the roots, do some under-cutting of weeds, but also inject tea with VAM spores in it.   You get the weeds and help the trees at the same time.

3. Tea Amount Per Bush 10/3/03 9:38 PM
DILUTION is NOT what you want to think about. What you have to have is COVERAGE of the leaf surfaces. OK, got that? Get dilution off your brains. Exit it as a consideration. The reason we have said 5 GALLONS PER ACRE is, so, with a typical, adequate tea, that contains the levels of bacteria and fungi that I talk about, you will adequately cover the leaf surface so the leaf surface will be covered and protect that leaf surface from all the bad things. If you have organism numbers too low, you won't get coverage. If you dilute inappropriately, you won't get coverage.

Question: So, 5 gal/ac is how much per bush?
Answer: Can I make the estimate that most rose bushes cover about 1/100th of an acre? So, 0.05 gal per bush. which is about 2 ounces or 13 ml.

Question: But you can't evenly apply 2 ounces to a bush, so how much water do you need to cover the bush evenly?
Answer: Shall we say 1 gallon? So, add 2 ounces, or 13 ml of tea to 1 gallon of water (remember to de-gas the chlorine!), and apply the gallon (plus 13 ml of tea) to the whole bush. Assuming I got the 1/100th of an acre per bush right, the 5 gallons is going to cover a lot of bushes.

4. Fungal-Dominated Over-Story Crop Plant
Plant a fungal-dominated over-story crop plant - like strawberry, or thyme, or lavender (a SHORT cultivar, from seed, not bunches, please), or marjoram, or some other native perennial herb (get Kirk to help you choose a good native).

5. Application at Bud Swell
About the time bud swell occurs, you want to do a foliar tea spray, at about 5 gallons per ac for each 6 foot height of tree. If the trees are really bushy and wide, then adjust appropriately.

6. Application at Bud Break
When bud break occurs, you want to get out with a second application of tea. If there is no disease early in the spring, you can wait another month to spray. When disease "season" comes upon you

(listen to the Extension folks, they'll tell you when the diseases start blooming, or the pests start to take off), then you need to spray every week if diseases or pests are bad. Every two weeks through a disease season, if the disease is present but not too bad. If you have perfect conditions for disease, then you may need to double up sprays, and do twice a week for a week or so.

We have a paper coming out on the work we did with JUST foliar sprays in vineyards. We didn't do anything about the disease inoculum in the soil in that study, and so we didn't get full protection. The study proved that you need to do something about the disease in the orchard soil. Don't listen to the people who want to claim that the study shows that compost tea doesn't work. Sigh. Foliar applications of tea can only do so much. That's what the study was about.

Question: Could just foliar sprays deal with the problems?
Answer: The answer is no, you have to do the soil drenches as well.

7. Too Much Tea? 5/7/04 9:01 PM
The only time you could put on "too much" is if you saturated the soil with water. And then it's an over watering problem, not too much AACT.

8. Less is Sometimes More 11/23/03 2:06 PM
You are correct. Just tea alone takes a very long time to improve the soil. Compost and compost tea together, plus some cover crops, and mulches usually speed things along, especially if the soil was devoid of organic matter. The critters need food, and you have to think about the right kinds of foods to add to feed the critters you need. Use the SFI organism reports to tell you what critters need to be fed, and use SFI to monitor how the organisms are responding. Sometimes, some organism groups NEED to go down in number. Do less biomass of bacteria, or less biomass of fungi, is sometimes what is needed, to grow the plants you want to grow. Less is more, sometimes........

9. How Much is Too Much 11/17/03 9:39 PM

Question: Anyone have ideas of how much is too much? What kind of potential pollution problems can arise in agronomic applications.
Answer: We have documented none, even after five years of applying tea. There isn't enough chemical in compost tea to worry about. The biology KEEPS the nutrients in the soil, so they don't leach.

Question: When you think that onion for example, which removes 50 pounds of N per acre, with a 40 ton onion per acre yield, usually requires 200 pounds of N applied per acre if working with inorganic fertilizer, where does the "excess" N go? What if you held on to all that excess N?
Answer: You wouldn't have to add any additional N for 4 years. And 2 tons of compost would more than supply the needed N on an annual basis. You could, alternatively, supply the N in the compost tea by adding fish, for example.

Question: Since ours is going on forage crops will the biology consume the additional nutrients the plants don't use.

Answer: Leaching goes away as a concern.

Question: Do we assume P & K levels will rise with compost and compost tea as they will with manure application?
Answer: You want to balance the P and L that you add with compost and compost tea with removal of those nutrients by the plant. So, if you put manure into compost, and that manure was from cows fed pelletized material, you may be elevating P or K in your soil. But, as long as you don't blow off the organic matter by tilling too much, the organic matter and organisms will hold that P and K in organic forms, which do not harm plant roots. Benign forms of P, K, etc, instead of "salts" which harm plant growth by holding water in the salt forms. I'm not sure that explanation is really clear if you don't understand salts.

10. 5% Fungal Coverage 5/14/04 4:52 PM

Question: If you want to get close or better than the 5% fungal coverage needed for effective out competition in the philosphere (Doc E, correct me if my % is off please!), then activate your compost/humus
Answer: This is correct. We need AT LEAST 5% coverage. And for those of you who have not read back through the list serve archives on this one, the data are on the USDA - WSARE website, written up in the findings from the SSI grant. The data are clear and un-equivocal.

11. Leaf Coverage of Organisms 2/2/04 7:55 PM
I prefer to have the coverage at 70% on the leaf surfaces, with 5% minimum of fungi.

12. 70% Organism Coverage 1/26/04 7:35 PM
One point that needs to be corrected in the SARE report; the level of coverage that SFI states as adequate is 70% coverage. The Rodale SARE report states that SFI says 60% coverage is adequate, and this is not correct. The total coverage, determined by summing both bacterial and fungal coverage, needs to be at least 70%. Some of the data used to show this level of coverage as being adequate was done for a SARE grant, and those data are in our 2003 WSARE website report.

13. Organism Survival on Leaf Surfaces 5/30/04 2:43 PM
To determine whether organisms have been harmed by high pressures or by hitting the leaf surface at high pressure, and to determine whether they have survived transit through the air un-harmed, we looked at both the biomass of active and total organisms in the tea and at leaf coverage by that tea when using different sprayer pressures and different leaf distances from the sprayer.

A tea was prepared using a tea maker, a molasses, kelp and humic acid recipe, with organism numbers all above minimal levels. Using a venturi sprayer, pressure at nozzle of 600 psi, we measured survival of organisms on leaf surfaces placed within 3 feet of the nozzle versus leaf surfaces 100 feet away. Leaves from tops of trees were retrieved using poles with cutters on the end. As I recall there was less than 10% coverage of organisms on the leaf surfaces that were within 3 feet of the sprayer. There was 70% or more coverage of the leaf surfaces that were 100 feet away. The leaves from the tops of the trees were more than 85% covered.

It is tricky getting the same amount of tea onto leaf surfaces 100 feet in the air as compared to leaf surfaces 3 to 100 feet along the ground. We estimated the time needed to spray leaves at 100 feet distance to get a certain amount of tea coverage by using the time it took to get the same coverage on leaves held at 3 feet compared to 100 feet away on the ground. Thus, the same amount of tea was delivered, given wind constraints, to the leaves at 3 feet versus the leaves at 100 feet. We repeated the work at lower psi, but you just can't get water to reach 100 feet distance at low psi. Coverage on leaf surfaces that were 3 feet away, using 100 psi, was similar to the leaf surface coverage at 100 feet distance when using 600 psi - in the 80 to 90% range.

14. Organisms and Survival 3/17/04 1:08 PM

Question: So I have tested a number of times before and after extraction.
Answer: Great, that's what is needed!

Question: The biomass before extraction is reduced by any pumping system used.
Answer: There are some pumps that do not reduce organism numbers, or perhaps the more precise statement is, some pumps in the place and way they are configured do not reduce organism biomass or activity. Don't ask me which ones. The testing was done on someone else's dime, and they don't want the information shared. And I'm not enough of an engineer to be able to make generalizations about types of pumps.

Question: Any sprayer using fresh water to dilute the spray causes a shift in osmotic pressure and many bugs die from that. The action of the spray also shreds any fungi and kills some of the bacteria.
Answer: You should not make generalizations of this nature. Survival upon addition to water depends on the quality of the fresh water, and what is in the "fresh" water. Many fresh waters have enough hardness that there is no loss of organism biomass or activity. Many sprayers do not shred fungi. In fact, most sprayers do not shred the fungi. The critical factor appears to be the nozzle configuration, and, again the pump.

Question: Bacterial/fungal mass after spraying -- of the types of sprayers we tried -- was disrupted. However, enough was foliar applied to get results.
Answer: That's why testing what ends up on the leaf is the most useful measure. If you get adequate coverage with bacteria and fungi, then the fact you may have lost some critters to get there doesn't matter.

Question: 4. After spray with dilution, the diminution of biomass was in proportion to the dilution.
Answer: Dilution is not the appropriate way to talk about this. You need to think in gallons per acre applied, or in gallons per 100 sq feet. If I stand and spray 5 gallons onto one spot, it doesn't matter how much water I used during that time. It matters how many critters end up on the leaf. Water is just the carrier. Figure that you need to get coverage. Water isn't the important point. It's how much tea actually hit the surface.....

Question: So effective coverage tested less dense. Since there was some food left in the tea, there is every reason to expect that some of the bacteria/fungi kept growing on the leaf. This showed during leaf assay. UV eventually wiped it all out on upper leaf surface but the biology was still present on the lower leaf surface after three days.

Answer: Yep, that's why adding food to the tea is a good idea -- food that the organisms did not consume during the brewing cycle. The organisms use the glue that they make to protect from UV. So I doubt it was the UV that killed the critters on the leaf surface. Dust. Air pollution. Pesticide drift. That's what kill the organisms on leaf surfaces most of the time. The bottom line seems to be that any transfer method kills some of the biomass and some of the protozoa. UV wipes out bacterial fungal populations within 72 hours but probably sooner if the conditions are correct. Lack of plant nutrition probably also plays a part - if the plant is healthy, then the plant should be feeding the organisms. Un-healthy plant - maybe no food.

Question: I have brewed and seen nematode growth and was looking for microarthropods but never seemed to find them. After picking up a book at a library sale about plant propagation, I came across a photograph of diluted soil showing parts of microarthropods. While they can and do exist in compost, it seems that a rapid food change or water change like brewing shreds these things. When I re-examined some of my brew samples, I was seeing bug parts but not whole bugs.

Answer: We generally turn compost way too much for microarths to want to hang around, or for nematodes to want to reproduce. So compost is usually lacking in these critters, except for Mark Sturges' worm compost, of course! Worm compost is more likely to have the bigger critters. 24 hours isn't long enough for nematodes or microarths to reproduce, so they won't grow in the tea.

Question: I found an interesting wormlike bug in a sample of reduced compost. We had been attempting to reduce the compost mass and produce a product suitable for brewing without the mass of compost. We could then refrigerate the "compost" extract and put the microbes to sleep. When brewed, the microbes would wake up and start multiplying. Anyway, I found these funny segmented worms. Some made up of three and up segments. Ninety-nine percent of them were dead but a couple lived. So straining and refrigerating killed off these worms. It didn't effect the fungal mass or the bacterial growth though and tea brewed with this stuff actually brewed the same as tea with compost but with a longer time. The brewing cycle is typically 72 hours with the biomass really growing in the last 24 hours. I had to come up with a different feeding strategy but all in all, this method holds some promise.

Answer: You were seeing insect larvae.

Question: Microscopic examination revealed a lot of fungi and rod bacteria. Protozoa were everywhere from little amoebas doing their gig to large swimming water bears and lots of paramecium (smaller). In relation to other brews, I found virtually no stalked ciliates and I attribute this to the lack of animal fecal matter in the compost, but I am not 100% on this.

Answer: *Vorticella* and *Volvox* (the stalked ciliates typical in soil or compost) relate more to anaerobic conditions, stagnant situations. Manures are generally anaerobic, so can have many stalked ciliates. But many other conditions also result in high numbers. We are just starting to use this in soil and I will send the reports when I get them.

15. Higher Organism Numbers 2/21/04 5:02 AM
Make tea with higher organism numbers, and then you can spray less tea.

16. Is Biology in Tea Adequate 1/3/04 9:06 Am

Question: Please, check your tea to make sure it really is what you think. Does it really have the biology needed?
Answer: We are working on a way for you to figure out certain parts of whether your tea is getting where it needs, and doing the job you need. The microscope for home-owners is just too expensive ($9000). The mobile UV light source would cost about $70,000. Gulp. So, not an option, right? It's cheaper to buy the scope we have at SFI, and pay to hire your own technician. Back to drawing board.

a. Stain to Determine Leaf Coverage
Then one day, Art Krunzel suggested a different stain that could be used. So we are working on testing that. This stain would be added to your tea, probably just at the end of a spray. The color of the stain on the leaf surface would tell you if the spray covered the leaf surface adequately. You could see percent coverage. Then, if the organisms were doing their job, the stain would be used as a food resource by the organisms, and the color would disappear. Doesn't tell you if you have the fungal biomass needed, so that would still need to go to SFI to be determined. But you would know whether the tea covered adequately, and if the organisms were active and growing, or whether they didn't survive transfer to the leaf surface. If the color did not cover at least 70%, you would know ASAP you have a sprayer problem. If the stain didn't disappear, you would know either the tea brewing process wasn't good, or you have a problem with your sprayer. We are trying to get the testing done on this by the end of January (must make sure the stain is food-grade. That requires some documentation). The stain is not expensive, and you need just a drop in a quart of tea being sprayed. So, something like a teaspoon in your last gallon of tea to be sprayed when using a back-pack. A pint (liter) of stain in your last 100 gallons when doing boom sprays or irrigation or circles.

17. Heavy Metals and Microorganisms 5/4/04 7:15 PM
The effect on the microorganisms depends on concentration. In general, when a heavy metal is chelated, it is must less likely to be toxic directly to the microorganisms, unless at high concentration.

Question: So, what is the level you will apply?
Answer: Generally trees need just a tiny amount of a heavy metal, especially when the metal is chelated, so I expect you would not apply much concentration. But expectation and reality can be far apart, so let us know how much you are putting on.

18. Toxic Salt Thresholds 1/7/04 11:33 AM
I expect every soil will have a somewhat different "toxic threshold" for different salts, but I also expect that the threshold won't vary that much between soils. Most of the time, we see salt effects begin to reduce microbial biomass at around 100 pounds of the salt added per acre. Doesn't really matter if it is gypsum or lime or anything else. Salt effects occur when water is "taken away" from

the organisms by the binding effect of the disassociated salt on H and OH. Variation occurs as a result of the disassociation constant for the particular salt, which you can look up in standard chemical literature. And it is per application. If you know the salt from the last application has been moved into the biology, then it's fine to put the next salt dose on. The simplest way to tell is to test by assessing biology before; add the salt at different concentrations, and test again.

19. Extension Service N Rates 11/18/03 11:41 PM

Typically the extension service has data on how much N is in a typical yield per acre of crop for your local area.

20. Soybean Application Rates 4/29/04 6:10 AM

Question: I need to determine the gallons per acre for one application assuming:
  a. 3 applications per season
  b. the crop is soy beans
  c. no manmade chemicals will be applied
  d. field was fallow last year
  e. located in eastern Arkansas

Answer: The basis of this answer needs to be in solid data. Please get the Compost Tea Brewing Manual, where there is clear data on the answer. But to summarize, the consideration is COVERAGE on the leaf surface. If you get the leaf surfaces covered, top and bottom, by AT LEAST 65% bacteria, and 5% fungi, we have always been able to protect the plant foliage from diseases. Please note that this is NOT a pesticidal effect. We are not killing anything. We are occupying the leaf surface with beneficial critters that do not cause disease. This is a very hard concept for people that are used to relying on chemicals to grasp. But it works. Same with human beings – it prevents disease. Combating disease once it is established means you are fighting a horrible battle. Don't go there.

Question: So, how much tea is needed to establish 65% bacterial coverage, and a minimum of 5% fungal coverage?
Answer: IF you have good tea (see SFI standards for compost tea), and you apply that tea so the organisms are not killed, then you will have that kind of coverage, if you spray 5 GALLONS of GOOD COMPOST TEA PER ACRE, in however much water (as a carrier) as you need to spray the 5 gallons of tea out evenly over that acre.
You need to spray a minimum of three times through the growing season - once at first true leaf stage, once pre-bloom, once post-bloom. Why the focus on bloom? Because it is easy for growers to know that the plant is at certain stages, and be able to time spraying based on something the plant tells you, not on whether you have the time to do the spraying.... Grin! IF WEATHER RESULT IN PERFECT CONDITIONS for the diseases to grow, then you have to spray more often. You need to make the leaf surfaces better for the "Good guys" than the "Bad guys", which means some effort on your part to change the leaf surface conditions. So, then you start spraying perhaps every other week, and if conditions are really perfect for the pathogen, spray once a week.

21. Can Tea Spraying Be Redundant? 1/27/04 1:16 PM

Yes, tea spraying CAN BE redundant. If you get the biology established, surviving, and growing in the soil, and on leaf surfaces, you should not have to keep applying.

Question: How do you know you have them in the soil, growing and doing their thing?
Answer: The answer is that testing is needed to see if things are present and functioning. With leaf sprays, you do typically have to apply several times through the year, because air pollution, pesticide drift, and dust will kill the biology on the leaf surface. So, foliar applications need to be repeated, and you need to know if the biology gets on the leaf surface initially. The leaf organism assay tells you when the biology needs to be replaced. I've suggested some other ways to know good coverage and activity too. In the soil, it is easier to get the right biology established, and have the roots keep everyone happy. Applying food is all that is needed, eventually. Just make sure not to kill the critters you want....

Chapter VI

SPRAY EQUIPMENT

SPRAY EQUIPMENT

1. Mesh Size of Spray Nozzles and Drip Tape 7/13/04 5:16 PM
Generally, you want to work on a mesh size of about 400 micrometers opening sizes, since fungal tend to grow in clumps. You want the larger opening size and therefore nozzle sizes as well. Drip tape with opening sizes of 5 micrometers will not be good places for tea to be used. But just about any other type of sprayer has nozzles with larger opening size than those. Aim for nozzles that have 400 micrometer opening size, or larger.

2. Sizes of Microorganisms 6/24/04 5:35 PM
Bacteria are in general 2 to 5 micrometers in length, 1 to 3 micrometers in width. Fungi are generally 2.5 micrometers in width. They can be miles in length. Protozoa vary from 5 micrometer width for the little guys to 100 micrometers for the big guys, all sorts of shapes. Soil nematodes are 10 to 50 micrometers width, to 10 to 20, up to 1 cm length. Magnifications were 1000X for the stained bacterial pictures, to 400X for some of the bacteria, 200 X for the fungi, to 6 X for the arthropods.

3. PSI Rates 5/30/04 1:39 PM
By the time a spray pushed out of the sprayer at 600 psi reaches 100 feet high in the air, the water is no longer moving at the same pressure as it had when it came out of the nozzle. The water slows down as gravity takes effect, and eventually starts heading earthward, which is the point at which it should contact the leaf surface. Pressure is about zero at that point, and therefore there is no harm to the organisms. But if the leaf surfaces are a foot away from the nozzle, there is no reduction in pressure, because gravity has not had an effect, and the force with which the organisms hit the leaf surface will be detrimental.

4. Droplet Size 5/26/04 4:05 Pm
The droplet size is important as the drops fly through the air. UV will kill organisms in small size drops, where the water is too limited to protect from UV penetration. Once that drop falls on the leaf, the organisms start protecting themselves by growing protective layers. The spreader/stickers help the bacteria and fungi grow those protective layers, as any spreader sticker that doesn't kill the organisms, are food for the organisms. This builds protection faster. So, spread the organisms on the leaf, so they find the foods the leaf is putting out. And pressure being pushed out the sprayer isn't the big deal. It's the pressure with which they hit the leaf surface. To push the tea to the top of a 100 foot tree, you need 500 psi. That doesn't harm the critters. If you spray the organisms out and they hit the leaf surface going 500 psi, they are dead. No different from you if you hit something with that force.

5. Pumps and Critters 31/7/04 11:05 AM
The bottom line with putting compost into the tea free, and then straining or running through a pump of some kind is to document that you don't lose your fungi by doing that. Straining the tea means loss of fungi as the fungi pass through the accumulating organic matter on the strainer surface. Using a pump means it must be checked to see what the pump does to the organisms.

Question: Some pumps don't harm the organisms. Some pumps are just terrible in what they do to critters. How do you know?

Answer: The only way is to test the tea that you are spraying out, after it has gone through all equipment, etc. If organisms biomass is great, then you are in-like-Mike. If organism biomass is low, then you have to play detective and figure out WHERE you are losing your critters. You CANNOT just assume that the critters are getting through the brewing process just because the water has a nice color.

6. No Copper Sprayers 12/15/03 9:28 PM

Please, not a sprayer made of copper. It only takes 3 ppm, or 3 micrograms of copper per ml of tea to kill a bunch of the beneficial bacteria. Or if copper is used, it must be carefully lined and you must be careful to not scratch or damage that lining. You wouldn't drink from a cup made of copper, don't make your beneficials do it either.

Chapter VII

BREWING TECHNIQUES

BREWING TECHNIQUES

1. **Different Kinds of Compost Tea** 12/19/03 10:19 PM

We need to clearly define the different kinds of compost tea, because that's part of the problem, too. Actively aerated compost tea is the only type of tea we can guarantee results, because we have studied it quite a bit at this point.

Question: The conditions to always make tea with good levels of bacteria, fungi, protozoa and nematodes are known. We need more replicated testing, but the scientific literature will have more of those published in the near future. Some of them are SFI pubs, some from other folks. What are the conditions?

Answer: Good compost. Needs to be documented, and the person selling the compost should document that the biology is present. Or make the compost right, and you know the good guys will be there.

a. Good Machine
Good machine.....documented to be able to extract the organisms, and maintain oxygen.

b. Foods
The foods you add need to be balanced for the aeration of the machine. Too many foods, you are in trouble.

c. Temperature
Temperature - 65 to 70 degrees, except in late fall when you might let the brew cool before putting it on soil at 40 to 45, or middle of a hot toasty summer where you will fry the organisms without helping them out with organic matter

d. Mixing
Mixing - just think about yourself. If you wouldn't like it, neither will the good guys. Roller coasters are ok, but....

e. Spraying
Spraying - coverage is important. The speed of impact is the important factor here. Drop size as well when in sunlight.

2. **Selecting for Organism Growth in Brewers** 2/25/04

Question: How fast will my bacteria grow in relation to any fungi I may extract and/or grow and at what point will the bacteria eat all the food that the fungi needs? Does the fungi keep growing or does it grow and what about protozoa? Are they growing in concert with the brewing time for fungi or do they need more time? How much time?

Answer: There is a continuum of species of bacteria and fungi, and the foods used are selected for the precise set of bacteria and fungi which grow. If you pick molasses, at a low concentration, bacterial growth is pretty much the only thing you get. The bacteria have enzymes that are better at grabbing simple sugars. If you use molasses in the 1% range, both bacteria and a few fungi

154

grow, but typically that's enough molasses to rev up the bacteria so they grow very rapidly, and the burst of growth they produce can drive the brew anaerobic. They typically produce some temperature, and so the stage is set for E. coli growth, IF E. coli is in the compost to begin. Increasing concentrations of molasses CAN result in a concentration high enough to inhibit bacterial growth through simple removal of water based on an osmotic binding. But it seems hard to consistently produce a concentrated enough condition to be assured of this working to allow fungi to rule, instead of bacteria.

a. Sugar and Different Foods
So, different foods than sugar seem to be the way to go. Besides, most DECENT compost seems to supply more than enough sugar to maintain bacterial growth. It is the fungal component that is hard to wake up and get growing, but a critical component to have in the tea.

b. Fungal Foods
Fungal foods are what need to be added to the brew, and sugars kept to a minimum. You need to understand your compost, so you know the potential to brew bacteria. Then, as suggested by MANY people on this list, temperature is important.

c. Temperature
When temperatures are low in the winter, adding sugar to get some heating as the bacteria grow might be a good idea. In mid-summer when temperatures are high, adding sugar is NOT a good idea. Use of cool water in mid-summer is a good idea. Warming the water is good in winter.

d. Understanding the Variables
Understanding all the variables is important when you are selling any product. Growers don't have to understand all the variables, if you can easily and clearly explain how to make the machine work for them in their conditions. Anyway, helping growers move in a more sustainable direction is what is needed.

e. Quality of Tea Machines
For example, some machines we have tested don't provide compost tea with all the organisms in it. I have never been able to produce a decent tea using some machines available to me - based on my definition of needing to have both bacteria and fungi, as well as protozoa and nematodes. It provides a bacterial tea, which can limit black spot, and a few other foliar disease organisms. But it doesn't give all the benefits one would want from a compost tea, because it doesn't allow all the organisms to be extracted from the compost, or allow them to survive in the tea. We can document that some machines do not produce teas with the biology that is needed to give the benefits that I talk about in my lectures. Facts are facts. Most other compost tea machines can make teas with the proper biology to benefit plant growth. Manufacturers need to tell their clients exactly how to achieve that with their machine. If the buyer chooses not to pay attention to "how to properly run the machine", then it is not the manufacturer's fault. If you don't pay attention to how to properly run a chain saw, it is not the manufacturer's fault if you cut your hand off. The instructions were clear on how to run the machine properly. Tools are tools. Incorrect use is in the operator's realm of responsibility. Getting advice from someone who doesn't know how to operate a machine

correctly just means you wasted your time and possibly money. You learn from that experience not to work with that person again.

f. Nutrient Cycling

Anyway, back to protozoa. Protozoa take longer to reproduce in the brewer than bacteria or for fungal growth to occur. Thus, nutrient CYCLING is not likely in a tea brewer, unless brewing occurs for days or weeks. Probably a minimum of three days would be required.

3. Microorganism Growth and Reproduction in Teas 11/1/03 11:31 AM

Both bacteria and fungi increase in biomass, or GROW, in the tea. (Strictly speaking, fungi don't reproduce in actively aerated compost tea - that is, they don't produce spores of any kind within 24 hours in stirred liquids. Picky point, but I am an academic. Bacteria can reproduce quite rapidly in tea). Both bacteria and fungi have to be extracted from the compost. It depends on the growth conditions you provide whether bacteria will be better able to grow, or fungi better able to grow. Fungi typically need a bit more help in tea than the bacteria. Beneficial fungi need a surface to attach to. Most bacteria do not.

Molasses at LOW concentration help bacteria grow. At HIGH molasses concentrations, you CAN select for fungi, as long as the other conditions I mentioned are also present. Certainly, high concentrations of molasses are not the best way to help the fungi. Molasses doesn't cause E. coli to grow to a greater extent than it causes ANY bacterium that can use molasses to grow. Nothing selective about molasses for only E. coli growth! So, we did some experiments that show that molasses does not cause E. coli to grow. If you don't have E. coli in the compost, E. coli will not grow. If you have some E. coli, low concentrations of molasses does not cause E. coli to grow. Really high concentrations of molasses will inhibit E. coli, and prevent its growth. Careful there, though. I said growth. Not presence. Even the reviewers of the scientific paper didn't get that straight in the first review.

4. Fungi Growth Rate in Tea 11/15/03 2:35 PM

Question: Someone asked for the rate of growth of fungi in tea.
Answer: Fungi start at un-detectable levels in compost tea at the start of the brewing cycle. And we want a MINIMUM of 2 ug, preferably higher, by the end of the brew in 12 to 24 hours. So, growth rate is quite amazing in teas, but they need proper oxygen, good foods and the right habitat - which means a surface on which they can attach and grow.

5. Spore Don't Grow in 24 Hours 11/8/03 5:00 AM

Spores usually don't germinate and start to grow in a 24 hour tea. I was thinking of "anaerobic" teas that may be brewed for three or four weeks. Often they go anaerobic, and then once the bacterial bloom is over because the bacteria use up all their food, then oxygen diffuses back into the tea and with enough time, the spores germinate and grow. But in a 24 hour tea, the fungal spores make it into the soil or onto leaf surfaces, and if the right foods and conditions are present, they germinate and start to grow.

6. Fungi Activity 11/8/03 4:54 AM

Question: Let's say we start with 2034 separate fungal organisms extracted into the tea from the compost. If we provide some "growing conditions" for them (food, a place to live), then we end up say 24 hours later with 2034 bigger organisms? (if so, what is the benefit of bigger fungi vs. smaller ones?)

Answer: Fungi grow at the tips. The cells elongate, and then put down a new cell wall, and the tip continues to grow outward. Fungi branch, as well, so a new side-branch will begin, and now instead of one growing point, there are two. So, yes, you just get bigger fungal bodies as they grow out. The benefit is that the longer strands of hyphae cover more leaf surface, access more nutrients. The long strands can break and as long as large enough strands result after breakage, both individuals continue to grow. Two individuals where there was one individual previously. Is that reproduction? The two individuals are genetically exactly the same. But, regardless of how much I'm going to have a tizzy about semantics here (grin), the fact is fungal biomass increases in the tea, and that means more coverage on the leaf surface, more biomass to move into the soil and find the root, or increase decomposition.

Question: What of the fungal spores in the compost? Again, providing growing conditions, could they typically hatch out and add to the number of fungal organisms in the tea? (if so, this must be a major benefit!)

Answer: The spores really like to be attached to surfaces before they will germinate and start to grow out. The hyphae (the strands I was talking about in the previous paragraph) really prefer to be attached to a surface in order to grow. Proteins, sugars, nutrients will concentrate on a surface because of ionic attraction processes, and that is most likely the reason that many organisms like to be in the same place. Increased food resources, and possibly a need to have a stable surface on which to grow.

a. Spores Are Important

So, yes, spores are important. If your tea goes anaerobic and the active, living strands of hyphae are killed, the spores survive the anaerobic conditions, and after air returns to the area, or after the bacteria stop growing so fast in your tea and using up any returning oxygen, then the spores can germinate and begin to grow.

b. Fungi Survive Bad Conditions

Fungi survive bad conditions by producing spores. But it typically takes several days for fungi to make spores, so they don't have time to use this escape mechanism when they are growing happily in tea, and then the bacteria bloom and use up all the oxygen, and kill the active fungi.

7. Testing and Ratios of Fungi 9/27/03 10:16 PM

Question: Can you clarify: More testing is needed to determine "aerobicity"(my quotes)? Do the tests you recommend a) monitor Dissolved Oxygen and/or b)use ratios of AB/AF to TB/TF to tell us more about whether our tea stayed aerobic? In the case of the latter, how may we use those data to interpret "aerobicity"?

Answer: I like having instant information on the conditions in the brew. So, the DO probe is best. It's just that DO probes are expensive, and they are subject to being finicky. So, learning to make the tea so it comes out correct, doing an SFI tea test with your first one or two or three teas, to make sure you are doing it right, is what is least expensive. Send your first tea in - if it's good, then there you are. If it needs help, you go searching for what needs to be fixed, and get the second tea right. We have a few people who have problems after two or three teas, and that's a head scratcher. Water too alkaline? Unsuspected water problems? Still working on a couple of those!

a. Ratios in tea - Active to total biomass

When bacterial activity is low, but total bacteria is high, it's a good indicator that you have lots of anaerobic bacteria present which will not take up the activity stain. The activity stain we use is taken up by aerobic bacteria, not anaerobic bacteria. Different sets of enzymes are used for anaerobic metabolism than aerobic, and the anaerobes don't use the FDA stain. So, activity of anaerobic bacteria is not detected. Low activity, and high total bacteria, especially in compost tea, suggests anaerobic growth was occurring. So, reduce bacterial foods, so the grow of the organisms in your tea doesn't outstrip the ability of your brewer to aerate the tea.

b. Low Fungi

Low active fungi can occur because the surfaces weren't present for the fungi to attach and grow. Maybe fungal foods weren't present. Maybe the bacteria bloomed and out-competed the fungi. These are things we need to spend more time researching - which bacteria are so competitive with the fungi? Could we add an inoculum of bacteria which do not compete with the fungi, so we could help the fungi be happier in the tea? Working on that, actually.

c. Low Active Fungi, High Total Fungi

Low active fungi, high total fungi - this can only have occurred when the fungi grew, and ran out of food, (or bacteria started to grow, and zonked the fungi) and are now not growing. Add more fungal food.

8. Equipment Design 3/30/04 5:47 PM

Question: What metals, if any, can be used for the tank and accessories in contact with the brew (stainless steel, steel, painted steel, galvanized steel, tinned steel, aluminum, anodized aluminum, brass, copper)?
Answer: Absolutely no copper, and brass is not a good idea either. Stainless steel would be about the only thing I would trust the organism not to solubilize.

Question: What range of temperature must be maintained?
Answer: Maintain temperature similar to the material you will spray the tea onto. Soil temps can be lower than 65, but I don't often use a temp lower than that. Soil doesn't get above 75 often so I rarely brew above that temp. Too warm and you can't hold oxygen in the water.

Question: What range of air flow rate (cu.ft./min.) must be maintained (for say 200 gal.)?
Answer: A minimum of 3 CFM seems realistic.

Question: Is it necessary to stir the mixture? If so, how often?
Answer: Yes. Constantly.

Question: Is sunlight helpful or to be avoided?
Answer: Only if you do not have protection from UV. Water provides protection at more than a few um depth of water.

9. Brewing Configurations 4/7/04 6:03 AM

Question: What size container would best match the following situation: aeration produced by a 30 gallon aquarium pump using 3-4" aquarium stones with the compost (vermi) suspended in the container at Dallas, TX elevation at 70 degrees F, with no sunlight? With those parameters: brewing time? Also, how much oxygen do those stone produce, and would an agitator benefit this set-up? One gallon? Five?
Answer: The 30 gallon pump will be fine for a 1 gallon, but could be limited on the 5 gallon size machine. Best way to know for certain would be test it in the parameters of the amount of compost, and the foods you want to use.

a. Aquarium Stones
The aquarium stones will drive you crazy. The issue is cleaning. Bacteria and fungi will grow in your air stones and plug them up. Each brew, you need to clean them by placing in bleach and letting them soak for several hours. So, have a set cleaning while you use another set. But it's a cleaning issue.

Question: So why not use plastic tubing with holes punched in it instead?
Answer: If you forget and turn off the pump while the tea is in the brewer, and tea gets into the pipe, then you can clean the tubing by having a rag on the end of a wire, and just pull the rag through the pipe. Usually, this kind of cleaning is not needed, so you only need to do this when you see any bio-film building up.

b. Brewing Time
Brewing time should be in the 18 to 24 hour range at your temp and elevation. Slightly larger air pump might be needed than what you describe, so borrow a 30 gal aquarium pump from a friend, try it out, and then borrow a larger pump, try it, with everything exactly the same as with the lower pump size. Given that time and a 5 gal brew, additional agitation should not be needed. You might note that this is very similar to the Fine Gardening article.

10. Brewing Techniques 1/18/04 11:06 AM

Question: What is the purpose of what we are doing with compost tea.?
Answer: A possibility, an alternate explanation is, that given the compost you are using, you don't have the lower temperature organisms in the compost. If the compost was made in such as way as to exclude the lower temperature organisms, so they are not present in the compost, then you can't get them in the tea brew either. So, go back to the compost you are using - how is it being made? If you can't get the median and cooler-loving fungi or bacteria in the tea, then it suggests that

someplace in the composting process the compost is getting too hot. Those cooler temperature organisms should be present in your tea.

a. Pre-composting
When people pre-compost worm compost, to lower E. coli, and other human pathogen numbers, they often let the pile get too hot. Just like thermal composting, you have to turn the pile when it gets too hot, or lose too much oxygen. There is a worm composting operation near you where they have that problem. The manure they use is heated to very high temperatures before they put the manure into the worm bin. If you happen to be using that worm compost source, that will be a problem, and could be biasing what you are doing. Probably have a nitrate problem with that compost too. Just a possibility but one that needs to be checked out. Just because manure was heated to a high temperature does not mean that ALL the lower, or cooler temperature organisms were killed. Some were killed, the ones that can't make dormant stages. So, the diversity has been harmed when compost gets too hot. Check your compost source.

b. Brewing Temperature
So, you brew at a cooler temperature to match soil temperature. If you are actually growing a plant when the soil is 40 degrees, then brewing the tea at 40 F is logical. Except how many of us are actually trying to grow plants when the soil temperature is that low? Think through the purpose of applying the tea. If you want plant litter decomposition at 40 F, then ok, select for the cooler temperature loving fungi by brewing at cooler temperatures. But please think fungi. Do you really need to be improving bacteria? Don't you have enough? Well, maybe you need a greater diversity, but don't exclude getting the fungi going too. But if you want to set the stage for when the seeds germinate and plant roots start to grow, perhaps the better choice is to grow more of the 55 to 60 F bacteria and fungi, and get them into the soil now, so they are ready and able to get to work later this spring. We add the WHOLE DIVERSITY of bacteria and fungi so that when the plant puts its roots into the soil and releases exudates to grow bacteria and fungi, the species of bacteria and fungi that the plant needs, and is selecting for with the precise mix of exudates sugars, proteins and carbohydrates, are present and can grow. If what you enhance are just the cool weather lovers, while you have the species of bacteria and fungi you need when the plant roots start growing?

Question: I have tried brewing at temps from 80 D.F. down to 55 D.F. and I have been looking at the tea with a Spencer 1000x microscope. I then take soil samples at different times and examine them the same way after dilution in distilled water. I try to make sure the amounts of soil and soil depth are as similar as I can get them and I use the same microscope technique every time. I look to see if what I am transferring from the tea is "taking" in the places I apply it. Because of the limits of my microscope, I can't tell types of bacteria but can see bacterial fields and I can see if the same organisms transfer to the soil. This, of course, means before and after soil examination.
Answer: You should be able to distinguish the different morphology of bacteria and fungi in your samples. You should be able to distinguish protozoa and nematodes too -- and you are doing the right thing, with respect to before you add something and after you add something. One important point though is how you prepare the samples for observation. You need to break up the water stable aggregates, and there are some specific things you need to do to make sure that you aren't being mis-led because you have bacteria and fungi establishing water stable aggregates, and thus

holding the bacteria and fungi that are growing in those aggregates, and not dispersing into your solutions. If you use tap water, you have to make sure the water is not lysing cells as well.

Question: From these results, I came to conclude that brewing closer to soil temp gave me a greater assurance that I would be promoting biology that was more in line with the temperature rather than brewing for one temperature and hoping I was getting the correct microbes for the soil.
Answer: But is it temperature that is the important point, or is it a specific function that you are trying to obtain? We don't want to get caught on the biomass alone point. You have to think activity. Are you getting the functions you want into the soil? what is the function you want when your soil is 40 F, or 50 F, or 60 F? Higher numbers of bacteria are nice, but is it what we are really looking for?

Question: By the way, I have been experimenting with the aerobe/anaerobe balance and the growth of protozoa. I am getting results and will forward those when I have some repeatable trends. Your comment about Bacillus Licheniformis during the mad cow discussions got me looking into ways to grow protozoa and bacterial/fungal eating nematodes within a brewing cycle of 48 to 72 hours. That meant that I had to rethink how I was brewing while still keeping the basic concept of ACT in place.
Answer: Good idea on the protozoa. We do need to think about how to make the tea brewing process better for them so they will reproduce. But they will only reproduce once, maximum, during a 24 hour tea brew. Have to have aerobic conditions in order to keep the good guys alive and happy. Nematodes will not reproduce during the 24 tea brew. They won't even think about reproducing while being whirled around in the tea. Nematodes need solid surfaces to hold onto, and they need specific fungi, and sometimes specific microarthropods to consume in order to go into reproduction. Not likely to happen in the tea brew. So, the nematodes in your tea brew are the ones you extract from your compost.

Question: I have been looking at bacterial growth, bacterial enzymes and the cultivation of higher order bacteria/fungi through enzymes produced by the critters. I have already grown protozoa and nematodes in brewers by using hay mixed with compost and molasses and blood meal with some other organic inputs.
Answer: Avoid the blood meal when growing the protozoa and nematodes. It can select for some nasty protozoa and nematodes that are human pathogens. OK? Please?

Question: I'm not a scientist by education, but I'm not ignorant of the scientific method and the need to document before writing or speaking. I learned this early on when I misstated that ACT can help control snails and slugs. It was a good lesson in humility. If I write something on this list, it is the result of over two years of experimentation and brewing and applying tea in "real world" situations. I am constantly experimenting and testing my own hypotheses and those I implement from other people. It is simply a fact of this type of business. Where I live, my business associate and myself are considered knowledgeable in this stuff because everything we have stated, we have proven. Every assumption we have made has been backed by prior knowledge and shown to work. I do all the brewing and experimentation and brewer/aerator design. Very soon, I will have my designs posted so anyone can build the systems from off-the-shelf materials and be sure that they are assembling a brewer that will work as stated.

Answer: Other tea brewer folks do that and have done it, so there are other places to go looking for designs as well. We can always use new designs, especially user friendly approaches, where the considerations and thought processes are included in the information.

11. Brewing Instructions 5/9/04 3:59 AM

Question: Okay. Instructions with my brewer say to use with watering can or backpack sprayer. Watering cans these days have roses with huge holes, so 5 gallons doesn't go very far.
Answer: Add about 1 gallon of water to 1 gallon of tea when you use your watering can. The 5 gallons is meant to be spread over an entire acre. If you put out more concentrated tea, that's fine, you just speed things along where you put down concentrated sets of organisms.

Question: What is there about the backpack sprayer nozzle that's so different from other sprayer nozzles?
Answer: Backpack sprayer nozzles tend to be bigger, since most homeowner and small scale people tend to put more junk in their sprayers. Commercial sprayers are variable in size, and you have to know what spray pattern you want to pick the nozzle you want.

Question: Yesterday we poured ACT on a 5X10 raised bed. This morning I noticed a weed we'd overlooked there (nothing planted there), and started to chop it off with my hand mattock. The soil was very loose, almost frothy in texture. Was this my imagination or can the tea make changes that fast?
Answer: Biology acts that fast. Especially when you give the organisms plenty of foods. Maintain that biological activity by giving them plant exudates to eat. Don't let all that lovely activity go back to sleep, by not giving them foods to stay active.

Question: Is it necessary or okay to use fertilizer before or after the ACT? I'd like to use some Alaska fish fertilizer on some plants, and spread alfalfa meal for others.
Answer: Generally you are putting back into the soil all the nutrient cycling ability that you need with the tea. As long as you have good organic matter, it may not be necessary to put in any fertilizer at all.

BUT, why chance it? Fish fertilizer contains lots of foods for the beneficial microorganisms in your soil. And the N that the plants need. But, the N in fish is in the form of PROTEIN, not nitrate. So, it doesn't leach, doesn't cause water problems, as long as the organisms in the soil are active and happy. And the fish feeds those organisms, you keep the bacteria, fungi, protozoa and beneficial nematodes and microarthropods happy and working for you when you add those foods.

The alfalfa meal is a better choice than fish fertilizer for plants that need more fungal dominance. Alfalfa contains cellulose, and feeds fungi a touch more. But you might want to consider some worm compost as well, as that will come with a great set of humic acids that can really help your beneficial, disease-combating fungal species. People often get confused about feeding fungi in order to combat fungi. Well, think of this in this fashion. There are good-guy fungi, the ones with the white hats (grin), and there are bad-guy fungi, the ones with whips and chains. The bad guys want to attack and chew up your plant roots while the good guys want to protect the roots. The roots will feed the good guys the food they want, if the good guys are patient and don't get greedy. Reasonable numbers, slowly growing. But the bad guy won't be patient and wait for the food to be delivered. Like a bandit horde, they try to grab the food they want, force the plant to give them what they want, and end up destroying the source of food.

The good guys try to maintain enough biomass to prevent the bad guys from getting too high enough numbers to cause real devastation. So if we can feed the good guys just a little, keep them active and happy, then they will always be strong enough to ward off the bad guys. If you don't have a good enough set of good guys present, you may need to enhance the species of good guys. We want the sheriff, the deputies, and the posse that does what the sheriff says. No sheriff? Need to add him. No deputies? Add them.

Question: How?
Answer: Compost. Or compost tea. But make sure the compost and the tea used were aerobic the whole time they were being made.

If it smells bad, it is bad. We need to hold classes that teach people what bad smells are. Pesticides smell bad, but no one has pointed out to them that if you can smell the chemical, you are being harmed. Maybe not out-right killed, but it's taking days, weeks and years off your life.

At least anaerobic stink is not doing THAT kind of harm. If you are losing the N, S, and P out of the tea (smell the sulfur smell?) -- that's your fertility being lost. Smell ammonia? Where's your nitrogen going? Certainly not staying in the tea!), and altering pH, and making some alcohol, which will hopefully be gassed-off before it hits your plant. It just impacts plant health, not your own health. But if you can smell the nutrients in the air, then they aren't in the tea anymore. They can't be helping your plant grow if you lose your nutrients before they ever get near the plant.

Buy the real stuff - aerated compost tea. Nutrients aren't being lost into the atmosphere before you even buy it. You aren't chancing acid conditions, or alcohol production. Anaerobic tea will not contain the full set of organisms you need in your tea. You will not have beneficial fungi, protozoa or nematodes left in the tea, if tea starts to stink. So, if you have stinky tea, don't expect the benefits to the soil that others have observed. Because the organisms that do the work for you were lost when the tea went anaerobic.

12. Temperature and Organisms   1/16/04 2:19 PM
There are a couple points to consider about temperature.

1. Organisms grow faster when temperature is warmer. This is the classic Q10 effect. Respiratory enzymes function more rapidly at higher temperatures. But look out -- that's respiratory enzymes, not all enzymes. Some leaf decomposition enzymes actually break-down leaf litter faster at about 4 C (which is about 40 F off the top of my head). If you are trying for the greatest bacterial biomass, then use higher temps. But the beneficial fungi grow better around 68 F, so I prefer 65 to 70 F for my brews. But then you HAVE to brew for 24 hours to get adequate growth, OR, precondition your compost so the beneficial fungi are already grown, and all you have to do is

extract and maintain activity in the brew. That's what the whole deal is with adding oatmeal to the compost.

2. Different organisms grow best at different temperatures. Which organisms are you trying to grow? More biomass may be produced at 75 F in a shorter period of time, but is that biomass the best set of organisms for 45 F soil? Well, the first question to ask here might be, what is the soil temperature you are going to add the compost tea to? If the tea is going into greenhouse soil, maybe 75 F is the more appropriate temperature for the tea. So, take-home message is: Try to match the temperature in the tea to the conditions in the system you are adding the tea to.

13. Brewing Temperatures-a 4/7/04 9:47 PM
There are quite a number of species of bacteria and fungi that do very well, and are actually selected to grow better, in cold temperatures. There groups of bacteria and fungi that do best at any temperature you want to talk about. Those species should be in your compost, should be extracted into your tea, and be placed into the soil, or onto leaf surfaces. Therefore, WITH WELL-MADE COMPOST, you will get a huge diversity of organisms, some of which function at each of these different conditions. The species with the highest number of individuals will be those growing at the temperature of brewing, using the foods, nutrients, etc., in the brewer.

Question: So, wouldn't brewing at the same conditions as where you will put the tea be wisest?
Answer: Except, the most rapid rates of decomposition occur in the winter, in litter materials, under the snow.

Question: Where did those organisms come from, on litter material? Did anyone incubate that dead leaf material at cold temperatures before letting that organic matter fall to the ground?
Answer: Don't always just go with the easier answer, especially if what's happening in the real world doesn't back it up.

Question: So, what is the right temperature to run the tea brewer?
Answer: Depends on what you are trying to achieve. If you are trying to make a brew to apply to foliage, you want lots of AEROBIC organisms. Aerobic, leaves are VERY aerobic environments. Anaerobic organisms won't stay active on leaf surfaces if the leaves are healthy. Anaerobic organisms don't therefore stick to the leaf surfaces. Anaerobic bacteria will wash off leaf surfaces pretty quickly. So, you want organisms that are growing in your tea. That means maybe slightly warmer temperatures than ambient.

Question; How much warmer is best?
Answer: We don't have the data for that yet. Most people are still just trying to get the balance of organisms right. It's not as easy as it sounds.

Question: In early spring, or late fall, doing soil drenches, would it be best to match tea temperature to soil temperature?
Answer: Probably. Also consider that what is really necessary for a soil drench is to extract everyone from the compost, and get them out in the soil, in as high numbers as possible, so your critters start occupying as much of the soil as possible, and get into growth mode.

Question: So, what is the best tea temperature? Surface? Plow depth?
Answer: If you plow as you add the organisms, then the organisms will go deeper, and the temperatures may be warmer than ambient.

Question: If I were a bacterium, what would I be doing now? What conditions would I like best? GRIN!!!!
Answer: I'd want my favorite food, good drink, warm and 9 hours of Star Wars to watch.....Air, water, food and comfort......

14. Brewing Temperatures-b 1/19/04 7:30 PM

OK, sounds like the worms are making good compost! You should have the lower temperature bacteria and fungi in the compost. So, when you brew, have you followed the growth curves of the bacteria and fungi as you go through the brewing process? Do you see the bacterial bloom first, and then the fungal? What are the times for both? Fungi are slower growers at lower temps. It might be that when brewing at 45 F, you might need to brew for two or three days instead of 24 hours.

15. Minimum or Optimum Mesh Size for Tea Bag 4/4/04 11:34 PM

You need something larger than 400 to 600 micrometer opening sizes. I don't remember what that is in mesh size.

16. Mesh Size in Filters 9/22/03 10:16 PM

I think they were described as 1/4 by 1/16 inch? Would that get through a #12 mesh? Could you express that in mm? If they are initiates of fruiting bodies, they won't survive if they get sliced or banged up. If they are fuzzy white tiny dust bunnies, they may well survive.

17. Tradeoffs in Straining 10/1/03 9:48 PM

So, it is better to use a mesh on the compost bag that keeps the particulate matter in the compost bag, than to strain the particulates out at the end. Or use a nozzle size that is larger, so you can spray a bit chunkier material. There are trade-offs in tea making.

18. Hyphae Build Up On Filters 10/1/03 6:03 PM

What I thought I said was that the hyphae get caught in the material that builds up on the filter or the strainer. As long as you don't get residue build up, straining is ok. When hyphae have to go through accumulated material, with small passageways, like felt bag material, small particulates that accumulate on nylon screens, then the fungi end up in the sludge, not in the tea.

19. Gluing Pipes 4/3/04 6:01 AM

Yes, you can use PVC for the pipes. The problem is the more glue you use to glue pipes together -- that glue has microbe-killing material in it, which out-gases for a period of time. Proper curing alleviates that problem.

Question: Is it possible to just push connections together, instead of using glue, especially when the connection is in water?

Answer: Remember, I'm a microbiologist, not an engineer.

20. Extraction and Aeration 4/3/04 6:02 AM
Yes, aeration provides exchange of oxygen for CO_2 in the water, but also the movement of water through the compost with enough energy to remove the organisms from the compost. Both are very important -- extraction and aeration.

21. Aeration Pumps 8/19/03 8:38 PM
Pumps that blow air into the tea work fine, if you test the aeration and mixing ability. Pumps that push the tea through the pump have to be tested to make sure aeration is adequate, and that they are not killing things.

22. Aerate Tea to Grow Huge Numbers 9/19/03 5:27 AM
If you do no application, you are really only testing whether plants need water to stay alive, and I think we all know the answer to that, we don't need to test that again. Water that is not aerated? But most of the water coming through your tap have adequate aeration. Tap water isn't anaerobic. You'd have to boil the water and cool it again, in the absence of air, in order to do the control you are suggesting. The reason tea is aerated is because we are GROWING huge numbers of bacteria and fungi. That takes oxygen. Normal tap water without the organism growth contains plenty of oxygen.

23. Difference Between Aeration and Being Aerobic 6/13/04 8:32 PM
When we first started testing "aerated compost tea", which in fact wasn't aerobic (there's a difference between aeration and being aerobic), we killed a number of tomato plants. Symptoms were browning of leaves, leaf curl, deformed leaves. We didn't always out-and-out kill the plants. Sometimes insects pests were attracted to the plants that had been harmed by the anaerobic teas, and the pests were what delivered the coup de grace and of course, there are the plants that did not receive adequate compost tea ORGANISMS to protect the leaf surfaces, and the plants succumbed to the disease we had applied. I would like very much to hear from folks that tea did not work for. I've always said that. We then try to figure out what went "wrong", so the problem is assessed and prevented from happening the next time.

24. Oxygen Content 4/1/04 10:01 PM
Oxygen content can be determined by using an oxygen meter, or a CO_2 meter, or by assessing bacterial and fungal activity with FDA staining. The CO_2 meter is least expensive, but not extremely accurate. Oxygen probes are a bit more spendy, and can be very persnickety. FDA assessment is relatively inexpensive, per sample, but you need to send to the lab by overnight mail.

25. You Can't Over-Aerate 4/3/04 5:50 AM
Unless you pressurize the air you pump into the water, you can't over-aerate. The diffusion of oxygen into water is dependent on temperature and barometric air pressure. Organisms use up the oxygen in the water, so that you need to aerate the tea to replace that oxygen faster than the organisms use it up. Thus, brewer design is critical to prevent areas that are difficult to aerate properly. Aeration is really dependent on how much you let the organisms grow, and is related back to the amount of food you add to the brewer.

26. Bubbles, Oxygen and Microbes 11/1/03 10:53 Am

Remember, it is the little critters we are dealing with, and they use up oxygen at the bottom of the tank just as fast as they use it up at the top of the tank. If you just bubble the surface, you are going to be making some really stinky liquids down there at the bottom of the tank. If you just have big bubbles, the exchange rate is not adequate to diffuse the air into the liquid at the rate the bacteria are using it up. Balance the uptake of oxygen by the microbes, throughout the tank where the organisms are using it, with the movement of oxygen into the tank through air bubbles released at the bottom of the tank, or mixed into the water to the bottom of the tank.

We add food into the tea, to grow the organisms, and therefore, we will have the protein films on the surfaces of bubbles and on the atmosphere-water interface. Exchange of oxygen just at the top of the tank is not going to be adequate to counter the use of oxygen by the microbes at any significant depth. The question of the upward movement of air bubbles is important. If you have very tiny bubbles that stay suspended in the water, and you have larger bubbles that move upward rapidly, you can shatter most of your fungi on those grinding surfaces. Therefore, you DO NOT WANT very fine bubbles that stay suspended in the water. You have to use a serious amount of pressure to produce those bubbles, and may get into the too-high pressure zone where super saturation becomes a problem, and kills the microorganisms. You may kill your fungi when the fine bubbles combine, and move more rapidly than the very fine bubbles, shattering the hyphae.

Be careful of the claims by companies that say tiny bubbles are a good thing. They aren't. I agree with the comments by the engineers on that point completely. But how big should the bubbles be? You and your oxygen probe should be able to figure that out. Don't want to go to all that work? The compost tea brewers that can show that the aerobic organisms stay alive and GROW in their tea brewers have done all that work for you. Buy their machines. Don't buy machines, and don't buy tea,8 from people using those machines, if they can't show you DATA about ACTIVE, living, growing bacteria and fungi and protozoa in their machines! The data should be on their web sites! Remember - bacteria, fungi, and protozoa.

27. Oxygen Concentration 5/31/04 7:09 PM

Yes, heating the air will reduce the oxygen concentration. Probably the best place to look to assess that would be the USGS website, but I'm not sure where that information would be on their site. Index......I'm not enough of an engineer to be able to give you much more help than that! Measure oxygen in the water when aerated with heated air. That's the practical approach, but I'm sure someplace, engineers have already tried this and figured it out.

28. Dissolved Oxygen Saturation Limits 5/7/04 9:37 PM

Question: Somewhere there has to be a baseline for O2 saturation limits in water at various altitudes and temps. My DO meter came with a table of measurement and I have taken that table and extrapolated beyond the table parameters and that seems to work. However, I am at sea level, right on the beach, so readings here will differ from readings in Utah or Washington. So we are back to localization and maybe somewhere we need a standard for zones. Geologists and cartographers use declination when working with maps and charts. This number changes depending on where in the world or even in the same state you are. So we shouldn't have a problem localizing recommendations for pathogen control in brewers in different locations using different composts.

Answer: The table is on the USGS website, and the link is on the SFI websites in the section about oxygen in water.

29. Microbial Respiration and Dissolved Oxygen 11/1/03 10:09 Am

Ah, we aren't talking mammalian respiration systems in compost tea. As far as I know, we aren't trying to send divers to live in the bottom of the compost tea machine. Could we stick trying to understand microbial respiration? The thing of concern is transfer of oxygen into the water. Oxygen is being used up in the water so rapidly by the microbes that oxygen concentration is dropping to below 5.5 to 6 ppm. Unless I am mis-remembering my courses on microbial respiration, high concentrations of N_2 gas don't really affect microbes much until you get to above 85% N_2 in the atmosphere. N_2 gas is at 75% in the total atmosphere, so you have to pressurize air bubbles a great deal more than we are, even with 20 foot deep, or 200 foot deep, tanks, to cause a problem for the microbes.

It is the use of oxygen by the microbes, and then diffusion of oxygen from bubbles into the water, that is the important balance. Since we are depleting oxygen in the water, the movement of oxygen from the bubble into the water will be more dependent on the diffusion co-efficient based on the gradient between oxygen concentration in the water versus the air bubble. The more rapid the growth of the microbes, the more rapid the diffusion of oxygen from the bubble into the water. The whole concern about the maximum movement of oxygen from the bubble into the water requiring at least 3 or 4 feet depth of water just went out the window.

Question: I think many of you still are hung up on the fact that you just can't believe that bacteria and fungi can be growing so fast that they can use up 3 CFM of air being bubbled into water fast enough that the water can still be dropping in oxygen content. But they do. It's what your oxygen probes are telling you. So, what do you do to solve the problem? Bigger and bigger pumps?
Answer: Hum, the engineering approach to life. Get a bigger hammer. Doesn't work with living systems. Bigger hammer? Bigger problems….How about considering LESS FOOD?! MATURE compost?!

30. Organism Death vs. Going to Sleep 6/11/04 6:01 PM

Death versus going to sleep depends on how fast the oxygen concentration is changing. If the organisms have time to react, they produce dormant stages, and go to sleep. If the change is rapid, and oxygen drops rapidly into the reduced oxygen range, death is likely. The determinant of too fast versus slow enough is species by species. But if you drop from 7 ppm to 5 ppm in under an hour, you are probably going to kill things.

31. Keep Air Blowing 12/17/03 8:51 AM

Again, remember to keep the air blowing through the aerator until you take it out of the tea, so you don't get tea in the air pipe. And of course, the bottom line is that all these tea makers I have mentioned make good compost tea that contains all the organisms present in your compost, growing the good guy aerobic organisms to high numbers in the tea. Tea that doesn't contain all the beneficials from the compost, and won't allow them to grow to high numbers in the brewing process should be called what? Brown water? In-sufficient tea? Anaerobe enhancers?

32. Bigger Pumps 10/9/03 10:22 PM
The more simple food resources that were added, the lower the oxygen was reduced by microbial growth. The microbial growth out-stripped the ability of your aerators to add air into the liquid. Kelp had the lowest "microbial growth" potential of the three foods you used, added fish was second, the fish-activated plus fish added was the lowest oxygen concentration. The best fungal readings were in the kelp brew, no added fish. Take - home message. Improve aeration in the bitti-brewers, or don't add any additional food resources besides kelp. Bigger pumps?

33. Aerator Unit Placement 10/4/03 8:20 PM
What the data showed was that an aerator unit needed to go in the pool at the bottom. The pool was a kid's plastic wading pool about 1/2 full. Additional aeration would be needed, and a bubbler in the pool would work great to maintain oxygen. Need to do it though, and show by collecting the data that it would work fine to maintain oxygen.

34. Micro Bubbles 5/17/04

Question: The shearing of fungi is the main concern. Doc E has said that 20 micrometer bubbles can shear fungi, and I think she said 1mm was a good minimum bubble size. I believe she observed that with equipment I don't have, so my data is limited...
Answer: Micro-bubbles which are small enough to stay suspended in water are the micro-bubble sizes that I talked about. These are bubbles with sizes around 1 micrometer, as I have been told. They do not move upwards in water, or at least, their movement is very slow. The problem is, based on sheer observational data, that these not-rising microbubbles impede larger bubble sizes as they rise through the water.

Question: Where did the larger bubbles come from?
Answer: I presume from condensation of smaller bubbles into larger bubbles, but the larger ones rise in the water column. As the bigger bubbles rise, and the micro-bubbles do not, the microorganisms get trapped between the bubbles. The bacteria just bounce around, but the fungi are shattered. Torn apart. Fragments all over the place.

Question: Interesting effect. Happens all the time?
Answer: Well, when we have folks try to work on "super-saturating water" with micro-bubbles, we always get shattered fungal hyphae. It doesn't kill EVERY fungus, just reduces active, living, growing hyphae to low levels. So, it is not good as a sterilant procedure, nor a fungal grow method.

35. Air Filter Stones 4/7/04 10:03 PM
Please realize that the air filter stones HAVE to be cleaned with each run. The bacteria love those crevices!!!!! Instant anaerobic biofilm!

36. Pipe with Simple Holes 4/8/04 10:23 PM
I like pipe with simple holes. When the pipe starts getting fouled, you can see it, and then clean it. With the air filter stones, you often don't know the insidious bio-film is present and the waste product killing the good guys.

37. Soaker Hoses, Cleaners and Microbes 5/16/04 10:02 AM
Both the cleaners and the microbes take their toll. So, soaker hose seems to be ok, relative to data shared. I appreciate the quantitative information. Do you see any loss of the fungi when your DO drops into the 3 ug range? Do you add EM?

38. Bad Stuff in the Pipe 5/14/04 4:09 PM
Your nose is probably right. The bad stuff was in the pipe, and exiting that probably was all that was necessary.

39. Cleaning Equipment 4/7/04 6:12 AM
It is as important to keep the sprayer clean as it is to keep the brewer clean. Yep. Absolutely must rinse, and a recirculation pump is a good idea. As you finish up each spray job, run the recirculating tea over the internal surfaces to keep the debris on the sides of the spray tank washed into the tea. Makes a world of difference in cleaning! You don't have to do this often, but on a truck-size sprayer, it helps a lot. With back-pack sprayers, swish the liquid in the sprayer around to keep sediment from building up, and the sides of the sprayer rinsed down too.

40. Hydrogen Peroxide and Cleaning 12/16/03 7:31 PM
A comment on hydrogen peroxide -- I've been known to use 15% $H2O2$ with really badly bio-filmed tanks, so you do what you have to in order to get the tank clean. $H2O2$ reacts rapidly in environmental conditions, so is typically less likely to stick around and cause problems. Most aerobic organisms make catalase, which is an enzyme that breaks down $H2O2$ into water and oxygen. Chlorine bleach is another alternative cleaner, but then you have to deal with the chlorine water. Oxy-Clean is another cleaner, which if I recall correctly, is OMRI approved? So using cleaners to remove bio-films is quite possible. The cleaners need to be degradable by aerobic microbes.

I've also been upside down in a few brewers in order to scrub bio-film out of places that were hard to reach. It is important to buy brewers and sprayers that don't leave little surprises. For instance, the brewer that uses disc-diffusers - please check the bottom of the discs. They accumulate bio-film with each brew. You HAVE to clean them. The manufacturer does not inform his clients about this problem when he talks about how "easy" it is to clean this machine. It is NOT 20 minutes to clean this machine. You have to take the pipes off that hold the discs, turn the discs over, blast the under-sides clean, and re-attach. Twenty minutes to clean? I don't think so. But not hours to clean. It is relative. I've used brewers that take hours to clean, even when using bleach, $H2O2$, or other cleaners. Pipes with 90 degree turns in them are not recommended. Brewer-makers that say that they haven't seen any effect of the 90 degree turn need to show you that on the fifth, sixth, or tenth brew, the tea organisms are still just as good as on the first tea brew. I don't argue with people about their machine designs anymore. I tell them what is what, and if they choose to ignore me, it just means that their clients will go elsewhere when their machine cannot get good numbers of organisms in the tea. My experience with bio-films comes from the Microbe-Brewer whose design was changed from the inventor's plan by Growing Solutions. That tea maker was then sold without being adequately tested for the effect of those changes. The manufacturer said that the pipes couldn't have that much effect. I think we showed how wrong that belief was. It isn't the first tea, or third or fourth tea that you start to see an impact of bio-film developing in a pipe. It's the fifth, the tenth, the twelfth.....

Question: Once bio-film builds up, you will not be able to make a good tea. When will the bio-film get going?
Answer: If you clean with a good cleaner, then you MAY get the bio-film dealt with and the pipe cleaned out. IF the bio-film gets really bad, you may have to take the pipe apart and scrub. But when you once could make good tea, but now can't, suspect a bio-film developing and getting worse and worse as time goes by. A 90 degree turn may not give trouble until the tea brewer has been in use for awhile. But it will, sooner or later, result in poor tea. Adequate MAY avoid the problem. We need more data on that.

41. Brewing Temperatures 5/7/04 9:32 PM

Question: I wrote a long time ago that the way I controlled pathogens was to use lower temps and more air. Things I read led me to believe that even if the pathogens have food, they don't like it cold (below 70DF) and they don't like O2. So I try to keep my tea temperatures lower. If I am brewing when it is hotter, I try to use 'green compost' which is one of the reasons I have been experimenting with Eucalyptus as much as I have. I have used Eucalyptus mixed with manures and just plain Eucalyptus (after processing to remove oils) and brewed with both and tested for pathogens. (Well actually I only test for E. Coli and Salmonella but these are the traditional indicators.) But I think if we come up with a protocol that stresses a brew environment that is hostile to pathogens by its very nature, we may have an inroad into certification
Answer: Problem is that many people do not have access to eucalyptus compost. And we have compost and compost tea with no pathogens even when brewed at 72 to 75 F.

Question: So, what is the critical factor? Or factors?
Answer: Aeration is one, clearly. Temperature may not always have to be held below 70 F.

Question: If you have great sets of lactic acid bacteria, then can you brew at higher temps? Or if you have diversity over some level, you can brew at lower aeration, and higher temp?
Answer: We still have things to figure out. But you are correct that if we figure out the SEVERAL sets of conditions that will be inhibitory of pathogens, then we can make tea in many different places, any place on the planet.

42. Tea Brewing Ingredient Amounts 5/30/04 3:30 PM
I recall writing that the recipes in the Compost Tea Brewing Manual (CTBM) were good places to START, given the brewers that were available then. At this point, with more brewers, the CTBM is still a good place to start to learn the factors you need to think about, but needs to be updated again, perhaps. In the fourth edition, I changed the CTBM to de-emphasize the recipes. Start with the recipe in the CTBM, but start modifying to fit your needs better. Remember, we are trying to

maximize organism biomass. If you don't have good compost, you have to grow a lot more critters in the tea brewing time. If you have a higher biomass of organisms in the compost, you don't have to brew as long, and less food can be added. But always keep in mind that it is organism biomass we are trying to achieve. Temperature, oxygen addition, food resource addition, compost quality, water quality, mixing, etc are all factors that have to be considered.

THE MACHINE MANUFACTURER has to do that work, so when they sell a machine to a client, those factors have been optimized. The machine manufacturers that sell machine without data to show that ACTIVE bacteria, ACTIVE fungi, protozoa and nematodes, as well as total bacteria and total fungi are maximized in their teas need to be removed from the world of compost tea. They are doing none of us any benefit, and harming the reputation of compost tea. It is then wise to do what the manufacturer says is right for that machine, unless you want to do a whole bunch of testing to figure out what other combinations of factors also work with the machine you have. With one of the brewers, the manufacturer recommends such high amounts of compost be added that it is not a brewer at all. They are hoping that enough soluble nutrients will be EXTRACTED, along with a few organisms possibly surviving the potentially anaerobic conditions of brewing, to be of benefit. So, if it's a 100 gallon machine, for example, and the manufacturer is recommending addition of around 50 pounds or more of compost, you know you are in trouble. All you can hope to have to give a plant response is some soluble nutrients and a few bacteria. Why not just add an organic fertilizer like a fish hydrolysate? It's less expensive. Quicker. Less fuss and mess. Just make sure you have the good organisms in your soil and on your leaf surfaces first. Or you may feed pathogens, not the beneficials.

43. Maintaining Biology 5/25/04
The local compost from the store may not have much biology. You may want to pre-activate the compost with some good fungal foods - humic acid or fish hydrolysate. Just a few drops in enough water to wet the compost to 50% moisture (just 1 drop barely squeezable water from the compost). Brewing for 36 hours may be a really good idea when the biology is a bit lacking. Smell the brew and get an idea of whether the tea critters are growing - the molasses smell should go away, or at least change, if the critters are growing in the tea. You can spray tea mid-day, if the drop size of your sprayer is large enough.

Question: How do you tell drop size on your sprayer?
Answer: Let some of the drops fall on apiece of paper, and measure the diameter.

Question: What would maximum tank temperature be for tea to be ok, if a person is already brewing at say 70 degrees? How warm can your tea get in delivery tank before it start becoming effected, or how warm is to warm?
Answer: The maximum temperature would be one where you start losing the beneficial biology.

Question: What causes the beneficial organisms to be lost?
Answer: Lack of oxygen. Boiling water. If the water temperature is too hot to put your hand in, you've lost the critters.

44. Balance of Food and Aeration 5/16/04 10:19 AM

The balance that is needed is one between enough food to get the organisms in the compost activated, but not to have lots of remnant foods after the brew period. I think it is up to the machine makers to work on exactly what that balance of food and aeration actually is, for their brewer design.

45. Does Temperature of Tea for Various Soil Temperatures Matter? 1/20/04 1:09 PM

Ah, can't recall any data on whether it is better to brew longer at lower temp or get the organisms growing and then let cool to the lower temps. Based on what people are reporting, it would seem better to brew at lower temperatures for a longer time. But doing some data collection would be the way to go. If you could run side-by-side tea brews using the same compost, same water, same recipe and then test organism numbers when you add the different teas to the soil, that would give us the answer.

Question: Which one gives higher fungal biomass a week after addition to the soil?
Answer: That would be the simple and most straight-forward way to assess. Hum, you would want to start the low temperature longer brew first, and in the last 24 hours of that brew, start and finish the 24 hour brew so they both could be put down at the same time on the soil. Otherwise too much possible variance resulting from applying the tea on different days and having different weather conditions affect the outcome.

46. Water Quality Issues 5/3/04 8:38 AM

Free chlorine is the component that harms the organisms directly, because it complexes with cell membranes and shuts down energy production and respiration. Talk about drowning in your own wastes, that is what chlorine does to cells - prevents wastes from being able to escape the cell, so the organism dies. Total chlorine includes the free chlorine, but also the chlorine complexed with, or bound to, organic matter or other cations (positively charged ions). So, free chlorine plus bound chlorine equals total chlorine. There is an equilibrium between free chlorine, and bound chlorine. As water is de-gassed, the free chlorine is lost as a gas. The bound chlorine that is not tightly bound will leave the surface it is bound to, and become free chlorine in solution. You have to then de-gas that as well. It's why you have to aerate water for so long, sometimes, in order to get rid of the smell of chlorine. If you have significant amounts of bound chlorine, you may have to aerate for hours to get rid of the chlorine moving off the surfaces and into solution. The less organic matter and particulates in your water, the less bound chlorine you will have, and the faster you can get rid of your chlorine smell. If it takes a long time to get rid of the chlorine smell, it tells you something about the level of "stuff" in your water. You may not be able to see the stuff, but it's there, if you have to de-gas for a lo-o-o-ong time. Hum, water quality issues.

47. Chlorine and Chloramine 5/3/04 8:21 PM

Chlorine is best blown off as a gas. Chloramine needs to be complexed with humic acid. Activated charcoal has also been reported to work.

48. Chlorine is a Microbe Killer 2/21/04 11:40 PM

Fussy Worms......or what? The lettuce mixes they sell in the store are washed in chlorine, and then dropped into nitrogen gas atmosphere in the bags

Question: So how good is chlorine-tainted food for humans?
Answer: Chlorine is a good microbe-killer, which means we lack the right biology to stay healthy when we eat food treated with these materials.

Question: They dip the lettuce when the bacteria and the fungi are both growing....
Answer: As long as it isn't for too long, it's probably not a concern. Wish I could study it more, however.

49. Neutral pH or Water 8/11/03 6:25 AM

Question: What am I missing? pH? Water condition?
Answer: Yes. That's right. I forgot pH (needs to be near neutral, may have to add acid or base, which is vinegar or citric acid, or ascorbic acid to drop pH, or baking soda to raise ph, for example). And that water may need to be degassed to get rid of chlorine or hydrogen sulfide. Or humic or fulvic acid need to be added to exit chloramine.

50. De-Gas Water 8/8/03 9:50 PM
You have to de-gas water that smells like rotten eggs. Sulfur is a good fungicide. If you smell sulfur in any of it's forms, you need to tie it up biologically, or if present as a volatile form, just bubble air through the medium, and blow off the gas.

51. Chlorine, Bacterial Resistance 5/3/04 8:24 PM

Question: The question becomes, which bacteria can develop tolerance? Are the beneficials, or the detrimental organisms going to show tolerance?
Answer: The organisms that are tolerant are those that have been exposed before to the material. Those would more likely be pathogens and pests, not the beneficials we deal with in soil.

52. Chloramine 5/4/04 6:56 AM
It would be very interesting to look into what beneficial soil biology develops resistance to chlorine, but I have a feeling, since it is relatively easy to exit chlorine from water. Typically if you allow the drops to fly through the air before they hit the ground the chlorine will de-gas adequately, which means sprinklers work.
Chloramines is the bigger problem, since it does not de-gas. But still, addition of decent organic matter in some form works well. Add fish hydrolysate, or emulsion, or humus, or humic acid, or kelp, or.... well, the list is endless. All organic matter will complex things like chloramine. You just have to know how much you need to add. A few tests of your tea to determine what dose is needed and you are on your way. Maybe that's what you and I could work out for other folks - how much of each material gets rid of the toxic effect of chloramine. Would the EPA be interested in such a research project, do you think?

53. Could Pathogens Slip Through? 3/1/04 1:42 PM
No data to show that a problem exists, but the possibility that maybe somehow a pathogen could slip through. There is more likelihood of consuming pathogens by touching a door handle, but we

don't do anything to prevent that danger. People may not wash their hands before eating a food raw after touching a door handle. So, is it true that applying compost tea, that might have some pathogens growing in it, to raw food could result in food borne illness? There is no data to show that this has ever happened with compost tea.

54. Human Pathogen Controversy 2/29/04

Question: Is there re-growth of human pathogens in compost, even after the temperature and turning requirements have been met in making the compost?
Answer: There are no data to show that human pathogens grow in compost tea that is made with properly made compost. We have lots of data points showing no human pathogen problems in compost tea, as long as the compost is properly made.   But these data are not replicated, which is a serious problem in trying to make our case. There are data showing that poorly made compost, or compost starting with E. coli, or not-finished compost made with manure, can result in human pathogen growth in teas with high levels of sugar added to the tea. Compost tea has to be made with properly made compost. The RISK is low that a problem would occur, as not only would the human pathogens have to survive composting, but they would have to survive the compost tea process, and survive being applied to the plant. Even on a plant eaten raw, the likelihood that a human pathogen would survive competition, inhibition, predation, and aerated conditions is pretty low. The risk is acceptable, relative to the benefit likely. There are many examples of benefit - reduced water use, reduced toxic chemical use, reduced inorganic fertilizer run-off, reduced erosion - the positive part of tea. There is no data showing there IS a problem.

55. Food Crops and E Coli 5/7/04 9:53 PM

Question: I don't think there is anything I would like to see applied to food crops without concerns. I actually want growers to be concerned.
Answer: The concern raised by the CTTF about quality of compost tea is valid, but the focus was wrong. There has never been any evidence that compost has caused food poisoning. Tea, even though it's been around since the Roman Empire, and earlier, has never been responsible for an outbreak of human disease.

Question: So why the hysteria about maybe E. coli could survive in tea -- especially based on the extremely poor science used to suggest there could be a problem?
Answer: Solid understanding of when there is a problem, and when there is not, is required. Time to get to work on this. Glad to know that others are finding the same positive benefits as we and others have observed. But remember, the positive findings go back to at least the Roman Empire. With a great deal of help, we have re-discovered the agricultural wheel, if you will. With a lot more help, it won't be lost again. We need to work together on this. I appreciate the recognition for my efforts, but you too have made the discovery now. Pats on the back all around. Now, time to be turning to the future. What's the next step?

56. EM Ferment 6/15/04 9:40 PM
When you make an EM ferment, initially the organisms grow so rapidly, they use up the oxygen, and the facultative organisms then begin to grow. And mycorrhizal fungi can survive just fine as

spores in anaerobic conditions, especially if there are no humic acids around - they won't germinate and start to grow as they will in aerobic compost tea. The longer you let an EM ferment go, the slower the growth of the organisms, until the organisms aren't using up the oxygen anymore, because they aren't growing. The ferment then returns to aerobic oxygen concentrations, and there is no detrimental effect of the ferment to plants, at least that I have seen. Maybe people out there have other experiences, and that's the info we need to have - what are the conditions that always give us good effects, what are the conditions that always result in not-beneficial effects. Need to get those figured out. So, with your brews, what are the conditions that always result in good plant growth? Have you ever seen not-beneficial effects?

57. Aerobic vs. Anaerobic Decomposition 11/15/03 2:03 PM

Response to the question about aerobic versus anaerobic decomposition - Aerobic decomposition is usually "complete" - in other words, the final products are CO_2 and water. Along the way, microbial biomass is formed, but it all eventually gets consumed, as long as we are talking aerobic conditions. In anaerobic conditions, decomposition is incomplete. Anaerobic metabolic processes leave you with a complex set of putrefying organic matter, otherwise known as sludge, which will never get broken down, until oxygen is introduced (or oxygen in the form of certain kinds of thermal vent compounds).

So, anaerobic digestion will always leave you with a problem. Aerobic leaves you with CO_2 and water, eventually. But, some anaerobic metabolites are good pesticides and so useful as organic forms of pest control. But I personally prefer to enhance biology, not toxics. We can develop the science to make sure that the conditions to consistently produce the organic pesticide are known. But there's a great deal of work needed to be able to provide the guarantee that is possible with the aerobic teas. Not so yet with the anaerobic - aerobic switching back and forth teas.

For example, European regulatory agencies are purported to have stated, or soon will state, that compost teas made without careful documentation of the conditions of brewing will not be usable in agricultural. Too many people making horrible messes using non-documented brews. So much for "European methods" being as wonderful as Brinton is trying to make us believe. Facts are, we need to be careful about making tea in a controlled fashion. And we have done that with the AACT methods. But lots of "folk-wisdom" out there that needs to be tapped, and developed. Let's just make it clear that these other ways of making liquid amendments are not, and should not, be called compost tea. They are plant teas. They are often anaerobic. Clearly not AACT. But they should be discussed on the compost tea list serve. There are interesting things that could develop from these forms of tea.

58. Anaerobic Teas 10/17/03 3:09 PM

We have some work to do to understand when anaerobic teas will result in killing plants, versus just not having much affect. Clearly it isn't just dissolved oxygen levels that are important. The difference probably has to do with just how much alcohol, phenols and other metabolic products were made by the particular set of microbes that grew in the specific conditions. The first anaerobic brew probably helped set the stage for the nastier organisms being ready to take off faster in brew number two. With the two brews, which one smelled bad? Color? Foam? What differences?

59. DO Levels Dropping Down 10/12/03 9:10 PM

I have never seen DO drop down and bounce back up all that rapidly, or perhaps I should say drop down and then recover so fast that readings at 5 minute intervals didn't catch it. We have backed off to reading every 15 minutes. Getting too much data to live with otherwise. If DO did drop below 6 ppm for 5 minutes, the organisms can deal with that condition and make it through short periods. We have seen loss of active fungal hyphae in as short as 20 minutes at low oxygen, but usually it is when oxygen is gone for 5 to 6 hours that the aerobic organisms really give up and go to sleep or die.

60. Oxygen and Anaerobic Conditions 10/12/03 12:47 AM

You asked about how we do our samples. We suspend the probe in the water and measure oxygen using the probe. Typically we take samples from several places in the tea brewer, usually focusing on places where the mixing might not be the best, such as below aerators, in corners, and so forth. Removing samples from the tea before measuring the oxygen concentration means you are allowing changes to occur to the tea before taking a true "in the tea brewer" reading. While I am not an engineer, in my experience in doing oxygen measurements, the instant that air bubbles are released into the liquid, gases begin to diffuse and equilibrate. If oxygen concentration in the liquid is less than oxygen concentration in the gas bubble, oxygen begins to diffuse from the air bubble into the liquid. Very rapidly, within micrometers distance, the gases have equilibrated. Thus, you need to know gas concentration in the atmosphere in order to know the maximum possible oxygen concentration in the liquid. If the microorganisms are growing, the can use up the oxygen diffusing into the liquid faster than you can supply oxygen. So, the oxygen measurement obtained from an oxygen probe is a sum of all these processes. Oxygen probes measure oxygen in the liquid and gas in front of the membrane and since oxygen concentration equilibrates rapidly, there should be no difference in oxygen concentration between gas and the liquid once you are a few micrometers from the aerator.

Given that the water in the tea brewer is well-mixed, then all the water should be at the same concentration. So, mixing is an important factor so no areas of poor mixing occur. It is critical to be beyond the rapid growth phase of the microbes in the tea brewing process before you take the tea out of the tea maker, or the tea can go anaerobic very quickly. IF YOU ARE BEYOND the rapid growth phase period, then you can have 5 to 6 hours before anaerobic conditions occur. If you are in rapid growth phase, the tea may only take a minute or so to be into anaerobic conditions. Of course, it takes a few hours to accumulate enough anaerobic metabolites, which we smell as odor, to be able to smell that the brew is anaerobic.

61. Rapid Microbial Growth May Cause Anaerobic Conditions 10/9/03 10:27 PM

The problem was not with the oxygen probes. They read within a few tenths of each other when calibrated at room air levels, and they were within a few mg/L of the temp - barometric pressure proper readings. If you boil water, and drive out all the oxygen, let the water cool without shaking, then that should give you a very close to zero reading. The differences in readings was the result of microbial growth in the tea brew using up oxygen faster than the bubblers were adding oxygen back in. The more rapid the microbial growth, the sooner the brew went anaerobic, and the greater the growth of ANAEROBIC bacteria.

62. Preventing Detrimental Effects of Anaerobic Conditions 6/15/04 9:34 PM

I think there is some very interesting and intriguing observations about the facultative aerobes/anaerobes, the lactic acid producing bacteria, the proprionic acid producing bacteria, and some of the yeasts. I want to understand the conditions that help them prevent bad-guy growth. If they grow too much, you could have too much acid production, and that could harm plants. What are the conditions where that could happen? And I THINK I've seen that happen - too much proprionic acid and it was detrimental to plants. The smell of the tea was very indicative. Need to work more with the Biodynamic people, because they teach people about the Smells that indicate when the brewed material is "not ready yet", versus, it is finished and ready to put on the plants. But I think your observation about preventing the detrimental effects that otherwise anaerobic conditions might result in is a good one. We need more data!

63. Best Way Not to Go Anaerobic 2/13/04 5:46 PM

Still the best way not to go anaerobic is to remember: LESS IS MORE (food that is) and a good recipe, plus colder water. I think that matching the water temperature to the soil temperature, or foliar temperature, makes sense. Many people have suggested and pointed this out, so I am not the only person thinking this one through. Brewing in cold water in midsummer isn't going to work too well, most likely, or brewing in hot water in mid-autumn, or early spring, isn't going to work too well either.

Question: The success of this method depends in part on how badly overfed the microbes are. Way too much food and it is unlikely to do the job without dumping out part of the tea and refilling with de-gassed water.
Answer: Exactly right. Too much food is not a good thing. The Goldilocks Principle applies.

Question: I think the next place we have to be careful with this idea is the pump's capacity. What happens to a pump that's on the brink of number of gallons it can handle when you top off the brew with more water? In terms of oxygen in the brew, does the extra water slow the rate of addition of oxygen? Moral: Have extra capacity. Don't brew at the top of your pump's capacity.
Answer: But remember that the water you add should be at max oxygen content, because you have aerated to blow off chlorine. That water should up the oxygen in the tea brew ASAP. The additional water will not slow oxygen transfer, but will enhance it.

Question: When it's time to apply the tea, do we need to make any adjustments in gallons per acre? We were trying to understand what adding water actually did -- I think Elaine would say "exit the notion of dilution" because we added space and oxygen for more microbes to grow, and helped keep some existing microbes from going inactive.
Answer: What SFI has shown, and even more so in the SARE grant we have just finished, is that coverage on the leaf surface is what is important. So, when you make tea, if you would have made 5 ug of active fungi per ml of tea, but you added water to the tea, and now have 4 µg of active fungi per tea (you added 1 gallon of aerated water into a 5 gallons tea brew), you would still add the same amount of water in the sprayer, since your active fungi is above the minimum level of 2 µg.

Question: However, the number of microbes per gallon is likely to be less with this added water, depending on how far into the brew the additional water was added. Should we adjust gal per acre accordingly by simply subtracting the water added from the water we would normally use as the carrier for the application? (EXAMPLE: If we were going to apply 5 gallons per acre, and had to add 195 gallons of water to be able to spread it on an acre at the 5 gallons/acre rate,

Answer: The tea itself is diluted, and you have to know what the active bacterial and fungal biomass was, and how much that was dropped with the addition of water. You can easily test that a couple times to know what the reduction would be. Or you learn what amount of food you can add that will keep the brew from going anaerobic when temperatures are hot.

64. Fungi in Teas 6/2/04 9:30 PM
Glad the fungi are improving in your teas! I'm sure you can get them even better. Try pre-activating the compost with some good fungal foods. Reduce the amount of compost in the machine, so you don't get so much sludge on the bottom of the machine which is hard to keep aerobic.

65. Calculating Biomass 6/1/04 11:09 PM
Biomass is calculated as follows: Determine biopolymer: length of the cell, times Pi times (diameter/2) squared. Biomass requires measurement of density of the fungus, so you can multiply fungal density times biopolymer to obtain biomass.

66. Food Additions after Brewing Stops 5/31/04 1:13 PM
There is a difference between turning the aeration off when a brew at 22 hours versus adding well-oxygenated water to a brew that has reached stable activity phase. Your brew at 22 hours, was not likely beyond the active growth phase of the brew. You probably had not gotten beyond the growth peak and into the period where oxygen demand has stabilized. Foods were still present and the organisms were actively growing, with a maximum oxygen demand.

Question: How about turning off aeration AFTER addition of well-aerated water but BEFORE any additional foods were added?

Answer: As far as I could tell, the question was about a situation where 100 L of brew at the well-stabilized phase was mixed with 100 L of well-aerated water. Aeration was turned off, and then foods were added as the tea was sprayed out. The question was, after two hours, would the tea in the sprayer, before food addition, be in aerobic range? I BELIEVE it would be. Given the constraints I have assumed, it would likely be fine. Given different conditions, my conclusions would be different. Of course, actual data would put an end to the considerations. But I get amazed at all the permutations we can come up with that need testing.

67. Organisms Need Tea Environment 3/17/04 11:28 PM
It is important to recognize that organisms need the tea environment. Too great a dilution can be a problem, causing osmotic disruption, unless you have humic acids, kelp, and other soluble materials from the compost. Tea needs those materials we add. As long as the remaining material is still active, the bits can grow out. So, again, making sure you know something about the pumps is a necessary thing. The person selling the tea brewer ought to check this to make sure the pump doesn't destroy the fungal biomass, protozoa or other organisms. If you get adequate coverage

with bacteria and fungi, then the fact you may have lost some critters to get there doesn't matter. The critical part is how much tea per area, regardless of how much water is used. If you put the same amount of liquid on each time, but more or less tea in that liquid, there might be a problem with not enough organisms getting on the soil or plant surfaces.

Question: Could be dust, heat or lack of food. My reading and the people testing (a very good lab on the vineyard) seemed to think it was UV and they had some tests to prove it when I cried foul. There might be pesticide drift but unlikely since none was sprayed anywhere near where we were working.

Answer: How far down wind can pesticide effects be detected? 15 miles. I bet there is every possibility that something was sprayed within that 15 mile upwind distance. The UV experiments are typically done in lab conditions, or with leaves in special containers, where UV dose is controlled, without any foods for the organisms to grow, and make the glue layers. A drop of 1 mm or greater is large enough to attenuate UV. If the organisms have a chance to grow on the leaf, usually about 20 minutes. If food is provided in the tea, or the plant provides the food, the bacteria and fungi are protected.

Question: It seemed to occur vineyard wide but we had them on a three day cycle anyway so the program worked. My reading seems to indicate that UV is bad for microbes. Am I reading something wrong? The microbiology texts I have read indicate that UV is the best antibacterial there is. What am I misinterpreting?

Answer: Unprotected cells are disrupted by UV, no doubt about that. But in the environment, cells have the ability to protect themselves. Look at a picture of the leaf surface with the microbes on it. Glue everywhere.

Question: Ok. I'm dying to know. On a leaf, how is the plant feeding the bacteria/fungi?

Answer: The leaf produces exudates, just like the roots. Sugars, proteins and carbohydrates are released from the cells, and that feeds the set of organisms around the surfaces. The plant does that to develop the protective layer of beneficial organisms.

Question: Test at the beginning, I see few and I see more after about 24 hours. Maybe it's that they are moving out of the compost looking for food or that as the bacteria grow and send out enzymes to feed, the nematodes respond.

Answer: That is the mechanism, as far as I'm aware. It takes time for the nematodes to extract from the compost.

Question: Yeah, I finally figured it out. What I was pointing out was that their bodies withstood the process but they did not live generally. I was unsure what exactly killed them in the process.

Answer: I think they drown.

Question: I may be off here but I have pumped tons of air into my tea and these stalked ciliates grow like crazy if they are there. They look like Greek urns on a string and every once in a while spring back. Around their mouths is an eddy of circulating water. They are cool to watch.

Answer: Stalked ciliates are cool to watch. If the conditions have been anaerobic, which selects for the growth of these critters, the competing flagellates and amoebae have been reduced significantly and the so the ciliates can continue their bloom without anything "getting in the way". Takes about 3 to 7 days after air returns to have the flagellates and amoebae finally get back to normal. I love watching the biology in tea.

68. Pathogen Survival 3/1/04 2:09 PM
I really dislike making broad statements about compost, or tea, based on incomplete understanding and testing. Think through the data - In perhaps 90% of the cases, when temperature and turning are done correctly, compost contains no pathogens worth worrying about. The beneficials are also present, and growing, and we get no re-growth of the pathogens. In maybe 8% of the cases, pathogens are clearly present, but don't re-grow.

Question: In perhaps 2% of cases, pathogens survive and are very happy. Why? What are the conditions that allow this to happen?
Answer: That's what needs to be understood. We need to still understand these unusual situations, and work to fix the problem. And the problem is in the composting, not in the tea. These odd situations need to be figured out!

69. Human Pathogens 9/16/03 12:07 AM

Question: As you suggest some compost piles are not under great management. Tests were conducted SFI to demonstrate that compost WITH E coli if brewed with good O2 eliminated that pathogen and others.
Answer: I would like to re-iterate that it is not just oxygen that eliminates the pathogens. Please, let us be certain to get the message across correctly each time. Please don't forget to include all the factors when talking about dealing with pathogens, ok? I want to also point out that if you start with an overload of E. coli per gram of compost, then the three factors, aeration, good competitors for food and space, and good numbers of protozoa and nematodes in the compost tea to consume the pathogens may not be able to deal with billions and billions of human pathogens. OK? You can push the ability of the "good guys" to deal with bad guys if the bad guys are just too many.

70. Getting Active Organisms in Brews 1/22/04 5:19 AM
Have to have active bacteria for the foliar protection to work -- 65% coverage with active bacteria, 5% coverage with active fungi is what we have seen as the needed levels. The high total bacterial biomass suggests good growth of bacteria in the brew, but they are not active. Please remember that the activity stain we use is for aerobic bacteria, and will not be taken up by bacteria growing anaerobically, either true anaerobes, or facultative anaerobes growing anaerobically.

Question: So, is it the sludge layer at the bottom of the tank?
Answer: Need to increase aeration during the time that the DO drops so abruptly? Need to reduce food resources so that sudden burst of growth that drops DO doesn't occur? All possible solutions. Which one seems easiest to try first?

71. Mechanical Failure 1/10/04 2:14 Am
When you have a mechanical failure, dilute your tea with aerated water ASAP. The colder the better. Use in your sprinkler, so at least the nutrients don't go to waste.

72. Sludge 10/04 1:37 AM

Sludge on the bottom of the brewer is not good. You tend to collect all the fungi in the sludge. They get caught in there and don't leave. Then as the brew goes on, bacteria MAY grow in the sludge, and since oxygen movement into the sludge may be limited, we have problems. I think the idea directing a stream of air at the bottom of the brewer is a good one, so that sludge doesn't collect or build up. Keep it in suspension as much as possible.

73. Bio-Film 12/19/03 7:26 PM

When I speak bio-film, I mean something that is thick enough to get a half inch depth of bio-film on your finger in a 1 inch swipe across the surface. That depth of film will harm your tea. Bio-film that harms tea quality is typically black in color, because of hydrogen sulfide formation. When you remove real bio-film, the smell, should you happen to get the sludge near your nose, is rank. The bio-film you show in these pictures will not develop to a level in a single tea brew to harm anything. If cleaned after a single brew, and maybe even after several brews, no problem should result. Bio-film has to be thick enough to prevent oxygen from moving into the film. That means thickness to the film you can accumulate with a single inch-long swipe. Films that will harm tea quality accumulate on the bottom of the disc diffusers in some tea brewing machines after three to five tea brews. To avoid development of these films, you have to take the machine apart and clean the bottom of each disc each time, which means that cleaning is far beyond the 20 minutes that some tea brewing machine manufacturers' claims. And they neglect to tell you that bio-film grows in the air bubblers they have in each compost basket. The air bubblers have to be soaked in bleach for a few minutes if you clean them each brew, up to three or four hours if you only clean after one or more brews. Cleaning is not even close to their claim of 20 minutes. Now, back to 90 degree turns in pipes. To clean bio-films from 90 degree bends, you have to clean the pipes with a cleaning agent each time. At times you will need to brush them out. If you buy brewers with right angle bends in pipes that the tea has to go through, the manufacturer should tell you about cleaning methods. It is up to the manufacturer of any machine to tell you about things you need to do to maintain the machine so that excellent results are possible.

74. Bio-Film and Tea Quality 12/19/03 8:04 AM

Question: Which people want to spend two hours or more cleaning the bio-film out of hard-to-reach places on your machine? Which of you want to volunteer to have to pop pipes apart after each brew so you can get to the bottom of the discs in your brewer? Discs which have bio-film so thick that you can run your fingers across the bottom and get smelly bio-film? What do you think that does to your tea quality?

Answer: No protozoa, no good nematodes, active fungal biomass barely detectable, and low total fungal biomass. You think you would have protection from mildew? Think again. SFI has a study currently in review in Applied Soil Ecology, the premier SCIENTIFIC journal in this area about our work for THREE YEARS in vineyards controlling mildew and grey mold. The bacteria, fungi, protozoa and nematodes in the tea are what determine quality of the tea. There is clear and unequivocal data on the Compost Tea Brewing Manual showing the studies we have done PROVING, in as much as anything can be proven in this world, that compost tea does what I say it does, and the REASON is the beneficial organisms in the tea.

75. Bio Film and Protection   12/19/03 8:04 AM

Question: Which people want to spend two hours or more cleaning the bio-film out of hard-to-reach places on your machine? Which of you want to volunteer to have to pop pipes apart after each brew so you can get to the bottom of the discs in your brewer? Discs which have bio-film so thick that you can run your fingers across the bottom and get smelly bio-film? What do you think that does to your tea quality?

Answer: No protozoa, no good nematodes, active fungal biomass barely detectable, and low total fungal biomass. You think you would have protection from mildew? Think again. SFI has a study currently in review in Applied Soil Ecology, the premier SCIENTIFIC journal in this area about our work for THREE YEARS in vineyards controlling mildew and grey mold. The bacteria, fungi, protozoa and nematodes in the tea are what determine quality of the tea. There is clear and unequivocal data on the Compost Tea Brewing Manual showing the studies we have done PROVING, in as much as anything can be proven in this world, that compost tea does what I say it does, and the REASON is the beneficial organisms in the tea.

76. Winter Brewing 12/16/03 7:06 PM

When brewing for winter application, it is better to brew at 65 F, and let the tea slowly cool (for example in the sprayer). You need to have adequate growth in 24 hours in the tea, so the temp needs to be 65 to 70. But then help select for less shock in addition to soil by letting the bacteria and fungi, protozoa and nematodes acclimate a little. There are always dormant stages of the organisms that grow at other temperatures, oxygen conditions, etc. so the inoculum is present for the other conditions. They wake up and start growing at those other conditions, so you are still applying inoculum for the cold-loving bacteria, even when you grow the tea at 65 F. Any organic matter addition, with beneficials along with, will be an improvement. What we are seeing is that it is important to get the soil chemistry turned around at the same time as adding biology. More to learn....Oh yeah, copper. It's the situation of the copper tank that has shown impacts on the beneficial bacteria. Which is different from what we are concerned about when considering drinking water.

77. Fish Oils 11/1/03 9:54 AM

Is it the fish oil that isn't coming off? If so, I'd think a gentle emulsifier would work. The yucca should foam quite nicely. It's probably the fish oils that are sticking well.

78. Think Biology, Not Mechanical 10/9/03 10:33 PM

When you provide more foods for microbial growth, guess what? More microbes grow. If microbes are growing, they use up oxygen. There's no major difference between the pumps. The difference is in the effect of more foods that the microbes can use. Try to think biology........

Question: Your numbers actually reveal some consistency that the air pump to your first brewer is not "identical" to the other two. The DO of the first brewer is consistently lower, in test 1 and 3, when fish was used. Fish has more N then Kelp does, I suppose. The third brewer was also producing less air then the second one and it became evident when the fish was used.

Answer: Please, think if you were dropped into a place where there was a little fish, just kelp, or double the amount of fish present. You wouldn't grow on the kelp much at all. You could grow on the fish, and you'd grow perhaps double on the double amount of fish. Under which condition would you use more oxygen, respire more CO_2? Think biology, not mechanical.

79. Stagnated Compost Went Anaerobic 10/3/03 9:57 PM
Data collected on flow forms made in Australia showed that each flow form added 0.5 mg oxygen/L. The problem was the non-aerated and non-stirred pool at the bottom of the flow forms where the compost stagnated in the water, and went anaerobic.

80. Carbonization Suppresses Fungal Growth 10/2/03 4:30 PM
As bubbles rise through the liquid, we see fungal strands caught in the interface between the small bubbles rising at different rates through the liquid. A factor of surface tension? But as the small bubbles move, the fungal strands caught in the interplay of the tiny bubbles are shattered and ripped apart. I think this is critical when some micrometer size bubbles are suspended basically un-moving in the water, while slightly larger bubbles move past the smaller size bubbles. I report what I observe. Not being a physicist, I am not certain what physical phenomenon this represents, but fungal strands don't do well in liquids with very small diameter bubbles. Another reason that carbonation works so well to suppress fungal growth?

81. Flow Forms 9/17/03 10:41 PM
I have some data done with Steve Capeness in Australia, on the flow form. Each flow form "step" increased oxygen by 0.5 mg/L. This was not enough to keep up with the growth of the microbes in the compost. Too much food added? Different CT machines can keep ahead of the oxygen demand from the microbes. Some CT machines do not manage to do that. Stirring is impossible to keep up, UNLESS YOU DON'T ADD any food. And even then, with some composts, there will be too much good bacterial food in the compost to have stirring keep the tea aerobic.

82. Temperature Flow Form System 9/17/03 6:20 PM
Heater in the pool is how you would keep a flow form system at temperature. Or if you are in hot climate, you have to be inside, air conditioned.

83. Biodynamics 9/17/03 7:17 AM
Allan Balliet is the better person to answer some of your questions, since he is an expert in biodynamics and does biodynamic farming. But, let me put my two cents worth in:

Question: Where can I get information on the Malcolm Rae machine or any other device to create an alternate left spin, right spin water vortex.
Answer: The Malcolm Rae machine is a small device that is supposed to impart energy into materials from a distance. Hugh Lovell is the person to contact about that device. Radionic machines are available from various sources, but you have to be very careful in the US not to run into legal problems when using them. The medical community has basically outlawed them, and you cannot use them for anything related to cures for human diseases or conditions. For agriculture, the legal situation is more nebulous.

a. Frequency Wavelength

The idea with these machines is to detect substances using the frequency wave lengths that are unique signals of any particular material or grouping of cells. These frequencies do exist, as the quantum physicists have shown. The ability to detect those signals reliably is the not-well-documented situation here. Each person can get very different readings for any item being measured. So, needs more work, huh?

b. Stirring BD Preps

For stirring BD preps and keeping them aerobic, which I think would serve to make the preps more consistent from batch to batch, you would need a compost tea machine. So BD preps are meant to go anaerobic for a while, however, I believe. Again, data are lacking on this, but in the case of the horsetail preps, I think the effective material in helping against weeds is actually an anaerobic product - but is it a product of fermentative anaerobic conditions or putrefactive anaerobic organisms? So, some work to do here.

c. Flow Forms are Aerator Units

The flow forms are aerator units. In the data we have, unfortunately only replicated one time so not publishable from a scientific point of view, each time the water went through a single flow form, the increase in oxygen in the water was 0.5 mg/L. If you knew the oxygen demand of your prep, you could then figure out the number of flow forms needed to keep the prep aerobic.

d. Preps Added to Teas

But remember that the preps are just ADDED to your compost or teas, as I understand. The preps are INOCULA that you use to add the right biology to your compost or compost tea as you are making the tea. Please realize that no biodynamic grower would use my terminology to explain what they are doing. They don't think of preps as inocula. That's a microbiologist adding their two cents worth in here. The preps are inocula, but BD practitioners don't think of them that way. But where I was getting to is, that a BD prep is not sprayed out the way you spray out a compost tea. You add the prep to the compost or the tea. Is that right, Allan?

84. Yogurt-Type Organisms 6/15/04 11:02 PM

You asked me to comment on the yogurt-type organisms under full aeration. If you had only those organisms, they would manage ok in fully aerobic conditions. But if they were in competition with true aerobes, the true aerobes will win. That's why the Biodynamic approach to obtaining these organisms is needed. You need reduced oxygen in order to develop conditions that allow the lactic acid producing bacteria to grow.

85. Getting Good Tea 12/17/03 8:51 AM

Remember to keep the air blowing through the aerator until you take it out of the tea, so you don't get tea in the air pipe. Tea that doesn't contain all the beneficials from the compost, and won't allow them to grow to high numbers in the brewing process should be called what? Brown water? In-sufficient tea? Anaerobe enhancers?

86. 90 Degree Turns 12/17/03 10:08 PM

The 90 degree turn on your brewer outlet should not be a problem since the tea doesn't circulate through it over and over, just once as liquid passes out of the system, and the velocity going through the turn is not high velocity. I agree that folks need to be told that they need to make sure that 90 degree turn needs to be kept clean. A manual with this kind of information needs to come with the brewer.

87. 90 Degree Angles 12/17/03 10:08 PM

The 90 degree turn on your outlet should not be a problem since the tea doesn't circulate through it over and over, just once as liquid passes out of the system, and the velocity going through the turn is not high velocity. I agree that folks need to be told that they need to make sure that 90 degree turn needs to be kept clean. A manual with this kind of information needs to come with the brewer

88. Manufacturers are Responsible 12/19/03 8:20 AM

Question: If the pipe with the 90 degree turn isn't in the tea, and is no where near the tea, how does anything that would cause a bio-film get into a pipe well away from the water?
Answer: Get to the specific problem. Solutions are only possible when the specific situation is dealt with. Cleaning is a serious issue. Manufacturers ARE responsible for their designs, and they have been sued for murder when proven willfully negligent. You have come forward to say the pipe really does have bio-film in it. The proof I have of my statements on the 90 degree not being a problem is also observational. I have never seen a problem there. But I'm entirely capable of recognizing a problem when the problem is put before me in a reasonable manner.

89. Microscope Manual 6/10/04 8:38 PM

The manual "Compost Tea Quality: Light Microscope Methods" has pictures galore, plus a step-by-step explanation of how to use a microscope to do the shadowing techniques needed to see what you want to see with a light microscope. A bit tricky, so the manual explains how. The manual has pictures of bad, poor, adequate, good and excellent tea, to go with the descriptions I sent out this morning. Many people don't know what fungi look like, especially the distinctions between narrow diameter hyphae (the "bad guys"), and wide diameter hyphae (the "good guys" for the most part). Most people don't know what debris look likes or protozoa, or nematodes. The pictures and explanations are all in the manual. And I plan on having a web page for additional pictures, with clear explanations of what the picture is. But the page will only be accessible if you have a manual. People can of course, put pictures that they take of their own tea up on their own websites.

Chapter VIII

INGREDIENTS

For
Actively Aerated
Compost Tea

INGREDIENTS FOR ACTIVELY AERATED COMPOST TEA

1. Brewing Recipes 10/1/03 9:50 PM
The recipes in the CTBM are starting places. You learn about your local materials by testing your first few brews, and fine-tuning.

2. Quantities in Brews 1/22/04 8:41 PM
…..a good point about too much "stuff" in the brew recipe. Simple is better, usually.

3. Different Foods Select for Different Organisms 2/26/04
Different foods, as with different salinity, will select for different organism growth

4. Think Like a Microbe! 10/18/03 10:40 AM
Grinding up shells isn't the same as having an extracted pure product. Microbes work on surfaces, and if most of the food resource is still in chunk form, the microbes can't get to it. It's like putting leonardite in your tea. Doesn't do a thing except destroy your pump, because the microbes can't chew through all the other stuff in leonardite (the pre-coal mineral that contains - relatively speaking - high amounts of humic acids) to get to the humic acids in a 24 hour period. The microbes can't do much to leonardite in even a few weeks, although maybe in a couple months some benefit of selecting for humic acid that use organisms would occur. So, leonardite into the soil makes sense, but add the organisms that can use this pre-coal material (mostly fungi). But adding to the tea? Not helping much.....

Same with chitin. Chunks of shell don't help much in a tea. Just not enough time for use to happen. If you ground up the material, then more surface area for the critters to chew on. But still, 24 hours? Not likely a benefit in the tea - but yes, benefit in the soil. Adding chunky foods to the tea and getting it spread on the soil works - the organisms will use the food in the soil and give long term benefits. If you want to have effects in the tea, you need to use extracted, higher percentage chitin containing materials. Or humic acid materials (see above discussion). Having the pure stuff means the chitin-using critters that seem to have highly competitive actions, and chew up insect larvae in the soil, will grow in the tea. The question ends up, cost-benefit. So, as we keep educating people to "think like a microbe", you'll all be able to answer these questions on your own. Must be the weekend, I just got a flash of the MTV platinum song "walk like an Egyptian" by Cindy Lauper (?- well, name is close) from a few years ago. "Just think like a microbe....." Who wants to go for this one?

5. Differences in Amounts of Foods 10/12/03 8:25 AM
When someone puts in kelp instead of fish, that's a significant change in the recipe for that brewer. The brewer used was identical between the tests. But the foods going into each brewer were different. One received fish, the next received kelp and no fish, the third had fish added to the compost as a pre-activator and then ALSO had fish added. The composts used in each brewer were different. There were significant differences in the three brews, and the most significant differences were the amounts of foods for the microorganisms to grow on.

6. Types of Foods 11/16/03 8:31 AM

Question: I (and the group I spoke to) would like to know - If the mixture was aerated, would the weeds and herbs break down more rapidly and be available to use in a much shorter time?
Answer: You have to distinguish between what happens to simple, structurally not-complex foods, as opposed to complex foods.

a. Anaerobic Condition
The anaerobic condition results in anaerobic bacteria, using anaerobic metabolic pathways, to consume the simple foods and produce alcohols, organic acids - some of which give the smells we all associate with anaerobic conditions - phenols, terpenes, putrescines, and other complex compounds, which may include antibiotics. Only half of these simple substrates will be completely metabolized, which means you end up with anaerobic sludge on the bottom of the container. That sludge will have to be dealt with using aerobic conditions.

b. AACT Brewers
In the AACT brewers, the simple sugars, simple proteins, and simple carbohydrates are pretty much all used (that means turned into either bacterial biomass, fungal biomass, a few aerobic metabolites which will be consumed by other bacteria and fungi, CO_2 and water) by the end of the brew. In AACT brewers, the fungi have the chance to begin breaking down the cellulose and other complex molecules in the plant tissue. They won't have finished that process in 24 hours, so those complex food resources continue to feed your organisms once you put the tea out into the real world. The break down of complex foods by fungal metabolism releases bacterial food. The way fungi chew up cellulose, humic acid, complex fish proteins, etc. results in the release of food resources for bacteria. And generally, just the foods for beneficial bacteria, not the bad-guy bacteria. Although, this has to be in aerobic conditions. No aerobes (if the tea is anaerobic, right?), then the bad guys can use the food resources.

Question: What if you have no good guys in the tea? What if you used stinky compost, where the anaerobes were the active critters?
Answer: The outcome of AACT could be questionable. You have to have the good guys. So, when you are using anaerobic processes, breakdown is much longer, and right now, we don't know enough to be able to predict the outcome of an anaerobic or fermentation type of tea. We have not studied the parameters enough to be predictive of whether or when the good guys finally start ruling again.

c. When is AACT Ready?
So the simple answer to your question is yes, AACT is ready in 24 hours, anaerobic or fermentation tea is "ready" in three to four weeks. Maybe longer. But, one other thing to think about. The end product of AACT is the whole foodweb, active and ready to go to work for you. In anaerobic or fermentation teas, the organisms are asleep by the time you finish the fermentation, and they are ready to work for you. You have to wake up the beneficials again, and in fact, most of the beneficials will not survive the fermentation.

d. Anaerobic Processed End Products Can be Toxic

OK, one more thing - the end products of the anaerobic processes CAN be (be aware, when someone says can, it means we have no guarantee that it will turn out every single time) highly toxic to a number of critters.

Question: What have we learned about doing the toxic thing?
Answer: That ultimately, it does more harm than good. A one time application of a pesticide can knock the bad guys for a loop, but you have also taken out a herd of good guys. You have to put the good guys back. So apply AACT to get t he good guys back. Or good compost, if you have enough to cover everything.

Question: So . . . . when the plant teas are "ready" would they be safe to add at the beginning of a AACT brew OR would it be best at the end, just prior to application???
Answer: You need to test this. I think (that means no data, just extrapolating from experience with lots of messing about with these things, and relying on talks I've had with lots of biodynamic people who have lots of experience, (Jeff Poppen and Alan Balliet, for example). It depends on what you want from the tea. If the nutrient you want needs to get directly into the plant, you add the plant tea into the AACT and foliar apply the mix. The high numbers of good guy bacteria and fungi in AACT elevate CO_2 on the leaves, and the nutrients released in the plant tea fermentation (we think), results in the nutrients being pumped directly into the plant, and getting the plant's nutrient levels to be super-charged. If you want to elevate the nutrient in the soil, you add the PLANT, or the plant tea, to the AACT compost bag, and let the brew occur with the plant. That way the nutrients are tied-up in the bacteria and fungi, and they don't leach when you add them to the soil. Especially in the fall, after harvest, you need to do this, because otherwise, the nutrients you worked so hard to gather, to ferment and release in the plant tea, and apply to the soil, just leach right on out if you don't have the beneficial organisms working for you in the soil.

e. Humic Acid Testing Results

Which reminds me, SFI did some testing on humic acids as fungal food resources, and I'm not sure I ever reported those results. The take-home message was this: Humic acids extracted using harsh chemicals (strong acid and strong base) are not as good sources of food for fungi as humic acids extracted using hot water, or less harsh chemical means. Humic acids that have been extracted using harsh chemicals can be revived, or biologically activated, however. The list I like? Terra Vita's highest concentration humic acid, Helena Chemical company's Hydra Hume, Horizon Ag's humic acids, a product out of Australia called Biostarter, made by Tryton. Tom Piatkowski has made a study of all these sources of humic acids, and he is a good resource to ask questions of. That's tom@healthysoil.com. Anyone else have a favorite humic acid? If we've tested it, and I can share the data, I'll let you know how it did in testing.

7. Tea Recipe 2/21/04 12:29 AM

Question: Can someone suggest a proper ratio for ingredients to end up with a balanced bacterial and fungal colony? I just eyeball it like the person that taught me to use the tea. I guess it's about a good handful of worm castings, 3 tbsp oats and a cup of molasses into 2-3 gallons of water.
Answer: Your recipe sounds reasonable. Test the final results, so you know for certain.

8. Tea Ingredients 3/27/04 11:25 AM

Question: I have compost tea machines and most of the ingredients to make a tea. Any suggestions?
Answer: Most worm compost has lots of sugars in it, and so you don't want to add molasses if you are using worm compost. Kelp is a good addition, as is fish hydrolysate, casein (milk protein), oatmeal (finely ground), or other protein meals.

9. Purpose for Ingredient Additions 7/27/04 9:13 AM

Sour milk? Why? Each component going into your compost, or into your compost tea needs to be understood. WHY are you adding each thing? I can tell you what to add, but then you don't learn WHY you need to add each thing. So, let's make this a learning situation. Why do you add kelp? How much? Why would you add ground egg shells? How much? What organisms do you select for if you put in sour milk? Or fresh milk? What will be the result if you add these food resources? Would you add an activator to the compost, or to the tea? What is your purpose in making compost, or tea? Different plants require different conditions in the soil. What are you trying to achieve?

10. Propionic Acid, Molasses, Any Simple Sugar 2/2/04 7:26 PM

Propionic acid is an organic acid; three carbons in the chain, and is a good food resource for most simple-food-using bacteria and fungi. The concern with molasses, or ANY simple sugar, is that it gets bacteria growing really fast, and you need to make certain that oxygen does not drop too low while brewing.

11. Carbon Sources 2/1/04 6:08 PM

The sugar will help the bacteria grow, maybe fungi, so they tie up the excess N. Addition of carbon sources - like sugar, humic acids, proteins, etc, allow the bacteria and fungi to grow, take up the N, immobilize the salts. It's both food and organisms. Doesn't work without both.

12. Sugars and Nitrogen 5/31/04 5:15 AM

Bacteria utilize simple sugars better than any other organism on the planet. Sugars can be pure carbon, practically speaking, so you need other sources of N in the tea brew; such as nitrogen in the compost, or in additives such as fish, humic acid, or kelp. People are often told that compost contains no nitrogen. That is not a correct statement. The true statement is that real compost contains very little nitrate. But in our corporate world, fertilizer nitrogen has been defined as inorganic nitrogen. And the nitrogen in compost is organic N for the most part. It doesn't leach. In properly made, aerobic compost, the organisms retain or hold on to nutrients, so they don't leach. Not the case with inorganic N, which is highly leachable and ends up in your drinking water. So, simple sugars get those bacteria growing really rapidly, as long as you have compost in the list of ingredients. But you may not want to enhance bacterial growth all that much, so most recipes for tea have less molasses in the mix, more protein which helps fungal balance.

13. Bacteria and Molasses 11/3/03 8:24 PM

There are only a few bacteria that consume other bacteria, and most of those bacteria that prey upon other bacteria are found in aquatic systems, as I recall. Not normal soil denizens. Molasses in of and by itself does not "cause" E. coli to grow. How could it?

14. Different Kinds of Sugars 3/27/04 7:09 PM

There are hundreds of thousands of different kinds of sugars. Most people think of sucrose as the only kind of sugar, but not so. Many, many different kinds, and worm compost has lots of the carbon present as sugar, which drives me nuts when the people who are making regulations try to suggest that we can't add sugar to compost tea. They are messing up by meaning glucose, but saying sugar. Worm castes and the slime on the outside of worms is probably very high in many, many kinds of sugars, some more complex than others. The bacteria that grow on these foods probably inhibit and compete with human pathogens. To say these sugars are "bad", i.e., grow E. coli, is incorrect.

The foods you mention are chock full of different kinds of sugars, many amino sugars, which again, are probably those the good guys do so well on, and help them suppress the bad guys. Addition of protein would probably help convert those sugars into something else, but it might not have the effect of inhibiting the bad guys. Maybe it would.

15. Too Much Molasses 11/1/03 11:10 AM

People should read Scott, the Daylily person in Ooze's e-mails about using 5% molasses in his teas. BAD news. Is it an aeration thing? Lack of fungi in his compost? Something in his water? What a mess he had! So, no, going with high concentrations of molasses to get fungi to grow is NOT the way to do this. It's a sticky mess. You think a pint of molasses is a sticky, gluey mess, think about adding enough to 500 gallons......And remember, you still have to have good fungal biomass in your compost to make the molasses thing work.

So, just work on getting enough fungi growing in your compost FIRST. Once you have that going, then maybe you would think about molasses at high concentration. SFI data shows that low levels of molasses resulted in no E. coli present at all. High levels of molasses, and the E. coli dropped SIGNIFICANTLY! Make sure your compost is human pathogen free. We have a simple, 3 hour turnaround, (costs $40 to do) test using molecular probes. Know for certain your compost is human pathogen-free. Make sure your compost tea is too. But, if your compost is human-pathogen free, and your ingredients are human-pathogen free, then the compost tea will be too.

16. Molasses Concentration 11/1/03 10:21 Am

What we have seen with molasses is that concentration is important. Remember the e-mail I sent out about 0.1%, 0.5% 1% and 5% molasses? We found that the lower concentrations of molasses JUST grew bacteria. Fungi were in fact HARMED. But at 5% molasses, the bacteria were reduced, and fungi grew like gang-busters. The trick is to maintain aerobic conditions, however. Probably, right at first, the shock of that much concentration of sugar, puts the bacteria to sleep. If you have good fungal biomass in the compost, the fungi probably start growing and the bacteria are out-of-luck. But, if you don't have adequate fungi in the compost, then the bacteria recover, and you better have SERIOUS aeration capacity to keep up with their oxygen use......... That much sugar! Phew! You're brewing beer.....

17. Sugar Source 11/1/03 10:13 AM

Question: What is the difference in cane, beet, and sorghum molasses in the use of compost tea?
Answer: You grow different sets of microorganisms with the different food resources.

18. Sulfur 8/4/03 3:03 AM
Sulfur is added to molasses as a preservative. So molasses from the mill should be non-sulphured (or non-sulfured, as the case may be, depending on whether we are using the Queen's English, or the American variety).

19. Kelp 8/21/03 5:42 Am
Typically weight per volume, as in kg of kelp per L of water. Or lbs. of kelp per gal of water..

20. Humic Acid in Tea 1/30/04 6:06 AM
If your compost tea has good humic acid content, which you can usually tell by color, then it definitely would have ability to absorb salts. So, compost tea should be dark brown. Not black. Be aware there is a dry, soluble kelp that is very dark in color (burned during drying?) which imparts a dark color to a tea , but is not humic acid and has none of the benefits. Sigh. When you buy tea, you need to ask about the ingredients that are actually in the tea, or you may get dark color without the benefits of humics.

21. Good Compost Needed for Tea 4/16/04 6:18 PM
If you make tea with good compost, you should not be dealing with soil-borne pathogens. Compost is not dirt. The heating and microbial processing prevent the human pathogen, insect and worm problems from being in the compost. Good compost, however, needs to be documented.

22. No Fresh Manure in Compost Tea 6/1/04 11:18 PM
If you flood something with incredibly high numbers of pathogens, you don't have the population of good guys to do the job of taking the bad guys out in 24 hours. NO FRESH MANURE in compost tea. We aren't making manure tea; we're making compost tea. Compost tea requires good, properly made compost. Fresh manure of any kind does not fall in the category of compost.

23. Compost, Nutrients, and Brewing 5/30/04 4:42 PM
The compost is just an inoculum of the good organisms, and a little soluble nutrient. Thus, you should not need lots of compost. Usually a pound or two for the 5 gal brewer, 5 to 7 pounds for a 25 gal brewer, 7 to 10 pounds for a 100 gal brewer, 10 to 15 pounds for a 250 gal brewer, 15 to 21 pounds for a 500 gal brewer. Range is relative to quality of the compost. Pre-activate and you only need the lower range. Foods are just to grow the good guys during the brew. Add more food when you spray out if you think the leaves need some food. Add food if the soil has low levels of organic matter, anything less than 3% OM is low. Brew for 24 hours. Longer just means bio-film has more chance to do interesting things to the brew. Hum, interesting...... there's a word with lots of possible interpretations.

24. Shelf Life and Preactivation of Compost 5/6/04 9:02 PM

Question: Has any one done any trials on the " shelf life " of pre-activated compost?
Answer: I'm not certain what you mean by pre-activated compost. As with all things, there is a certain time that compost is most active, and that falls off as the organisms use up the foods. With compost, that is about a two year time period after the compost "finishes". If you pre-activate, activation lasts for as long as the foods you add are being used by the organisms.

Question: Do paper or plastic containers make a difference?
Answer: Paper usually can breath on it's own, while plastic cannot. Aeration is easier in paper, but then you have moisture issues. Plastic retains moisture better - which can be a problem if things are too moist.

Question: Does any commercial service offer pre-activated compost that arrives ready to go?
Answer: Simpli-tea offers pre-activated compost, but if it ships a long distance, then it has to be sent in breathable containers. Nature Technology offers breathable containers for their compost, which they send pre-activated, I believe. Pre-activation is probably best done when you know you are going to use that compost. Otherwise, your critters may be out of food before you use the compost!

25. Compost Used in Tea Based on Purpose of Application 7/29/04 12:56 AM
When you think of compost to be used for compost tea, you need to consider your purpose in using the tea. If you are applying tea to soil, use of a fully mature compost is just fine, because the organisms will be put in the soil, and will have plenty of time to wake up, and use the foods as they become available, or as temperature, moisture, etc. select for the different populations of bacteria, fungi protozoa, nematodes.

But when making a foliar tea, you want the organisms to be as active as possible, because you want them to glue themselves to the leaf surfaces as soon as possible. So, compost for a foliar application should be made, possibly, from a slightly immature compost -- say, a compost that still is warm, in the maturation phase of the composting cycle, not the fully mature phase. From a worm bin, use worm compost that is just drying down from 70% moisture to 50% moisture, so the fungi are as active as possible.

26. Diversity and Balance of Microorganisms 10/18/03 12:10 PM

Question: Compost doesn't vary that much on a daily basis, as long as it is mature, and you are maintaining environmental conditions. Yes, species in compost, or any real world sample, varies daily in exact numbers of each species present, but that variation has never been demonstrated to be a critical factor in tea making. Day-to-day variation in exact number of individuals of each species?
Answer: Not important in tea making. Much more important to know that you have the DIVERSITY of bacteria and fungi, and that you have the right balance of bacteria to fungi, that you have the nutrient cycles, i.e., the protozoa and nematodes. And please, listen to all the

academics who, if they know anything at all about environmental samples, will agree with these statements -

27. Increasing Fungal Growth 3/28/04 3:22 PM

Question: What do you suggest to increase the fungal loading in the tea? Will adding feathermeal, oatmeal etc, encourage fungal growth even though I may be starting with a compost that is not ideally balanced for fungal growth to begin with? How about Alfalfa Meal?
Answer: The protein meals encourage fungal growth. We have put whey, casein, and milk into teas, and see some improvement in fungal growth. VERY little is needed, so beware getting too much into the tea. A little goes a long way.

28. Fungi Need a Surface To Grow On 6/14/04 10:27 Am
Fungi need a surface to grow on, and rock powder, dust, flour, whatever you want to call it, provides surfaces. The mineral powders are micronutrients that the fungi can solubilize. If the tea, or soil, lacks some micronutrient, then addition of that nutrient will result in growth, where before its addition, the organisms would not grow. That is the practical application of Liebig's law. Add the limiting nutrient, and growth occurs.

29. Beneficial Fungi 1/10/04 2:12 AM

Question: Ah, remember I said beneficial fungi? The fungi growing out of the decaying logs?
Answer: May not be good guys. Shelf fungi, which form the shelves on logs are the fruiting bodies of the fungus that likely plugged up the water-uptake mechanism of the tree. So, the fungi we want are the thick white (yellow, pink, lemon) fungal strands that appear in the forest floor, in the humus layer. I think we have some pictures of these on the SFI website. David Loring has pictures on his web site too. Anyone else have pictures of happy, healthy, good-guy fungi?

30. Fungi 12/22/03 2:09 Am

Question: Fungi are a whole different issue. I have read on this list that hyphae indicate fungi. That isn't 100% true. Those are the roots. Evidence of roots is no guarantee that fungi will develop.
Answer: All hyphae are fungi. Period. Full stop. Look up the definition of hyphae. It is extremely easy to differentiate roots from hyphae. Come to SFI, and I will SHOW you the difference. Fungi grow in compost tea ALL THE TIME, if you have food and air for them. Anyone who wants to doubt that fungi grow in tea are welcome to come to SFI, any SFI lab, and take a look at their tea and at a tea made properly. I will demonstrate fungi growing in tea. If anyone wants to say that fungi don't grow in properly aerated compost tea, I can show you reams of data clearly showing that beneficial fungi grow in actively aerated compost tea.

a. Anaerobic Tea
Now, if anaerobic tea was meant, then that's a different story, but a goodly percentage of the time, truly anaerobic compost tea will kill your plants. Too much variability, and too poorly

documented parameters with anaerobic teas. Lots more work to be done before the reliability of no-air tea can be proven.

b. Aerobic Tea

AACT is what I discuss, because we are getting really close to being able to guarantee that if you make sure the tea stays aerobic, and has good growth of beneficial bacteria and fungi, plant surfaces will be protected. You can't document that kind of success if fungi aren't growing in the tea.

31. Grains and Fungi 1/3/04 3:29 PM

Grains are not added for the purpose of inoculating species of fungi. Fungal diversity in dried, milled grain materials is not really worth worrying about. Not all grains work really well. Through trial and error, several materials have been singled out, since they often give good growth of the fungi that are present in the compost. Oatmeal, feathermeal, soybean meal, etc are foods to grow the fungi.

32. Carbohydrates and Tea Brewing 2/14/04 3:11 PM

Question: I apply a tea of worm castings, oats and molasses (plus alfalfa meal and humics) about every month to the soil in my tomato greenhouse. Doing only this, I've been told, won't supply a month's worth of carbohydrates for the colony and "they" will have to take carbohydrates from the tomato plants to survive (even though the sugars in the plants aren't ideal. To keep the fungi and bacteria happy, and keep my plants from being robbed of carbohydrates (and me of my yield) it's been suggested I add a blend of proper carbohydrates about once a week. I was told the above from a company selling such a blend of carbohydrates. Is it sound science or just marketing? And/or could I, alternatively, just add some diluted molasses or a homemade blend of complex and simple carbohydrates from different sugar sources?

Answer: The molasses will be used quickly, but about 20% is worked by the bacteria and fungi (mostly bacteria however) and released as waste material, which is more complex food resources for other microbes. The oats are also used, but more slowly, and it may be three to four months food supply for some microbes. Depends on how much food you added. The soluble material in the worm compost, which you extract during the tea making process, also supplies foods. If you make or use a strongly fungal worm compost, then these foods may last for 4 to 5 months. If you use a strongly bacterial worm compost, then the foods may last for only a month.

So your source saying the tea doesn't supply enough food MIGHT be correct IF the worm compost is strongly bacterial (food added to the worm bin is strongly bacterial). But the part they have flat incorrect is that the microbes in the soil will not "take" carbohydrates from the plant. Sorry, most of the organisms in the soil cannot force the plant to release more sugars, proteins or carbohydrates, unless they are pathogens, or Rhizobium. That is not the problem. The problem is if you have rapid microbial growth in the soil, stimulated by TOO HIGH addition of sugar (molasses for example), protein (oatmeal, for example), or carbohydrates (flour, plant material, for example), then when the microbes grow, they take up nitrogen, sulfur, phosphorus, etc and immobilize it, preventing the plant from getting the nutrients needed.

Too rapid microbial growth can take up oxygen in the soil, result in anaerobic conditions, which means alcohol is being produced in the soil, and the plant will be harmed. So, to prevent this, make sure you use good compost because then you also add the protozoa and good-guy nematodes to the system, which eat the bacteria and fungi, and release the nutrients plants need in the root zone. So, if you see your plant suffering a slow down in growth, it is not because you need to add more carbohydrates. That may harm the plant if you don't have
enough protozoa and nematodes. The thing to do would be to add more compost tea, with perhaps a shot of fish hydrolysate, or kelp with extra organic N in it.

Because you are exactly right, more tea would solve whatever problem. Just make sure to add to the tea the materials that will fix whatever visual problem you might be seeing with the plants. So, additional kelp, ferric citrate for a low iron condition, fish for N, P, S, add calcium to the compost pile to make sure you get enough calcium into the tea. You could use corn gluten (just a little! it goops up in water), with added N, you could use oatmeal, or alfalfa meal (ground to soluble, ok?) as both sugars, some fungal food and additional organic N. Check your local SFI advisor and get their help for specific questions, such as, "what does it mean that the leaves are purple".....

33. Nematode Presence in Tea 9/16/03 12:35 AM
Someone has claimed that nematodes aren't present in compost tea. If you have good nematode numbers in the compost, there will be good nematode numbers in the tea. Want proof? If you use a decent compost with normal nematode numbers in the compost, we'll run a nematode extraction using your compost tea, and show you the nematodes. Of course, if composting wasn't done correctly, and there are no nematodes present in the "compost" material, you can't expect there to be any nematodes extracted into the tea.   Talk to any nematologist who has ever actually extracted decent (non-stinking) compost, and they'll set the story straight. Compost can contain lots of nematodes, and if the nematodes are present in the compost, then they'll be extracted into compost tea, given that the machine being used really makes compost tea.

My husband is a an internationally known, and well-recognized nematologist. He's also a professor at Oregon State University. I have actually spoken with him from time to time, and we work together on research projects. In case you don't want to believe my data, then he can demonstrate that nematodes exist in high numbers in good compost, and that nematodes from decent compost are extracted into compost tea. If there are nematodes in the compost, and no nematodes in the compost tea, then you have a bad compost tea maker. Most likely, the tea machine killed the nematodes, and if the nematodes were killed, then the fungi and protozoa are not likely surviving either. The tea might have lots of bacteria, which could give some benefit, but nothing close to the full benefits that should be seen from a good compost tea. The take-home message to be learned when someone claims that nematodes don't exist in compost tea is that the person making such a claim knows very little about decent compost tea.

34. Nematodes 9/29/03 8:40 PM

Question: Do you have tests that can verify *Nematophagus* fungi in AACT or compost?
Answer: We have found *Arthrobotrys* and *Paecilomyces funosoroseus*, based on spore morphology. Presumably the others are present too, just haven't seen them. As long as the fungi

are in the compost, they will make it into the tea. I have not seen the spores germinate and grow in the tea, however. So, the inoculum
makes it into the tea, but growth does not occur in the tea. At least, that I have observed.

Question: Have you had experience with the following fungi that are available in Australia and are being sold as nematophagous fungi *Arthrobotrys oligiospora, A. conoidus, Paecilomyces funosoroseus, P. lilacinus* and *veticillium chlamydosporium?*
Answer: I do not have experience with *Verticillium chlamydosporium.* The others, yes.

Question: Would it be feasible to use an inoculation of these organisms in an AACT machine(zero bacterial) grow them out, then inoculate into fungal dominated compost and thus have some of these organisms in the AACT that is used on pastures?
Answer: I think the better choice is to obtain an inoculum and place it in the compost. Let the fungi grow in compost with good numbers of nematodes. It is really the presence of nematodes in high numbers that enhances these fungi.

Question: Can we assume that *Nematophagous* fungi are already in the AACT if it meets the SFI criteria for high quality AACT?
Answer: No, can't assume that. If the compost doesn't have many nematodes, it is quite likely that the *nematophagous* fungi are not present in high numbers, and may not be present at all. Sorry I can't be more hopeful on this one. We need to get more nematodes in compost. An inoculum of nematodes for the compost might be the best bet.

35. Predatory Nematodes 1/29/04 9:19 PM
There is no inoculum of predatory nematodes that you can buy on the market. You can buy entomophagous nematodes, such as *Steinernema* or *Heterorhabditus*, which go after root-grubs, soft-bodied insects, and weevils. You can add these nematodes to your compost, and let them increase in numbers in the compost, and then extract into your tea. Nematodes do not grow in compost tea, since tea brews for a short time, and nematodes require very specific cues (generally seasonal, or kinds of prey present) in order to reproduce.

36. Temperature and Microherds 4/16/04 5:57 PM

Question: What if I brew 5 gallons of ACT at 70°, and pour it on a raised bed that has not been planted yet? Will the microherd establish itself before I plant? What if the temperature drops below 40° some nights thereafter?
Answer: Anyway, You will likely have a few of the critters go-to-sleep because the temp is lower in your soil, but they just go to sleep, generally, if the temp is not that much lower. All the lower-temp-loving organisms wake up, however, to compensate for the ones going to sleep. The microherd will establish, given adequate food, and no pesticides or high levels of salt in your soil. Sometimes we see significant die-off if there are toxic materials in the soil. In soils that have been anaerobic, we can see reductions in organisms on compost addition, since the anaerobic conditions produce toxic products. As long as you have good structure in your soil, you have the condominiums for your critters to move it and be protected from cool conditions. And remember,

soil temperature does not vary nearly as much as air temp; so the soil will not likely drop that much because of one night at cooler temps.

37. Total Dissolved Salts 4/10/04 8:33 PM
Total dissolved salts includes other salts than just sodium chloride. Anything that dis-associates in water is a salt.

38. Water High in Salts 4/10/04 8:13 PM
When you use water high in salts, you need to have good levels of organic matter in the soil, with good biology present, to sequester the salts, and incorporate them into the organic matter.

39. Anaerobic Waste Materials Are Killers 4/8/04 10:21 PM
The data we have seen says no - even if most of the water is aerobic, the anaerobic waste materials are killers of the other good guys, AND the anaerobic bacteria seem to have a search and destroy mission when it comes to beneficial fungi. Protozoa being spun past the anaerobic zones are killed as well, so maybe you don't take them ALL out, but you drop the numbers which is not good when you need nutrient cycling.

40. *Bacillus subtilis* 7/10/04 8:50 PM
Bacillus subtilis, generally several sub-species, are usually present in aerobic compost. Therefore, it is in the tea. Only if you have a specific insect problem, which you know a specific *Bacillus* culture would help alleviate, would I add a single, specific inoculum of any *Bacillus* to a tea.

41. Live Worms in Compost Tea Sediment 6/18/04 11:46 Am
Yep, if the worms survive in the tea, especially if down in the sediment you have developed on the bottom of the container, the material has stayed aerobic. But I don't think you really made tea. You made a water slurry of the compost, and stirred it around for awhile. You did not likely grow much of anything in the slurry - fungi probably didn't make it through the brew. The worms were happy eating the bacteria in the compost, but in terms of increasing the microbial life in the liquid - probably didn't do much. A true compost tea gets the organisms growing, increasing microbial biomass significantly through the 24 hr tea brew. Liquid compost slurry is a different thing - still probably going to do good things if applied on the field, but not the level of improvement you would expect to see with a real aerated compost tea. I define tea as something where we have BREWED and increased ALL groups of microbes in the tea during the brew cycle. Extracts and liquid slurries are something else. They can give you benefits - just not the same benefits we expect from tea. But live worms in the sediment shows conditions are aerobic. But live worms in the sediment - shows conditions are aerobic.

42. Milk and Coffee and as Food Resources? 5/10/04 5:01 PM

Question: Milk - which is lactose, a kind of sugar, and protein, is food for beneficial fungi, especially when placed on the leaf surface, which is going to be very aerobic. So, is milk actually toxic to the disease-fungi, or grows the fungi that combat the disease fungi?
Answer: Not sure what microorganisms coffee would select for. In coffee cups, Bacillus species rule the microbial community (I worked on that for one of my senior projects in college). I expect

the impact on slugs with coffee is a direct toxic effect of caffeine, but I don't know for certain. Caffeine would act as a food resource for microbes, most likely bacteria. Maybe negative for some species. Cations are positively charged chemical compounds -- like calcium, sodium, potassium, etc. Cations combine with negative ions, so the charge is balanced.

43. Nitrogen in an Organic Form 3/22/04 10:44 PM

You need to make certain that nitrogen (N) is added as an organic form, not as nitrate (which is present in high concentration in most manures that have aged a bit), or as ammonium (fresh manure), or as ammonia (anaerobic, reduced form of N). The best form of N to add to compost or tea is organic forms, such as the organisms, or proteins. Fish hydrolysate is great material to add to get N in the tea. Corn gluten with added N (typically was added as urea, which usually is converted to nitrate, which can give a real benefit to the pathogens and weeds if you don't make sure the biology is added too!) Be careful of adding any inorganic N if you have N fixers or desire N fixation to occur. N in inorganic forms shuts N fixation right down. Come to the SFI compost class to learn about how to deal with these materials. We also go through the N cycle so you can see how these different compounds are used by the biology, and the transformations that different organisms perform.

44. Guano 3/22/04 10:38 PM

Guano works quite well in tea, just please be certain that the guano has been composted, or allowed to age a significant time. Guano is bird manure, and needs to be composted, just like chicken manure. Generally guano is not collected until it is well dried, and so, aged. Pasteurization or sterilization of some kind is typically required for most guano coming from outside the US, so pathogens are not as much a concern as with non-composted, fresh manures.

45. Fish Hydrolysate and Fish Emulsion 2/23/04

It is relatively easy to make fish hydrolysate, but fish emulsion requires removing the oils, and that requires separation technology. Fish hydrolysate - You need to grind up the bones, scales and other materials to small sizes, and then use some enzymes to digest the fish protein and calcium. Oils need to be incorporated into the mix using a surfactant. It isn't easy to make the oils stay in the liquid and not separate. Best to use a fish that will not be high in heavy metals or other toxics. Careful of the source of fish. It is much easier to buy a good fish hydrolysate from Organic Gem, Neptune's Harvest, or Geofish.

46. Bonemeal 1/9/04 7:15 AM

You know Elaine you didn't comment much on my adding bonemeal for calcium purposes. Is that ok? The wife rarely eats eggs, I don't, so we hardly ever have eggshells. Bonemeal is fine from a microbiology point of view, although others have concerns about bonemeal from a prior point-of-view, so think about that when you buy bonemeal. Maybe getting bonemeal from a known source instead of the God-only-knows-where-it-came-from-but-cheapest-source would be a good idea.

47. _Beauveria_ 1/5/04 10:05 PM

Question: Can I apply _Beauveria_ in compost tea, added before or after brewing and apply it to the seasonal growth of grass around my fruit trees or should it be applied to the bare soil and then mulched?

Answer: Typically add _Beauveria_ at the beginning of the tea brew so the spores can germinate and be ready to attack and destroy insects and insect larvae. If you add at the end, you have to hope the conditions in the soil or on plant surfaces will be good enough to get the fungus to grow. You apply the tea where you have the insect problem. If you have insect adults, then take out the adults by applying to foliage. If you are earlier in the season, and you have a problem that has a soil stage, apply to soil. But please use it only when you NEED to, as this fungus will take out beneficial insects as well as the bad guys. You want to have a background level of _Beauveria_ always functioning, so the bad guys can't escape their normal predators. When you have an outbreak of bad guys, then get _Beauveria_ going extra strong.

48. Hay and Protozoa 12/7/03 1:02 PM

If you use hay that has not been treated with a pesticide (VERY important to know that), then the protozoa like to hang out and go-to-sleep on the surfaces of the hay. So, brown stuff, right? The plants went senescent (dormant) in the field, and were harvested. That material usually has lots and lots of protozoa on the stems and crowns. So, take hay, add just enough water to cover the hay, let it set for 3 days, and the water will have hundreds of thousands of protozoa. If the bacteria on the hay stems grows really fast, you get mostly ciliates because ciliates do best when the water gets oxygen limited. the more fastidious flagellates and amoebae do better when really aerobic conditions remain in place. So, for most diversity, put the hay into the compost bag, and let the protozoa be extracted from the hay surface, and get into the tea. The protozoa will not excyst in the tea and start growing, but they will be put out into your soil, or onto the leaf surfaces. What is it that protozoa do for you? Why do you care that they are there? Testing to see if you all know the answer........

49. Saponin and Ionic Associations 11/30/03

In trials that we did with yucca, specifically material from Desert King, the biomass of beneficial fungi increased significantly in the teas to which this material was added. Please don't throw the baby out with the bath water. Just because something says there is an anti-fungal effect, don't throw something out. Try to ask what fungi were killed. If the material being discussed killed the fungal pathogens, but not the beneficials, would that not be a good thing to add to your tea? Data on the effect of different saponins in tea is what is required. All saponins are not created equal.

Question: What exactly is a spreader?

Answer: It means that the ionic associations between particles (which may be cells, should be salts, could be organic matter, could be sand, silt, clays, etc) are lessened. That is the spreading effect. As you change ionic associations (that's the positive and negative charges on the surfaces of things), the charges on the surfaces of bacterial, fungal, protozoa, nematode, etc will be changed. In some cases, this modification can alter physiological function of the cellular surface, and can result in lysis of the organism. Synthetic saponins tend to have higher osmotic concentration, so these materials are harder on organism cell walls, and result in greater lysis (break-up) of the cells.

The higher the concentration of saponin added to the tea, beyond some threshold level of benefit, the greater the negative effect on the organisms in the tea. So, let us not throw out all saponins as potential fungal foods. There is benefit there. Attempt to understand the mechanisms of why and when something will work, and why and when it will not work, before blasting out a conclusion that is too broad.

50. Aloe in Teas 11/3/03 6:57 ASM
As I understand this (I haven't checked it out myself), the layer of material just under the skin surface of the aloe leaf contains a high amount of fairly toxic material. You must not use that layer when making something to feed people, animals or microbes. So when growing aloe, you need to find out from someone who knows about aloe just how thick that layer is. My understanding is that the alloin is a normal ingredient in aloe, and this complex molecule has antimicrobial properties as well. Or maybe the layer under the leaf surface is the alloin which gets into the jelly-like material during harvest. We have had people add aloe to teas, and see no benefit. BUT that may be as a result of other factors, such as they added too much food, and the microbes grew so fast they used up the oxygen in the brew. We all know what that does to the beneficial fungi. Ask questions of how much food, what were oxygen levels during their brew, and getting the actual data, not just the "summary statics" is probably a good idea. I don't mean to have people not use aloe. I think it very wise of Judi to ask questions before jumping into using something new. Getting the facts, and not just swallowing hype, is a good approach.

51. Aloe 11/1/03 7:28 PM
Ah, where's the DATA? Anything can be said about any product, but without some DATA to support the claims, ah, hem. Aloe also contains a very toxic material in the leaf, and unless your source of aloe is very careful about extraction, the material can be very bad news. Be careful with pure aloe. Can have great results, but be sure it's just the gel part of the plant, not the leaf surface.

52. Peat Bogs 11/2/03 2:46 PM
First, some history. Peat doesn't develop overnight. I don't mean that statement to be a put-down, but many people just plain don't understand the time element when it comes to making peat. So, some history on bogs and peat. Skip to the bottom of the e-mail if you already understand the process of making peat.

Peat bogs are a phenomenon of the far northern parts of the globe (We don't have significant land mass in the southern hemisphere at the right latitudes for this to happen, except maybe in New Zealand, and that's too young an island to have developed real peat bogs yet). Harsh winters are required to stop decomposition and allow the accumulation of reduced oxygen layers that inhibition complete decomposition.

In semi-tropical and tropical areas, black water systems, swamps, marshes and bogs are very different from areas where the soil freezes, and can remain frozen year-round. Peat does not develop in warmer climates because decomposition does not stop during the winter. Instead we get acid sulfur soils, for example, as the land rises along a shoreline. Lakes as they fill in - in tropical areas - might undergo the terra piedre (hum, spelling isn't quite right there, but hopefully close enough) process, which was mimicked by the Mayans apparently with great success. But, different process there, back to peat.

During formation of peat bogs, organic matter from leaf drop from trees, needle drop from conifers, grass resides, annual plant residues, etc. begins to be decomposed by soil organisms in the late autumn, but then the process is stopped by freezing conditions. If the snow layer is deep enough, decomposition picks up and can be quite rapid under the snow. But before the last year's layer is fully decomposed, the next summer's plant material falls on top of the previous layer. Same process is repeated. Some decomposition with each year, but not complete. Humus develops.

With several years of this happening, in places where summer is very short, a thick layer of leaf material, plant residue and humus builds up. The lower layers of the organic layer, where humus is developing, may not thaw in the summer or thaw only in some years. Decomposition is very slow. Water typically gets "hung-up" at the surface of this semi-permafrost layer, and reduced oxygen concentrations develop. Decomposition slows down even more, and some serious tannins and phenols build up. Anaerobic gasses develop, and the bog is underway.

Unique plant species begin to develop - those that can tolerate the wet-feet, anaerobic conditions in the lower organic matter layers. In certain places, sphagnum moss was best able to grow, because water didn't drain out of the bog all year. The reduced oxygen conditions in the water, and the particular mix of gases in the water selected for the growth of sphagnum. So, a certain kind of peat contains a high amount of not-fully decomposed sphagnum moss.

With time, the weight of the organic matter being laid on the surface each year compacts the lower layers more and more, so the lower bog layers develop a dense consistency. Some bogs accumulated tens to maybe 100 feet deep of this organic material over the hundreds of years they were in existence. What if a layer of sand was laid on top of a bog, as the result of seas shifting, or a volcanic event occurred, and the bog was buried? Or ash from a far-distant volcanic event put a blanket over the bog surface? Through geological time, compaction and anaerobic processes will eventually turn this old bog into pre-coal, with continuing pressure, coal, then petroleum, and eventually, given the right conditions of pressure and temperature, diamond will be formed. Fun to think about that as you burn your gasoline. That was potential diamond, if you waited another, oh, 100,000 years.

If people drain bogs, the bog material can be burned like logs when it is dry. It is compact organic matter, with wood-like characteristics. If you fluff compacted bog material (put air into it; sphagnum is particularly notable for it's ability to fluff again), it makes great potting material, and can have some great anti-microbial impacts.

Dr. Harry Hoitink at Ohio State University has spent a great deal of time working on the plant-beneficial properties of peat, so if interested, read some of his papers. Or Mike Boehm's papers - he worked with Hoitink for his Ph.D.

Question: But why can peat be disease-suppressive?

Answer: Anaerobic products. If properly fluffed, there won't be alcohol or other volatile stinky gases by the time you use it, but the phenols, terpenes and tannins may still be there. Certain peats can be very disease-inhibiting, others not so great. With some peat material, there's enough N, P, K, etc still left in it, with other peat moss, the nutrient were lost through anaerobic volatilization of N, S, P, etc. PH can be really acid in some peats, not so acid in others, depending on the layer of the bog you take the peat from, and what happened with respect to the anaerobic processes. How long anaerobic? What was the interplay between anaerobic and frozen? All kinds of variables.

Quality of the humus can be quite variable. And the biology can be non-existent. In fact, most of the time, unless the biology is added back into peat moss, you don't have on-going benefit from the peat. The anti-microbial properties don't remain, because when biology does return to the peat in the pot, the anti-microbial products get eaten by some microbe that views those materials as food, not as inhibitory materials.

However, unless you have a peat bog near you, peat is no longer either cheap or abundant. The world's supply of peat is dwindling rapidly, and the loss of peat bogs is a serious problem on a global scale. There are global efforts underway to stop mining peat from peat bogs. We're losing a sink for carbon dioxide that we can ill afford to lose. Don't believe me? Read any issue of the Ecosystems journal from the Ecological Society of America. Serious problem.

There is a difference between a peat bog and the humus layer in a forest. The humus layer developing at the bottom of the O horizon in forest soils is a great source of humus. This source of humus hasn't gone anaerobic and lost the good guy fungi. Forest soil still has the good guy fungi, as long as the forest is still healthy and growing. So, there is some need to recognize what is a healthy forest.

But no matter if you want to use peat, or forest soil, trying to routinely cover your garden with that material alone is just too expensive. So, you get a handful of good healthy forest humus, and add it into your COMPOST pile. Make your compost tea from your "humus-enhanced" compost. The "spent compost" from your compost tea still has the good guys in it, so add that back into this year's compost pile. Let it go all winter and bingo! next spring, you have more humus-enhanced compost.

Peat moss is not very useful as an inoculum to your compost or compost tea, in my experience. If you buy peat moss from the store, it has been pasteurized, and does not contain beneficial organisms. Peat moss from a bog? Very iffy about whether it will have the beneficial organisms in it.

Humus layers, as long as they are aerobic, are good. Even better if you can see fungal strands in the material. So Alaska Humus? For those of us who live no where near an old growth, healthy forest, guess what? Alaska Humus is that humus layer we need. Do you buy 100 tons of it? No way. Well, one Hotel did, because they were losing their palm trees and needed to save their $30,000-or-more-each palm trees from certain death. And they did. As I understand, there were 600 palm trees in danger of certain death, and all but 5 or 6 were brought back to health. I believe there are still a couple of the trees where the fight has not yet been won. Its a foliar crown problem, so soil amendments do not directly combat the problem. Getting compost tea into those crowns is problematical too -- 50 feet in the air, trying to spray into a thick crown? But the trees health improved significantly and surely would have died long ago except for bringing the biology back. Alaska Humus was used for the recovery job, and it worked. It was expensive.

For those of us with less money than the Hotel, we are going to find the least expensive source of excellent humus. I've talked about ways to buy expensive humus, and make it feasible to spread that benefit through the next couple years. AH has worked in many situations, at this point. For many people, it is economic and a great way to get the inoculum and the fungal foods they need.

Question: Can you get other kinds of great humus and repeat the same thing?
Answer: Sure, but please make sure the biology is in that humus you use. Without the right biology in the material, you may be putting the food out, but instead of Santa Claus, you get vermin. Please make sure the right biology is in the humus you use, or add the right biology if you are not certain. AH has the right biology most of the time, so it's a good investment. But, buy enough to inoculate your compost pile, or add to the potting hole of your expensive tree you just planted. Another possible approach is to make compost tea with the few pounds of AH you buy, and apply some of the tea to your compost pile. Last year's compost and next year's. Gee, does that sound exactly like what was recommended for the good humus layer you got from your forest, if you are lucky enough to live next to a forest? Yep.

I'm trying to make it clear that there are always alternatives. There are multiple ways to get the right biology into your soil, your potting material, onto the foliage. Pick the method that works for you. Having troubles figuring out the right method, what will work, in your climate, in your particular area? Talk to your closest Soil Foodweb Advisor. The list is on the SFI website.

53. Extracted Amino Acids 10/11/03 6:27 AM

Question: Would the extracted Amino Acid from Fish product (fertilizer grade) an alternative to Fish hydrolysate in making AACT?
Answer: The information needed would be whether the amino acids are selective for some groups of microbes more than another group of microbes. Bacteria use the simple sugars, protein and carbohydrates better than most fungi. By simple, I mean linear, non-branched, straight-chain carbon substrates. Fungal enzymes typically aren't as capable as bacteria at pulling in the simple foods. Thus amino acids that are simple, non-complex, not much tertiary structure, are more likely to be bacterial foods. More complex amino acids would be more selective of fungi. So, I'll answer your question with another question (grin). How complex are the amino acids produced in the product? Another question, how were the amino acids extracted? Were they denatured in the process of extraction?

54. Yeast 9/24/03 9:30 PM
Yeast are occasionally in tea, but rare, because they are rare in good compost. We almost never see active yeasts in soil, compost or compost tea. But they are present, and can be cultured on plates. But that doesn't mean much, because the yeasts have dormant stages that allow them to be

present, but not active in conditions they do not grow in. Yeast often produce alcohol in anaerobic conditions.

55. Biodynamic Preps 9/16/03 8:01 PM

The biodynamic preps CAN be useful for addition to compost teas, as some of the preps, when fresh, are nicely fungal. Some outstanding fungal diversity in some of the preps. But once dried, the fungal biomass isn't so great. I think (please note that means no solid data) there is some validity in the imparting of energy to water when a vortex or Malcolm Rae machine (I think that's the right spelling) is used. Measuring the benefit is not that easy. What exactly do you measure to show benefit? Perhaps 75 to 80% of the time, we see increased bacterial and/or fungal activity, and resultant increases in total bacterial and/or fungal biomass.

Question: What about the other 20 to 25% of the time? Decreased activity, or no change as compared to the control. Lots to yet test here. Why the 20 to 25% no-benefit seen? What other factor exists here that we are not paying attention to?
Answer: Someone suggested moon phase to me when I was in Australia, and so I went back and looked at the dates. Not related to the phase of the moon, as far as I can tell. Or maybe biodynamic folks need to teach me more about moon phases than I am aware of? Anyway, I think there is something to at least some biodynamic approaches. We need to discover what those basic repeatable factors are, and weed out the factors that give variation. When something fails to give a benefit 20% or more of the time, it's too great a failure rate.

a. Consistency in Actively Aerated Compost Tea

Compost tea production has been very much the same in the past. Too variable and too inconsistent. Sometimes you'd get good results, sometimes not. The failure, or the no-benefit rate was too great. But once we started making actively aerated compost tea, then the results were consistent and reliable. OK, you have to make actively aerated compost tea to get consistent results. If you let the putrefactive microbes take over, and don't return to aerobic conditions before application, you can be in trouble. Or really, your plants will be in trouble. The only times I've killed plants is when I've let brews go anaerobic. Not all brews that appeared to be anaerobic killed the plants, but too often they do kill plants.

b. Adding EM Inocula in Teas

Now, there are some interesting results when you add EM inocula in teas. Steve Diver talks about this, and I would like to do more work on these bacteria. They are fermentative bacteria, and when anaerobic conditions occur, they produce lactic acid, malic acid, and other fermentative products. You get less production of ammonia, hydrogen sulfide, or the really smelly organic acids. Or, most of the time you don't. Still more to be understood here.

Question: How beneficial are the fermentative bacteria for plant growth?
Answer: I am not aware that anyone has made a study of this. Maybe the EM folks could set me straight, and send some data for the group to look at?

In any case, do the biodynamic preps, the liquid manures (look out for the human pathogens please!), or the plant extracts benefit microorganisms? Sure. But the variability in beneficial results is too great.   I don't like to write things off just because some people have messed up while doing the methods......So, there's something useful there.   It's going to take some work to figure out exactly what, and how to management it reliably.

56. Effective Microorganisms (EM) 2/21/04

EM Lacks Diversity. There is an interesting situation going on with EM. These are facultative anaerobic bacteria which do not produce the anaerobic compounds that are so detrimental to plants. These bacteria MAY also suppress human pathogens. But, research is needed. There is one paper, which Steve Diver has quoted,

that shows EM bacteria prevent the growth of human pathogens. So, adding EM to a brew of good compost, which accidentally may go anaerobic because too much food was added, or a heat snap occurred, MAY prevent the brew from being something that would select for pathogen growth. The question remains whether the EM bacteria would be helpful, harmful, or just neutral for plant growth.

57. EM and AACT 2/21/04 11:40 PM

Question: Has anyone brought in Teas to be tested in which EM has been used? I've just bought some EM and I'm reading up about the different ways of using it. Any suggestions?
Answer: We have done some testing, and I'd like to do more. The EM bacteria out-compete the human pathogens. There's a good paper that shows this.

58. EM Brews and Rock Powders 6/14/04 10:25 AM

I don't see the need to "brew" for weeks and weeks to get the rock powders incorporated into the biology. And I prefer biology that isn't going to potentially be a detriment to the plants. Note the potential word there. I think there's some interesting things going on with EM bacteria that needs further understanding. And I will be working on this project next Feb in South Africa, so information should be forthcoming. The lactic acid bacteria, and proprionic bacteria, both of which grow a better reduced oxygen concentrations, and appear to be VERY competitive with human pathogens, are major components of EM. There are some yeasts in there which function in a similar fashion to the bacteria. Could we put them in our compost teas, and then even if the oxygen dropped a bit, the human pathogens would still not be a problem? Intriguing, yes?

59. *Bacteriophage* 9/11/03 12:34 PM

Bacteriophage exist in the teas, but usually the diversity of bacteria is so great that even several types of phage doesn't harm the effectiveness of the teas. In fact, maybe the phage are good, because they may selectively target disease bacteria.

60. *Mycorrhizal II* 6/16/04 12:41 AM

Most fungal spores are fine to germinate and start to grow in the tea. But *mycorrhizal* spores are NOT. ANY pump will harm them, ONCE THEY HAVE GERMINATED. Even being spun around, once they have germinated, it will kill them. As long as they stay as spores, not germinated, they are fine. But humic acid will cause them to germinate - and guess what is in most composts....Having *mycorrhizal* spores germinate in the tea is not a good idea. Other commercially available spores - no problem. If someone bought mushroom spawn, and added that to the tea, I'd want them in at the end of the brew, since most of the basidiomycete fungi are just as "tender" as *mycorrhizal* fungi. They just can't take being knocked around once they are out of the dormant phase.

61. Organic Acids and Preservatives 6/15/04 11:33 PM
Concentration of these organic acids are important too. Typically in preservatives, the concentrations of the acids are much higher than you would get in any fermentation.

62. Organic Materials 6/15/04 11:31 PM

Question: These microorganisms are capable of generating minerals such as tocopherol, lycopene, ubiquinone, saponin, and powerful anti-oxidant flavonoids, such as quercetin, quercetin-3-O-glucopyranoside, and quercetin-3-O-rhamnopyranoside
Answer: Hum, the things mentioned in this sentence are not minerals. They are organic materials, not minerals. Most of these are beneficial foods for many microorganisms, and quite a few are plant-growth promoting materials. But they aren't minerals.

63. Raccoon Scat 3/27/04 7:48 PM

Question: Do raccoons eat lots of insects, whose exoskeletons end up in the scat? Do the chitin-using fungi grow on those dead exoskeletons?
Answer: I don't really know, but perhaps you do, and can let me know. If they do, then a small amount of the scat, VERY early in the composting process would probably get the inoculum into the pile, and would be good.

Question: What is the normal diet for raccoons?
Answer: Grin....yes this is related to compost tea. We want the good guy fungi in the compost, so we can get the good guys into the tea. What you feed the critters is all important.

64. Plant Tea 1/5/04 10:30 PM
The only way to know what's in the plant tea is to look at the microbes. The only way to know what effect it will have on the AACT is to measure the biology in the AACT BEFORE adding the plant tea, and then AFTER the plant tea is added. Then you would know what happened, and hopefully, you would tell the rest of us!

65. Comfrey Compost Tea 5/25/04
Luckily, I don't think anyone is going to be drinking comfrey compost tea made for plants. The take-home message info on comfrey is: none of us should make alkaline or acidic extracts of comfrey to be added to tea. Just add the plant. The idea would be to add a small handful of comfrey in the compost bag, or into the water (later would need to be filtered out, be careful of the fungal consequences). But is that just the leaf part of the plant, or the whole plant, with or without the roots? B vitamins would be nicely water-soluble.

66. Comfrey Tea vs. Comfrey Compost Tea 5/17/04

There's a difference between comfrey tea, and compost tea made with comfrey. One has no compost in it, and is not compost tea, it still has some interesting properties, however. But like any plant, the interesting materials are variable. How much of the important chemicals are in healthy plants, versus sick plants?

Question: Comfrey is known for high calcium, right? Lacking calcium in your soil?
Answer: Add comfrey to the compost, or to the tea.

Question: How much calcium will be added per what unit of fresh, or dried comfrey?
Answer: I don't know that answer.

Question: Can comfrey only be used fresh? Anything else known about comfrey benefits? Effects on organisms in comfrey tea, or when the comfrey is added to compost tea?

Chapter IX

COMMERCIAL BREWERS

COMMERCIAL BREWERS

1. Anaerobic Tea 11/1/03 9:42 AM
There are "compost tea" machines on the market that only leave you with anaerobic bacteria. And make no mistake, even those sorry set of critters can improve dead dirt. But anaerobic tea returns only the first miniscule part of the soil foodweb to the soil. But every journey starts with a single step. So, step miniscule-part-of one.

a. Aerobic Tea
Actively aerated compost tea machines return the good-guy bacteria, the good-guy fungi, protozoa and some nematodes (depending on what is in the compost). You get steps one, two, three, four, five, six, seven and sometimes eight.

Question: What do you want to spend your money on? Something that won't return but a tiny benefit, or something that will move you well down the road?
Answer: With repeated applications, using good compost, will get you to "Go, Collect Your Money". When you buy a coffee maker, do you then try to make your own beans, your own milk and sugar mix? No. You follow the directions of the manufacturer.

b. Buy the Manufacturer's Starting Mix
So, with the tea machines, buy the manufacturer's starting mix. Figure out what is in the manufacturer's material, which you can do with time and a good nose. See what amounts the manufacturer used to make the tea machine you bought work right. THEN start fooling around, if you have time. Once your plants are growing so much better, you probably will be spending your time where you should - harvesting your crop, selling a better tasting crop and figuring out what you want to grow next year. What others plants could you be successful with, now that you know how to fix your soil?

2. Tests and Posted Data 6/16/04 11:29 AM
On one "tea machine" website, the testimonials are all from relatives of the person making the machine -- but it does tell me what I want to know. There's another site that I have to laugh at - the compost tea machine seller shows ONE test from a plate count lab, and ONE test from a direct count lab. That doesn't tell you anything more than ONCE they were able make an ok tea. How many tests did they have to go through to get those "decent" results? What about routine tea production - what about on the second run? the third run? They won't show you data from anything except the first tea run - because while the first run looks ok, the second isn't so good, then the third is poor, the fourth has no decent biology to speak of, and ..... as a buyer of any product, you should be able to expect to be given information about performance of the product that with time. You should be able to get names of people who have bought the product, that are not associated with the company. Testimonials from the person selling the product don't count. People not associated with the company, who, when you call or e-mail them, can tell you exactly what they think without getting a kick-back from the company, without being punished by the company for telling the truth. Reputable products have data from many production runs on their websites. Not- reputable products show only one piece of data, because they can't repeat that one

success. Any product manufacturer has to first show me data that shows they can at least once make what they claim, but then they also need to show me their product consistently can perform.

3. Easy To Clean 12/17/03 8:27 AM

Question: You are right - the machines have to be designed to make it easy to clean them. How long do you take to clean your machines after a batch of fish production?
Answer: Most homeowners want easy-to-clean machines. Some brewers have 90 turns in the pipes. They HAVE to be cleaned on occasion. Not every time, but you need to be able to SEE when they need cleaning (see a color change that tells you the pipe is dirty), or you do have to clean them every time.. No pipes to worry about. Other brewers take some cleaning, but they have followed your advice, and make it EASY to pop the pipes and diffusers off and clean them. With some brewers you have to replace the soaker hose each time. You have to cut soaker hose up with each brew which is time, but it is pretty easy. We shouldn't automatically shy away from 90 degree turns, except if you really hate to spend time cleaning. Guess what? I hate to spend time cleaning......

4. Tea Brewing Equipment Manufacturers 12/16/03 7:33 AM
Think about the fact that you have to have the right sets of bacteria, fungi, protozoa and nematodes to get the benefits of compost, or compost tea.

The "rightness" of the biology depends on the plant you are trying to grow. So, if the machine you are talking about does not result in BACTERIA, FUNGI, PROTOZOA and NEMATODES from the compost being extracted and surviving in the tea, then the material should not be called compost tea.

We differentiate real compost tea, that can give all the benefits of protection from disease-causing organisms, retention of nutrients, cycling into plant-available nutrient forms, improvement of soil structure, reduction in water use, and increases in rooting depth, from tea not able to give all these benefits. Anaerobic teas do not have the organisms required to give these benefits. The tea able to perform properly is called Actively Aerated Compost Tea. Any tea that drops into anaerobic zones (less than 5.5 to 6 ppm oxygen), will no longer have living beneficial fungi, protozoa or nematodes. The beneficial organisms do not survive lack of oxygen for much length of time -- just like people.

One Tea Brewer Manufacturer has recently changed the bag in their machine. They sent all their clients nylon bags, to replace the felt bags they used to have. Reason? Mildew grows in the felt. You can't get the beneficial fungi through the felt. I am VERY happy to see this change. Maybe, just MAYBE, that will be enough to put those machines over the edge into OK, BUT they must have DATA to document the improvement. That manufacturer has no data to show that their machine makes compost tea. You might suspect that the manufacturer has data to show that their machine does not make a material that contains adequate sets of organisms, but they don't show that data, of course.

Please note that folks showing great results in the field, not just the lab, have hard data on their websites. Please note that plate count methods are totally inadequate to show whether active organisms are present in tea. Plate counts cannot tell you whether you have adequate diversity in the bacterial community, and they are beyond hopeless in telling you anything about fungi. They miss protozoa and nematodes completely. So, trying to shore up the reputation of a compost tea using plate count methods is just proof that the tea couldn't make the grade with methods that show what is really going on.

Everything we do at SFI involves direct observation of the organisms in your sample. We can differentiate active from total bacteria and fungi. That's what you need to know - what organisms are GROWING in the tea at the time you put the tea out. Talk to the manufacturers that have DATA, and often they have scientific trials reported on the effects of their tea makers on plant production. These machines can work just great. You have to use them properly, and that can take a bit of learning curve, but the probability of success is high. The probability of success is not there with machines that can't even extract or keep alive the organisms you need to give improvements.

Now, other tea brewing machines do on occasion make teas that kill black spot fungi, or give a short term control of certain problems on leaf surfaces. But the anaerobic bacteria that grow in those machines (how do you know they are anaerobic?) Use your nose. The tea stinks) do not last on leaf surfaces. Leaf surfaces are aerobic. So control is short-lived. Addition of anaerobic bacteria to the soil means the soil is moving more anaerobic, not aerobic, and plant roots require healthy, AEROBIC conditions in soil in order to grow. We have to keep working on those other manufacturers to make their machine do what they say it does. But right now, you cannot call what comes out of some machines compost tea. It is not compost tea. Compost tea should contain all the beneficial organisms you find in compost. Based on all the data I have, that machine is not capable, ever, of giving you the set of organisms your plant needs. Go to the those manufacturer's websites and look for any DATA. Not testimonials, they don't count. Please notice that the testimonials on their website, at least the last time I looked, are from employees of the manufacturer, or from family members. Not exactly confidence inspiring. Yes, they may have a pretty website, but why would you buy a machine based on prettiness? Are you trying to make pretty, or are you trying to help your plants?

5. Inadequate Brewing Equipment 12/16/03 7:33 AM
You asked why there is negativity to some tea brewing machines. Some machines are not capable of routinely delivering the biology needed to get the benefits that have been documented to be possible with real compost tea. Think about the fact that you have to have the right sets of bacteria, fungi, protozoa and nematodes to get the benefits of compost, or compost tea. The "rightness" of the biology depends on the plant you are trying to grow. So, if the machine you are talking about does not result in BACTERIA, FUNGI, PROTOZOA and NEMATODES from the compost being extracted and surviving in the tea, then the material should not be called compost tea.

We differentiate real compost tea that can give all the benefits of protection from disease-causing organisms, retention of nutrients, cycling into plant-available nutrient forms, improvement of soil structure, reduction in water use, and increases in rooting depth, from tea not able to give all these benefits. Anaerobic teas do not have the organisms required to give these benefits. The tea able to perform properly is called Actively Aerated Compost Tea. Any tea that drops into anaerobic zones (less than 5.5 to 6 ppm oxygen), will no longer have living beneficial fungi, protozoa or nematodes. The beneficial organisms do not survive lack of oxygen for much length of time -- just like people.

One machine has recently changed the bag in their machine. They sent all their clients nylon bags, to replace the felt bags they used to have. Reason? Mildew grows in the felt. You can't get the beneficial fungi through the felt. I am VERY happy to see this change. Maybe, just MAYBE, that will be enough to put these machines over the edge into OK, BUT they must have DATA to document the improvement. This particular company has no data to show that their machine makes compost tea. You might suspect that they have data to show that their machine does not make a material that contains adequate sets of organisms, but they don't show that data, of course.

Please note that folks showing great results in the field, not just the lab, have hard data on their websites. Please note that plate count methods are totally inadequate to show whether active organisms are present in tea. Plate counts cannot tell you whether you have adequate diversity in the bacterial community, and they are beyond hopeless in telling you anything about fungi. They miss protozoa and nematodes completely. So, trying to shore up the reputation of a compost tea using plate count methods is just proof that the tea couldn't make the grade with methods that show what is really going on. Everything we do at SFI involves direct observation of the organisms in your sample. We can differentiate active from total bacteria and fungi. That's what you need to know - what organisms are GROWING in the tea, at the time you put the tea out.

They have DATA, and often they have scientific trials reported on the effects of their tea makers on plant production. These machines can work just great. You have to use them properly, and that can take a bit of learning curve, but the probability of success is high. The probability of success is not there with machines that can't even extract or keep alive the organisms you need to give improvements. Now, those other machines do on occasion make teas that kill black spot fungi, or give a short term control of certain problems on leaf surfaces.

Question: But the anaerobic bacteria that grow in those machines -- (How do you know they are anaerobic?)
Answer: Use your nose. The tea stinks) do not last on leaf surfaces. Leaf surfaces are aerobic. So control is short-lived. Addition of anaerobic bacteria to the soil means the soil is moving more anaerobic, not aerobic, and plant roots require healthy, AEROBIC conditions in soil in order to grow.

We have to keep working on those other machines to make their machine do what they say it does. But right now, you cannot call what comes out of those machines compost tea. Call it something else. It is not compost tea. Compost tea should contain all the beneficial organisms you find in compost. Based on all the data I have, those machines are not capable, ever, of giving you the set of organisms your plant needs. Go to their website and look for any DATA. Not testimonials, they don't count. Please notice that the testimonials on their website, at least the last time I looked, are from employees of the company, or from family members. Not exactly confidence inspiring. Yes, they may have a pretty website, but why would you buy a machine based on prettiness? Are you trying to make pretty, or are you trying to help your plants?

6. Back-up Claims with Data 12/7/03 1:12 PM
Whenever a company says great SFI results, please make sure that the product SFI tested is what they are selling now. One company, for example, did testing with SFI on a previous machine that they were making. It wasn't until that machine had been used for more than 4 to 5 brews that the problems started to occur. They don't show any of the data from the later tea brews, do they? That's why on the SFI website, we're doing time documentation of the tea machines. How do the tea machine do over time? Of course, you have to clean them properly. Use good compost. Use enough food, but not too much. You need to follow manufacturer's directions. This list serve is the place to post data that shows what happens when you do or do not follow directions. Doesn't have to be SFI data - you can post information about how the plants responded, or tasted, or whatever you want. As long as you back-up your claims with data, with solid information. So, with people trying to sell you a product, be just a little bit questioning before you buy.

7. Buying a Brewer 11/15/03 12:34 PM
When buying a brewer, there are a few steps you want to think through.

a. First Step: If you can put out 5 gal today, and 5 tomorrow, and 5 the day after, why buy a machine that makes 50 gal? If you own 10,000 acres, ok, you need a big machine. If you own an acre or less, a 5 gal machine will likely do fine.

b. Second Step: Who sells machines in your size? Narrow your choices down just based on that.

c. Third Step: Compare the different brewers.

d. Fourth Step: Ask the compost-tea list serve for comments on each brewer you are looking at.

e. Kind of Pump: If you are going for the bigger machines, pay attention to the kind of pump on the machine. Did the manufacturer check to see if his pump kills organisms? Where is his data? Don't accept "trust me". There's a machine on the market that we demonstrated to the manufacturer that his pump to take the tea from the brewer into a holding tank was reducing numbers of fungi and bacteria by 50%. Keep that in mind, when buying something. How are you getting large volumes OUT of the tank?

f. Ease in Cleaning is important. Can you get to the bottom of the tank? Are there square corners in the pipes, knowing that in a month or so, that corner will be bio-film filled. It isn't right away that the problem develops. With one commercial brewer, altered from the original design we tested at a University, the pipes and pumps were changed to make the machine look prettier. The numbers on the changed machine were similar to the original, not-pretty design for the first couple of runs, but then, look out, the numbers dropped terribly as the bio-film developed. The manufacturer claimed that our methods had gone awry, that we didn't know what we were doing, because the numbers were coming out lower. It wasn't us, it was bio-film. SFI just tests the tea, we don't have to know why the numbers are coming out poorly. Usually I try to figure it out, and with the Microb-Brewer, we did figure it out. But not until after the damage was done. That brewer is no longer for sale in the US.

g. *Surfaces to Clean:* Next thing to check - Are there surfaces in the machine you can't see, can't get to clean? Those places build-up biofilm. There's a brewer on the market that has discs in it, and you can't see, and you can't reach, the bottom sides of the discs. It is not fun getting the discs out to clean their bottomsides. Think about the time involved in cleaning. Most LARGE brewers should have a way to rinse the tank down as you pump the tea out.

h. *The Compost Container* has to allow free movement of the compost. Solid baskets that don't allow compost movement, that allow the compost to compact in the bottom, are going to cause you fits. Compost should be in bags, so easy-flow is possible. Some baskets are there to keep the bag of compost from twisting in the water flow, so the compost isn't constricted in that bag-basket design. But other brewers with a basket have to have an aerator inside the basket, or the compost compacts, and goes anaerobic (happens at about 10 hours into the brew, so beware of the brewer that only has data for hours 0, 8, and 24)

i. *Bubble sizes* should be medium to large, not micro-sized. Tiny, tiny bubbles are a bad idea. They shatter the fungal hyphae. Ask for the data showing good FUNGAL results. And please make sure the lab they are testing with uses decent methods. No data? Don't buy the machine. Only plate count data? Don't buy the machine. They are trying to pull a fast-one on you. Ask them what plate count data mean. Ask about documenting the relationship between plant growth and plate counts.

8. Problems With Some Machines 11/14/03 8:31 PM

a. *Inside of the Machine Needs to be Clean:* There have been a couple of groups of problems with some machines. First, people who don't recognize that the INSIDE of the machine has to be clean. It's the inside that is important in tea quality. A clean outside of the machine is a good idea, don't get me wrong, but it's the inside that really counts. With compost tea, cleanliness is next to godliness, huh?

b. *Checking the Water Source is Important:* If the water being used is highly alkaline, there's a problem. You don't have to be terribly careful, just make sure the pH is near 7. But several people with well water with a pH near 8.5 have had trouble making decent tea, until they realized the problem.

c. *If a Little Food Resource is Good, More is Better:* Not with tea it isn't. More food than the manufacturer recommends means too much microbial growth, and therefore, lack of oxygen in the brew. Less is more, sometimes.

9. Soaker Hoses From Petroleum Products 11/4/03 8:15 AM

Thank you for clarifying what brewers use old tire materials. I didn't know soaker hose was made from that material. Sorry, I don't know everything. The danger of using old tire materials in a tea brewer probably comes as microorganisms in the tea brew attack and begin to chew up the petroleum materials. Yes, there are herds of microbes that attack petroleum products. In a compost pile, at the right heat and temperatures, microbes will chew old tires up in a couple months, to the point you can't find anything left of the tire, except maybe the steel-belts. What tea brewer uses old tire parts? I think you are very wise to avoid that tea brewer!

10. Break-down Products Pretty Toxic

The break-down products of petroleum products are initially pretty toxic. The first step or two in the decomposition process takes a complex, often toxic material, breaks it down by removing phenolic units, or releasing heavy metals, chlorines, bromines, carboxyl groups, or carbonyl groups, etc. Those can be not-great news to other organisms in the vicinity.

The remaining undecomposed material, as well as the first step breakdown materials, will be further decomposed in a compost pile, resulting in long-chain fatty acids, organic acids, more phenols, terpenes, as well as production of some simple sugars, carbohydrates and amino acids. With more time, more of the toxics will be metabolized to the simpler materials, which are used by bacteria and fungi to make more biomass, and the toxicity of the breakdown products becomes less and less. But that is in a compost pile.

In a 24 hour tea, the first time you use the soaker hose made of old tires, probably not enough time for any significant break-down or metabolism of the tire material has occurred. In the second tea, however, if the microbes have been active and chewing on the hose material, you could have some breakdown and release of toxic material. By the time you have done three to five brews, the microbial population in the soaker hose material has really gotten going, and the bio-film is pretty hefty by then. You have some toxics being produced and possibly being released in to the tea brew. We've seen that compost tea made with machines that use soaker hose material make barely decent tea after five to six uses, even if the first tea made was great. I attributed this to the development of bio-films, and therefore production of anaerobic materials. Maybe release of toxic material from the tire materials is another component of why the tea quality rapidly goes from great to good to not-good at all.

The answer? You can't clean out soaker hose well-enough by soaking in bleach, or hydrogen peroxide to get rid of the bio-film inside the little pores and passageways in the soaker hose. The bio-film is the layers of microbes that are chewing away on the soaker hose material. You need to replace the old soaker hose with new materials every five to ten brews, depending on how good you were at cleaning the soaker hose between tea brews to begin with. The better you clean, the longer the tea stays fine. Just depends on how much grow you allow in the soaker hose between runs. But the fact that soaker hose is made from old tires was something that had not crossed my mind. Thank you for bringing out that new information. It explains why the teas in soaker-hose brewers can so rapidly go from great to not-great within just a few brews.

11. Why Buy a Commercial Machine? 11/1/03 11:14 Am

The reason to buy a commercial machine, that has the data on their website, is that you don't have to worry then.

218

Follow manufacturer's instructions. Use their nutrient mixes, use good compost (look for the fungal strands, add some fungal foods, or ask for data about fungi from the person you buy the compost from). The tea should then be great!

12. Tea Makers Compost and Nutrient Mixes 10/12/03 9:46 PM
The reason most tea machine makers sell their compost and their nutrient mix is because they have tested those in their brewer, and therefore have biological data to show that their mix and compost makes good tea. Ask them for those data. Standard recipe, standard machine configuration. A good tea machine should get repeatable and consistent numbers. And most of the people who make tea machines that SFI works with routinely get good tea. Important to follow directions however.

13. The Point Is To Make Good Tea! 10/12/03 9:02 PM
The way to know if you are getting enough air is to measure it when you use your typical recipe and your typical compost. Start from that knowledge, instead of from the CFM, or air pump horsepower. The deeper the water column, the greater the pressure has to be to make bubbles. The configuration of one machine we had in the lab might have been different from other designs. They did not produce much surface movement of the water. I have seen the same machine at a different location, and they really bubble nicely. Different pump? I don't know, and it isn't up to me to police different tea makers. I have said, over and over, that you need to have data from the makers of the tea machines that show, with the pump, recipe and compost they recommend, that the tea will contain the aerobic organisms needed.

I find myself getting very frustrated with all this. The point is to make good tea. Measure that end point, and determine what the CFMs need to be in YOUR machine, in order to make good tea. As machine makers change the container size, depth, height, the pump used, etc, it is hard to remember to ask all the right questions about exactly what was done. The point is to make tea that has the organisms in it. Aerobic organisms, because we have even less data on anaerobic organism tea than aerobic tea, and with certain conditions in anaerobic tea, we can make some really horrible brews. I've killed quite a few plants with anaerobic tea. I've never published that data, because you don't publish negative results. Hope to get some replicated studies in on that this winter however.

Chapter X

COMPOST
and
WORM CASTINGS

COMPOST AND WORM CASTINGS

1. Compost Gets Calcium in Soil 5/2/04 9:40 AM
I don't think I was saying compost TEA was the way to get the calcium back into the soil. Compost is the way to get the calcium into the soil, at less cost and more effectively than adding inorganic sources of calcium.

Compost tea, made with compost with elevated calcium in it, over the course of the summer, can elevate soil calcium levels, but not from the leached-out low levels most soils in your part of the world are at to begin with. Compost tea might be the way to maintain calcium levels, once you have them back to where they need to be. Having the biology to retain Ca is critical, however. If you don't get the biology into the soil, and keep the organism active, you will still keep leaching out the Ca.

2. Worms in Compost 10/21/03 5:50 Am

Question: I left the heap to "cool down" for 6 months before using a thin layer of it as a mulch. During that six months some kikuyu grass had grown up onto the pile and when I took the manure from there I saw the most amazing thing. Under the grass and amongst its roots were 1000's of big native worms but elsewhere there was not a worm in sight. What were the worms "eating"? Roots? Decomposed manure? Bacteria?

Answer: The manure is a great source of bacteria food. By combining with sawdust (a fungal food, but often not a great sole source unless a mix of different woods), and leaving it compost for 6 months (it's going to compost no matter whether you mean for the material to do something or not), it was developing some good populations of bacteria and fungi for your native worms. Probably with the manure/wood base, the pile of material was somewhat to very anaerobic early on, but with time, microbial growth slowed, and oxygen was not used up as rapidly. So the pile became more aerobic, and the protozoa and nematodes, maybe some microarthropods, moved in. The worms found the pile a great place to live. Because the pile is probably quite highly bacterial-dominated (typical of manure-based materials), and therefore nitrate-dominated, the grass was selected for, and is what is growing on, the pile. Without testing to know what is home, however, this is what is likely. Don't know for certain unless we have some data.

3. Human Pathogens in Compost 10/8/03 1:30 Am
If the compost is not made correctly, you might have human pathogens in the compost, and that might be a problem if you allow conditions in the tea to match the growth conditions for the human pathogens. Generally these conditions are reduced oxygen, poor competitor growth. So, aerate and maintain the competitor organisms.

4. Compost Has The Diversity Needed 10/1/03 9:09 AM
I have spoken about making your own inocula from your own soil for years. It's great that there is a story about someone in the USDA doing this, but please, we've been doing this for decades. Differentiating between the good guys and the bad guys is what stops most people from doing these cultures themselves. You have to be able to ID and test what you are growing. But if you know that the soil is growing great carrots, then you are pretty well assured that that soil has good organisms in it. So, use that soil. For carrots. Will it be good for corn? Maybe not. Carrot soil

has organisms that carrots have selected for, and you need to develop a good corn soil. Agri-Energy has some good inocula for corn in the mid-west US, but are they good for the south, or Pacific north-west? Hum, less than stellar results with some growers. So, as I've pointed out for years, each plant requires it's own balance of organisms. You need to know that the critters you are adding are the best for the crop being grown. Using soil to make a soil tea may result in less than the right diversity needed for other plant species. Compost, if made correctly, has the diversity needed in most cases. That's why we use compost, not soil.

5. Worm Compost, The Better Choice 9/25/03 1:31 PM
If you allow the microorganisms to grow faster than you are adding oxygen through aeration, you may think something is aerobic, when in fact it is not. That's why you have to test. Kelp gives similar benefits as yeast, with respect to minerals, and with less likelihood of anaerobic problems developing. Worm compost gives the enzymes and hormones, in fact, a better range of enzymes and hormones. Use worm compost, as a better choice

6. Grey Gritty Liter 9/21/03 6:03 PM
Where exactly were you hiking? The grey gritty liter could be the ash from St. Helens, or from Mt. Mazama when it went off. East side of the mountains in Oregon, the Mazama eruption is more likely. These ash layers are not typically high in fungi. Or, it could be E horizon. Wet forest systems develop E horizons, which are very high in fungi, and roots, without much of any other biology present. I don't believe anyone knows why these layers develop - although I have not kept up in forest floor development in recent years.

7. Time versus Money 8/19/03 1:15 PM
It is always time versus money. If you have a year or two to allow composting to occur, and can keep the pile decently aerobic, then you don't have to turn, ever. But if you want compost in 6 to 8 weeks, you have to turn each time the pile gets up to 155 to 160 F. Don't let it go anaerobic. And then there's all the intermediate time/turning/food resource mixes/pipes into the pile/ etc. You need to learn which things are important at which times. Or let the organic matter compost for two years or so. Your choice.

8. Mulch and Vermicompost 8/2/03 5:52 AM

Question: Re. mulch composition to mimic tea critter dominance. Correct me if I'm wrong: straw, hay supports protozoa dominance HAY has protozoa, straw may or may not, wood-based compost/mulch supports fungi dominance.
Answer: That's correct

Question: Vermicompost supports fungal and protozoa dominance.
Answer: No, it depends on what foods you put in the worm compost

Question What mulches/composts are dominated by bacteria?
Answer: Green plant material supports bacteria.

9. Green Foods 8/1/03 5:56 PM

All the green foods, the sugar, protein and carbohydrate is in the hay, if cut green and not let it go anaerobic before drying.

10. Microbial Biomass in Manure 6/4/04 11:25 PM

Question: What was it that any of the posts on organisms in manure, or age, or what causes death doesn't square with what your doctor said? The previous posts didn't say anything with respect to how much of human manure was bacterial biomass.
Answer: Bacteria can double every 20 minutes. Only if they have enough food will they attain that growth rate, but think about human manure - pretty good food resource. And if you are a bacterium selected to be able to grow in human manure conditions, nothing about the human digestive track is going to be a disturbance. Unless you take an antibiotic, that is.

Question: So how much of any manure is actually microbial biomass?
Answer: Your doctor was probably a bit on the low side, actually. In order to maintain the high numbers of protozoa in manure, you HAVE to be growing a lot of bacteria on an hourly basis.

11. Worms and Pathogens 6/3/04 7:52 AM

Question: The trick is to know what rate of raw food addition to the bed will actually have the worms completely process it before the next addition. You also have to think about the liquid added to the bed - where does the unprocessed, possibly pathogen-contaminated liquid move to? Do the worms process that adequately?
Answer: The one experiment that SFI did, and have had a grad student attempt to publish, showed that contact with the worm killed the pathogens. Sigh, the grad student has not followed through, since he now thinks that a job and his thesis are more important than getting reviewer's comments responded to and getting the manuscript re-submitted. Life happens, huh?

Question: But if contact with the worm kills the pathogens, then the critical knowledge is, how many worms must be present, relative to the food you are adding?
Answer: No one has the answer to that, based on data. And it seems critical, don't you think? Research is required. Two different sets of information are needed. First, holding food addition constant, increase the concentration of worms in the beds from no worms present to 50 worms per cubic foot of bin, to 100 worms, to 150 to 200. Look at how far the water from the food penetrates, and if the worms process all that material, or if water escapes un-processed, especially if particularly wet food additions are made. Check E. coli presence. Show that E. coli occurs in the food, but disappears before the next food addition or disappears as the casting material moves out of the active zone of worms.

The second experiment needs to be with the correct worm concentration, as determined from the above work; add increasing amounts of food, and determine the maximum amount of food that can be added before the worms can no longer process the food adequately to remove E. coli. If we had both of those pieces of information, there would be no question about whether worm beds were able to adequately process waste material. But no one has those pieces of information. So, we get stuck with not knowing exactly what that food to worm density ratio is needed to make pathogen-free worm compost.

12. Worm Manure 6/2/04 9:23 PM

Eric asked if worm poop was worm manure. If all fresh manure has to be composted, then what is the situation with worm "manure". The joys of language. The digestive system of a worm is so different than the digestive system of mammals, birds, or even insects. Worm digestive systems don't appear to harbor pathogens, as long as you make a decent effort to not over-feed the worms. So, what's the best way to express this? Fresh manure from higher animals has to be composted, because of the potential for pathogen contamination. Is that better? Or does it lead to argument about the definition of higher animals?

13. Dead Insect and Pathogens in Compost 6/1/04 11:44 PM

Dead insects need to be composted, just like anything else. Who knows what pathogens they might have? So, add the dead insects at the beginning of the composting process -- heat, or passage through an earthworm digestive system will kill pathogens. You would not want to add dead insects to anything, except the start of a compost pile. In with the dead insects, you could have eggs that the insects laid. Eggs are dormant stages, survive dry conditions, and will hatch when conditions are right

14. Nematode Types 5/17/04 9:24 AM

Question: If added to compost during mesophlic (cool) stage, will these nematodes multiply while in the pile? Would it be a good idea to give them a while in the pile before application of compost or making tea? What is the best time to inoculate a pile?
Answer: One company maintains their *Steinernema* their worm compost bins. Addition to thermal compost should be after the pile has cooled to about 100 F. And once added, do not turn the pile again. Nematodes do not like disturbance. They will only reproduce once every so many heat units. In the summer, this means they can, if moisture is maintained, reproduce (hum, memory, don't fail me now) every 30 days. Once temperature drops below 65 F, their reproduction falls off considerably, and there may be only one reproductive event through the winter. Q10 effects apply.

Question: Is it possible to identify these specific nematodes during testing or does the test show good and/or bad nematodes?
Answer: Yes, to both. SFI will ID to genus, and we will point out *Steinernema*, if present.

15. What Type of Fungi is It? 5/17/04 10:26 AM

Make sure you even have fungi in your compost. A good, decent level of fungi. Home test? Add the oatmeal, humic acid, fish hydrolysate (all three in small amounts, ok?) to your compost, and wait overnight. Observe the results.

1. No obvious fungal growth? Find some real compost, compost that has fungi in it.

2. You see fuzzy-wuzzy growth? You have compost that isn't really compost, because you have mostly bad guy fungi. Inoculate your pile with some beneficial fungi, with whatever local source you might be able to find that you KNOW has good fungi (talk to Highlands Soil & Water in Salinas and Monterey -or New Era Farm Service - they both make compost with good amounts of fungi - check the SFI website. Actually, Highland's compost is SUPER high in fungi, just like Leon Hussy's compost - the KIS brewer, or Alaska Humus)

3. If you see "Santa's beard"; then, ok, you have some ok fungi. You may still want to improve the species diversity by adding some additional fungal sources, like Alaska Humus.

4. Thick threads of fungi growing IN THE SOLID PART OF THE COMPOST, not fuzz on the outside of the pile in any way. This is the primo stuff. If you see these guys, you have the fungi.

16. Ergot Fungi are Fungi 5/9/04 6:05 PM
All of the ergot fungi are fungi. These are a group of fungi that produce ergot as a by-product of their metabolism. They are, without doubt, fungi. Unless the oatmeal that you added to the compost was infested with ergot, the fungi that grow on the oatmeal is not going to be ergot fungi. I think we can safely assume that the oatmeal used is NOT infested with ergot, since it was food-grade material added to the compost. Ergot fungi colonize certain kinds of seeds, only under certain, fairly specific conditions. We don't have those kinds of seeds, those kinds of materials, or those kinds of environmental conditions in compost. The fuzzy fungi that grow on oatmeal, or other protein meals that have been suggested are additives to compost and are not ergot fungi. Ergot fungi are not that fast growing. And in no case has anyone suggested that you would eat these fungi. And please be clear that I have said, over and over again, that you want the thick, thread-like fungal growth, NOT the fuzzy-wuzzy fungi.

17. Animal Droppings in Compost Piles? 2/9/04 12:13 PM
I would avoid adding the fungi growing in animal droppings into a finished compost pile. There is too great a possibility of adding pathogens along with the animal droppings. It is amazing what dogs and cats will eat (stomach churns with the thought), and that material passes out in the fecal material. The organisms that thus grow from that material can be less than desirable. Different case if you have a starting compost pile. If you are yet to reach high temperature, then addition of VERY MINOR AMOUNTS of animal droppings is possible. But you must make sure that temperature is reached, or you'll be setting yourself up for problems. Cats and dogs can carry helminthes, or little worms that are happy to parasitize you if you aren't careful. So, if you add animal manure to the pile, you have to make sure that if reaches temperature long enough and enough to kill the parasites, or all parts of that material are visited and either touched or are ingested by earthworms.

18. Evaluation of Landscape Soils and Compost Materials 2/8/04

Question: I need a quick "breakdown" of what these ingredients break down to in soil...or if they are harmful to the biology. I know Gypsum has a salt effect. I don't have specific percentages. Sorry. I looked in the email book to get general info, but didn't find these ingredients.

Question: Chicken Manure / Rice Hulls
Answer: High in nitrogen, can be high in nitrates, if not composted correctly, Check smell, which tells you a great deal about how the material was composted. Rice hulls generally are fungal foods, if fungi are present. They can simply absorb some NO_3, but depends on the ratio of chicken to hulls to determine whether enough.

Question: Volcanic Sand
Answer: Provides micronutrients, and a surface

Question: Gypsum
Answer: Calcium sulfate, kills fungi at high concentration. Adds calcium, which can be beneficial if there are enough fungi to hold the calcium. The sulfate is a problem.

Question: Fir Bark
Answer: Can select for growth of good fungal species, wide C:N is good at absorbing NO_3 from the chicken.

Question: Sawdust
Answer: Fungal food, ties up excess NO_3

Question: Sonoma Amendment 50 -- A well-balanced soil amendment to be tilled into clay soils. Composted Chicken Manure / Rice Hulls, Fir Bark , Sawdust
Answer: See above for effects of each component. It really depends on whether it was actually composted or not.

Question: Mushroom Compost (Salt effect?) -- Great for tilling into clay soils or as a top dressing around flowers and vegetables.
Answer: Probably not all that great. It wasn't really composted, most likely. So typically high in salt, antibiotics present, just peat moss as food resource, so it is good for improving fluff.

Question: Composted Straw Steer Manure
Answer: Lacking green material typically. Usually got very hot. If black, it has been burned by too high heat in the composting process.

Question: Composted Yard Waste
Answer: Actual ingredients in the pile? If actually just yard waste, the pile did not get hot enough to kill the pathogens.

Question: Composted Chicken Manure -- An organic fertilizer high in nutrients.
Answer: Usually became way too hot during composting, with toxic nitrate levels, and black color.

Question: Composted & Screened Chicken Manure / Rice Hulls
Answer: Screening means the fungi were reduced even more than by the too hot composting process. Check color - if brown, then it might be ok, if black, it is just high nitrate charcoal.

Question: Nitrolized Sawdust -- A soil amendment to be tilled into clay soils.
Answer: They added urea to help reduce the huge N suck-up demand of the sawdust. Urea generally helps fungal diseases.

Question: Nitrogen added (.5%) Redwood or Fir Sawdust Vermiculite (will kill mo's...yes?) -- Used in potting mixes or for top dressing seeds. Retains water or nutrients.
Answer: Retains water, but not friendly for microbes. Depends on concentration used....

Question: Kiln Fired Expanded Shale
Answer: Clay pot shards by any other name. They actually do great at improving fluff, and helping add physical airways.

Question: Perlite - Isn't this dangerous? -- Used to aerate planting bed or container plants. Does not retain water or nutrients.
Answer: Expensive. Adds salts usually, since salts are absorbed in the perlite. If the perlite is soaked in tea or organic solution, then it might not harm anything, might even benefit. It does add physical fluff.

Question: Soil Mix -- Used for general planting, trees, new lawn, under sod, flowers, shrubs & gardens. River Loam, Loam Sand, Nitrolized Sawdust, Composted Chicken Manure / Rice Hulls Organic Compost
Answer: Could be fine, depending on the amounts of each component. Nitrolized sawdust should be a small component

Question: Raised Bed Mix -- Above ground planting, large containers, wine barrels, raised beds for flower or vegetable gardens. River Loam, Loam Sand, Volcanic Rock, Composted Chicken Manure /Rice Hulls, Fir Bark, Mushroom Compost
Answer: Salts!!!!!!!

Question: Veggie Mix -- Great for vegetable or flower gardens and raised beds. (River Loam, Loam, Sand, Volcanic Rock, Composted Chicken Manure / Rice Hulls, Mushroom Compost, Fir Bark, Bone Meal & Feather Meal
Answer: Asking for disease with the bone meal, but could be a good mix, if bonemeal is a minor component.

Question: Acid Mix -- For acid loving plants such as: azaleas, rhododendrons, and roses. (River Loam, Loam Sand, Nitrolized Sawdust, Volcanic Sand, Composted Chicken Manure / Rice Hulls, Mushroom Compost, Fir Bark)
Answer: What is acidic about this? They aren't telling you everything here.

Question: Amended Soil -- Excellent for under sod lawns, building mounds or general planting or anytime you need a heavier loam based mix. (River Loam, Nitrolized Sawdust, Composted Chicken, Manure / Rice Hulls)

Answer: Again, they aren't being fully honest, or they are suing for not high N plants, or plants they plan on putting fertilizer on quite often.

Question: Plain Screened Loam -- Used for fill or building mounds. Product is screened to remove large stones. (Sandy River Loam)
Answer: Just a nice mix of sand, silt and clay. Could be nice.

Question: Fill Dirt -- An unscreened soil.
Answer: Lots of rocks.

Question: Plain Dirt (may contain stones up to 6") Tailings -- A by-product of screening soil mix.
Answer: Even more rocks.

Question: Plain Dirt (may contain stones up to 6")
Answer: Same - rocks, but could be a good soil.

Question: Wood Products
Answer: Mulch

Question: Top Dressing -- Used for dressing an existing lawn. (River Loam, Loam Sand, Nitrolized Sawdust)
Answer: Hello disease. Although could be ok if very little nitrolized sawdust was used.

19. Compost Breakdown 1/8/04 12:40 AM

Question: Looks like Bacillus subtilis also makes materials that allow the breakdown. So you need both Bacillus species, or just licheniformis, and then a surfactant.
Answer: It is good news. You will have all of the above in a decent compost pile.

20. Resuscitating Compost 12/31/03 10:02 PM
The need for reviving - and thus the use of oatmeal, or alfalfa meal, or feathermeal - occurs when the worm compost has NOT been treated properly, and needs to be resuscitated. Can you point me to the data that shows three years as good response? How was the compost stored? I've only been able to get two years as the limit for storage, before seeing a significant loss in bacterial diversity.

21. Composting 12/31/03 9:56 PM
If you do plastic barrels, put a pipe with holes in it down the middle, to get air to the lower levels of the material. I prefer wooden containers with slits, or spaces that allow air to move into the compost. Need to keep the compost moist, so in dry climates, not very large slits! Or just put the compost in the ground, and use compost fabric to cover the pile. I actually use plastic sheeting at times. Just make sure not to tuck the edges all under so air can't get into the pile. Sometimes you just have to go with what you have.... Another thought - if you use plastic barrels, another way to deal with the lack of air flow is to put holes in the bottom so air can get in. Up on bricks too, possibly?

22. Molds and Fungi? 5/10/04 4:49 AM

Question: The grey fuzz on your compost is not good. Avoid disturbing it, ok? If you do disturb this material, do not breathe the spores produced. The cloud of "dust" is a cloud of spores, and you don't want to breathe that. But give the nose a trial here, and tell me what you smell when you approach - but don't touch - the fuzz. Get a moldy smell? A mildew smell?

Answer: Now, terminology again. ALL molds, or moulds, are fungi. Got that? Don't say molds and fungi. That's like saying human beings and men. The green fungus you are seeing - can you describe it a bit better? Can you see little balls on the surface of the colony? Low to the substrate? That means, the fuzz is close to the surface of the compost. Is the growth compact? Or tall, slender strands, with green fuzz at the top? David Loring put together a great set of pictures of these fungi that grew on his compost. David's pictures are accessible on the Rincon-Vitova website, I believe.

23. Pathogens and Regrowing 3/8/04 1:15 PM

The compost program is VERY needed in the USDA, but in order to keep it funded, there has to be public hysteria, and a crying concern about it. Compost tea is the way to exit having to use toxic chemicals in farming, landscaping, etc. Compost is needed in it's production. Could it be possible to justify the program by making it clear that we need to understand compost, and why SOMETIMES pathogens are present even if compost has been properly composted?

Question: Can pathogens in compost re-grow?
Answer: No, the pathogens aren't regrowing if you have proper sets of diverse, aerobic organisms in the compost. If the compost was made improperly, such as it got too hot, and lost the good guys, or the good guys were never there in the starting materials, then the compost isn't really properly made compost. Another possibility is that the compost that is apparently re-growing pathogens was actually contaminated by another source after the compost was finished. If the compost pile is about 100 yards downwind of a dairy waste lagoon and manure pile -- and the wind BLOWS.......

24. Compost Temperature 4/7/04 9:59 PM

80 F overnight. The older books used 105 for 18 to 24 hours, but that's out-of-date. Too high a temperature, and you volatilize carbon, N, other nutrients.

25. Compost Moisture 4/7/04 9:57 PM

Compost is not often sold by DRY weight. It's sold by volume (cubic yard, for example) most of the time. It can be sold by the ton as well (2000 lb), but then figure that decent compost is about 50% moisture. Dry it down, and you put the biology to SOUND sleep at less than 25% to 30% moisture.

26. Eucalyptus-a 5/1/04 4:22 AM

Question: This is partly because the C:N of Eucalyptus is about 1000:1. Also there are oils in Eucalyptus that tend to act as antibacterials. I have found a way to nullify the oils in a very short time. So don't be afraid of the boogey-man mentality of Eucalyptus. With proper handling, it is as useful as any other soil additive. You just have to think the right way about it, treat it and then use it.

Answer: I don't think I have ever seen a C:N on eucalyptus of 1000:1.

Question: Have you actually determined the C:N in the wood, in the bark, leaves, etc of eucalyptus?

Answer: It would involve sending samples to a lab and would require paying money to do that, neither of which are approaches that you support. So I expect you have not in fact determined the C:N for yourself before making that statement. There are different C:N ratios in each of the different components of plants as well. And, if the C:N of the wood was indeed 1000:1, then simply removing the oils would not result in decomposition of the wood. Addition of nitrogen in some form would be absolutely required to speed the composting process.

27. Significant Carbon in Biosolids 4/29/04 7:54 PM

Just as an aside, there is significant carbon in biosolids. If the bio-solids have digested (composted) already, the carbon that is present is recalcitrant, and not easily used by bacteria. High N MAY be present, if the biosolids haven't sat around and been anaerobic for a long time. The simple sugars, and other simple carbon sources have been used up in digested biosolids. Bacteria need those simple food resources to grow, and tie-up the N, S, P, etc in their biomass. So adding sugar gets things started again.

28. Beneficials in Composting Process 4/18/04 1:25 PM

Most beneficial bacteria and beneficial fungi survive just fine through the normal heat produced during composting. The temperature should not reach above 155 to 160 F (65 to 70 C), because then the beneficials will be lost. It is most important to define "high heat" when you ask about survival of organisms through the composting operation. The beneficial bacteria and fungi, protozoa and nematodes may become dormant, or may search out protected areas, such as the middle of aggregates, when temperature reaches high levels. Not until temperature moves above 165 to 170 F will a significant number of beneficials truly be lost.

Human pathogens, many plant pathogens, some beneficial organisms, and root-feeding nematodes are lost as a result of temperatures above 131 F, for three days continuously. Thus it may be a good idea to re-vitalize compost with compost tea; especially tea made with a mix of good worm compost and good thermal compost.

29. Diversity is Critical 4/18/04 1:25 PM

Diversity is critical in compost. So, in your first compost tea, you might want to use a little commercially available microbially rich compost or humus! Anyway, add these materials to improve the species diversity that you inoculate back into your pile. The concept that organisms die during composting comes from plate assessments of compost. The organisms are still very much present, and will return to normal functioning as the compost cools. Composting is not like pasteurization, as no pressure is involved during the heating process.

30. Pay for Beneficials, Not for Problems 4/26/04 2:08 AM
The "micro" nematodes are not micro-nematodes (there is no such thing). The description is that of insect larvae, and probably a sign that the "compost" was not in fact compost. Someone paid compost prices for mulch, and probably mulch that was anaerobic. Flies are attracted by the alcohol and other putrefactive anaerobic materials produced during anaerobic decomposition of the organic matter. They laid eggs in the material and those eggs hatched when water was added. The description is of the larval stages of flies -- not pleasant, and certainly not organisms that you want. That's why asking for DATA about what organisms are present in your compost is so important. Pay for beneficials, not for problems.

31. Keep Compost Aerobic 4/30/04 7:15 AM
A nematode life cycle is a week to a year long. So, nematodes will not reproduce in compost tea. They don't like being swirled either, so disturbance associated with making tea will keep them from reproducing. Nematodes need to be grown in your compost, and again, the beneficials grow in aerobic conditions, the root-feeders like reduced oxygen. Keep the compost aerobic!!!!

32. Eucalyptus-b 4/30/04 4:35 PM
Main difficulty with eucalyptus mulch is the phenols in the bark, leaves and wood. You have to allow those phenolic materials to de-gas before you use it as mulch, because these materials are trouble for many of the organisms in your soil or compost. Put the eucalyptus material in a pile, and let it age before use.

33. Nematodes are Transparent 5/1/04 10:31 AM
The real reason microscopes are needed to see nematodes is because they are transparent, for the most part. Without a microscope, and without proper extraction, the nematodes sitting on organic matter will not be seen. They blend in.

Question: So, what extraction method are you using to pull the nematodes out of the material?
Answer: Most nematodes can, barely, be resolved by the naked eye. But nematodes are a great deal easier to find with the help of a microscope. So, there is a slight controversy in the scientific world about whether nematodes are truly "microorganisms", or not.

a. Nematodes are Microorganisms
One definition of microorganism is that it requires a microscope to see microorganisms. Nematodes would then sit right on the fence with respect to that definition. You can see them without a microscope, but you sure can't ID them without a microscope. That last point is what usually clinches any argument with a microbiologist. You can't tell who the critter is if you don't use a microscope, so nematodes are microorganisms. But, no such thing as micro-nematodes. Let's not confuse the lay public, or even the academic world, by inventing new terms. We have enough inappropriate terminology and jargon as it is. Let's not invent more.

b. Nematodes Come in Four Functional Groups
1. Bacterial-feeding nematodes
2. Fungal-feeding nematodes
3. Predatory nematodes

4. Plant-feeding nematodes, which includes the root-feeding and foliar-feeding nematodes

People separate out a fifth group, "switchers", or nematodes that have the equipment to feed on roots, or feed on fungi. I've seen the same species chewing on roots, and chewing on fungi, so I take the attitude that they are capable of doing both.

Question: How much do these nematodes actually switch, in the field?
Answer: Well, if they are strictly root-feeders, I've seen these organisms living happily in soil that has no plant in it, just fungi. I've seen them happy as campers living in soil with no fungi, but lots of roots. The plants aren't happy either. So, strong suspicion that they can indeed eat fungi and roots, as they need to. But - no published papers showing the switch, so the final chapter is yet to be documented.

c. Bacterial Feeding Nematodes
There are small size bacterial-feeders, but most of the bacterial-feeders are large size. Some bacterial-feeding nematodes consume pathogenic bacteria, and some bacterial-feeding nematodes eat good-guy bacteria. There is no clear grouping of bad-bacteria feeders or good bacteria feeders. So, most likely, the bacterial-feeders just eat whatever they can put in their mouths, without regard to what is good, bad or indifferent for the plants. But it means distinction of "big" versus "small" nematodes as being "good" or "bad" is a bit iffy. Still, it might be a generally useful distinction. The little nematodes are in general root-feeders or foliar-feeders, while the bigger ones, are in general the more beneficial species. But not a perfect fit, and they ALL require a microscope to be identified.

34. Worms in South Africa 5/3/04 8:24 AM
If you had worms in the soil previously, there are eggs left in the soil (they can hang around for years); then addition of compost tea, with good plant roots in the soil too (on-going food resources); then the eggs can hatch and the worms survive. But, if something was applied that could kill the worms and their eggs, such as pesticides and high levels of inorganic fertilizer, then you will have to hope that some larger critter will bring the worm eggs, or adults back in. Humans can provide that function, as well as birds, voles, shrew, etc. If you don't know for certain, it would be best to get a small amount of worm compost from someone, and spread it in places where you know the area will stay moist. That way, you can bring the worms back faster.

a. No Worms in Organic Fertilized Areas
Just to relate an experience from South Africa - we went on a field day with some grower's and brought a fertilizer salesman with us (un-beknownst to me). In the first orchard, one that had been converted to biological a year ago, there were worms everywhere. Worms were in the soil below the trees, in the grass strip between the rows, down into the soil a good half meter (they should be deeper, true, but a half meter, in an orchard that had been totally inorganic fertilizer up to a year ago - that's good!). This made the fertilizer salesman cocky. He said "These soils around Capetown are very rich, and worms abound here. We'll find them in the inorganic fertilizer orchard, just wait and see." The farmer who owns the farm grinned, and said, "Do you want to bet? We see worms here, but will they be in the fertilizer area?" The fertilizer guy was adamant that earthworms would abound in the inorganic fertilizer treated orchard too. These were fertile

soils, after all. So, they made a bet for a case of whiskey. The farmer would give the fertilizer guy a case of whiskey if there were worms in the continuing-to-be-treated-with-inorganic-fertilizer orchard, while, if there were no worms in the inorganic fertilizer treated orchard, the fertilizer guy would owe the farmer a case of whiskey.

So, we went over to the continuing inorganic fertilizer orchard, just a few meters away - same soil type, same past practices, except no compost for the last year. The fertilizer guy took out his digger, and.... no earthworms. I wasn't aware that a bet had been made, so I just snorted, shrugged my shoulders, and said, "What did you expect? Inorganic fertilizers are salts, and worms can't tolerate that kind of water stress. Of course there are no earth worms in this area. They were killed long ago, and won't come back until the high inorganic fertilizer applications end." The fertilizer guy gave me a look of, well, whatever, and insisted he was going to find earthworms in this inorganic fertilized orchard. He dug up the grass strip, the soil under the trees, around the trees, and by the time we got done looking at the soil pit that had been dug, he was in a frenzy. No earthworms. So the grower said, "You owe me a case of whiskey." The fertilizer guy started to hem and haw, but he had been caught fair and square. No earthworms where you use high levels of inorganic fertilizer for more than a few years.

At lunch time, the fertilizer guy and I went through a rendition of "compost isn't adequate N, P, K, S, etc to keep plants healthy". He insisted, and got a bit rude about his point of view, that compost couldn't possibly provide the nutrition for a plant. After going through the math with him, over and over, I finally stopped responding. These growers were seeing that compost did the job, got them off pesticides, and was fully capable of giving them all the nutrients, and in fact, improving nutrient levels in their apples, pears, etc. But the best was left for last. A different grower this time taught the fertilizer salesman a lesson in humility. We arrived at a four year old orchard, with big, beautiful fruit, great yields (not yet picked so no numbers, but you could see the harvest was going to be good). The apples were solid and juicy (I couldn't resist eating one - juicy, sweet and not mushy at all). The grower looked at the fertilizer guy and said, "No inorganic fertilizer used here for nearly three years. A full two years on compost alone, without any inorganic fertilizer." The owner of the company looked at the fertilizer guy and said, "How do you explain this? If compost can't supply all the nutrients these trees need, how can we be seeing these results?" There was nothing the fertilizer guy could really say, except that sometimes, under some conditions, maybe compost would work, for a limited period of time. No one wanted to argue. He'd been wrong enough that day. And of course, we do have to show that compost will work, give high yields, for the whole life-time of the orchard. But there is NO reason to expect that compost will not do the job. You have to add compost to equal the removed nutrients; make no mistake that compost-maintained systems will require input. But far less than the current inorganic regime people are following, but the fertilizer guy was a very quiet person all the way back to town. Good compost is the trick. Compost that is aerobic the whole way through the composting cycle. Not stinky, not smelly, because that means you are losing nutrients.

Question: You want compost to be a "fertilizer"?
Answer: The nutrients aren't in the form of nitrate, ammonium, or inorganic forms. They are in organic forms - in the bacteria, fungi, protozoa and nematodes. Just adding bacteria is NOT

adequate -- just fungi - not adequate. Protozoa, beneficial nematodes and microarthropods are all needed. Compost supplies them all, but only if WELL-MADE, aerobic conditions are maintained.

b. Stinky Organic Matter is Not Compost!
So, the lie is that stinky organic matter is compost. It is not. If someone talks about compost as not having adequate nutrients, they don't know what compost really is. The "compost" yards that stink are not compost yards. They are waste reduction centers. Don't buy their stuff. They should pay you to haul it away. Buy the good material - and the results will be spectacular.

35. Sell Compost to Growers 5/7/04 9:05 PM
I think what we need to do is have the compost for sale for growers to just buy. Don't expect them to make their compost, or pre-activate it. Sell it to them. Still cheaper than buying toxic chemicals.

36. Compost Quality 5/7/04 9:24 PM

Question: If we follow the Luebkes, we learn that compost is best if localized.
Answer: Exactly. The testing we have done supports the conclusion that the local organisms are best adapted to the local environmental conditions.

Question: So importing compost from vast distances doesn't necessarily make for better product in your local area. Yes there are some similarities but there are also a lot of differences. If we use imported compost as a base and then localize it with local green inputs, aren't we really just taking one extra step to get localized compost? How can this be standardized?
Answer: This is a bit more difficult, because we need to recognize the local sub-species, the local adaptations. Probably the best way to deal with this is to make compost LOCALLY, and then check that you have the max diversity possible. And total bacterial, and total fungal biomass are the simplest way to test that at a gross level.
Then, we can start testing using molecular approaches.

Question: Do you have the 20 most beneficial local species? Do you have a great diversity of FAME, or PFLA signatures?
Answer: We're working on a method to ID your top 200 species of bacteria, and then the top 100 species of fungi, using molecular approaches, because, guess what? The top 100 species don't grow on any plate count medium we know about.

37. Temperature for Organisms 7/29/04 12:38 AM
There are different temperature optima for different species of bio-remediation bacteria and fungi. Given that we have some 650 different active ingredients in the pesticide formulations used today, and that the combinations of chemicals results in a nearly infinite number of toxic mixes that have to be dealt with by the biology in soil, or compost, we cannot state that there is a single best temperature, a single best set of starting materials, a single best moisture, etc that will always result in decomposition of ALL the toxics in the organic matter.

The best approach is to make sure the compost process goes through a full range of conditions, so that decomposition is optimized, no matter what the combination of pesticides might be present. If you know the specific toxin in your compost, then you could search for the SET of bacterial or fungal species that are known to decompose that ingredient, and make sure it is in the compost pile, and make sure the conditions in the pile at which that set of species functions most rapidly.

There are thermophilic fungi, and bacteria, that decompose a number of pesticides. Because microbial decomposition processes are faster (Q10 effects) at higher temperatures, IF you have thermophilic species present in your compost that can attack the toxics, given the food resources and moisture in the pile, higher temperatures mean faster loss of the pesticide.

Question: But, do you always get the heat-loving species in your pile?
Answer: People have shown good rates of pesticide decomposition at "intermediate" temperatures, and at ambient temperatures, as well as at high temperatures. Sometimes it has been shown that the fastest rates of decomposition occur at temperatures that are not considered even in the warm temperature ranges. Why play the game of saying that all compounds will be optimally decomposed at some temperature? It just isn't that simple.

The "take-home message" is that you have to know the species of bacteria and fungi in your compost pile in order to know what temperature, moisture, oxygen, food resources and chemical composition are best to maximize decomposition of any particular material. We do not have the methods to allow us to assess the bacterial or fungal community on a routine basis, even if we were lucky enough to know what species of bacteria and fungi are best for decomposing any pesticide. Therefore, it is best to add the widest diversity of kinds of high N, green, and woody materials, in ratios designed to select for a temperature regime that will not result in extremely high temperatures that will kill the organisms, but will allow microbial growth to be rapid, in many different temperatures, moistures, etc.

Temperature in a compost is strictly the result of BACTERIAL and FUNGAL growth. That means, the proper foods must be present to get the bacteria and fungi to grow. You have to have enough high N FOODS to get growth rates rapid enough to generate the growth that will result in elevated temperature, but not too much food, so you kill organisms because the pile bursts into flame.

Question: Inadequate food? Inadequate growth to decompose anything. No organisms?
Answer: I don't care how much food you have, without the right biology, there won't be enough heat generated to kill weed seed, human pathogen, plant pathogens or pests. As the organisms grow very fast, they use up oxygen. That means, when temperatures reach high levels, the organisms are using up oxygen faster than oxygen can diffuse into the pile BASED ON THE AIR PASSAGEWAYS INTO THE PILE. Chunky materials will allow air to diffuse into the pile, fine-ground materials will result in lack of oxygen diffusing into the pile.

Therefore, temperature gives you a good idea about oxygen in the pile, as long as you control particle size carefully, and don't let the pile become anaerobic. Once the pile has crossed that threshold into anaerobic conditions, and the metabolic products produced in anaerobic conditions, all bets are off about the relationship between oxygen and temperature.

Decomposition of complex ring-structures in pesticides is an AEROBIC process. The catecholases, or the enzymes made by microbes to break down the most toxic portions of many pesticides, are only produced in aerobic conditions.

Question: So, is it really important to categorize whether decomposition processes are occurring in cool, warm, or hot conditions?
Answer: Only if you know what organisms are present, and whether the pile will remain aerobic. And, whether the organisms have adequate energy sources (food) to grow, and adequate moisture. Generalizations are just plain not-useful, given what we don't know about the organisms in compost, and what makes them grow, or not.

38. Biosolids 6/9/04 10:21 AM

Question: So my question is: biosolids = sewerage solids (yes /no), biosolids do not equal putrescible waste (yes /no)
Answer: This is part of the definition problem. People use the term biosolids to cover quite a few situations. Biosolids are the solid part of human manure after the initial sewage treatment has been performed.

Question: So - how many different ways of doing the initial sewage treatment process?
Answer: At least a couple, that I know of, just to begin -- activated charcoal beds, trickling filter beds, anaerobic digestion chambers, aerated ponds - all different ways of handling sewage. Each method results in different kinds of processed waste material.

Question: Does the sewage treatment plant separate industrial effluent from residential sewage? Offices?
Answer: That is critical. If industrial waste was allowed in, don't even think about using those biosolids. The heavy metal problem is a killer. If the biosolid material is from residential or office areas, then most likely it could be processed into good compost. So, definitions are required, and we need to use the same words to describe things.

39. Inhibitory Compounds and Mushroom Compost 6/7/04 9:02 PM
Some of the other inhibitory compounds are:

- salts (not always NaCl, but other inorganic nutrients such as KCl, magnesium salts, etc)
- antibiotics to inhibit things that compete with Agaricus
- antibiotics to inhibit bacterial diseases of Agaricus
- antibiotics to inhibit fungal diseases of Agaricus, including yeasts
- antibiotics to inhibit algal growth

Many mushroom growers will tell you that they don't add any toxic chemical, but they don't recognize that antibiotics are toxic chemicals. The mushrooms don't take them up, so we don't eat them, but the antibiotics have their effects on the organisms in the compost. In the soil you might add the mushroom "compost" to. Thus, it shouldn't really be called "compost"; it is officially called "spent mushroom waste". Call it what is it. It can have great "fluff" effect, which gets oxygen into the medium you add it to, but that fluff doesn't last unless the biology gets going. So you can see benefits of adding spent waste, but not all that you should see. And the benefits don't last if you don't bring the organisms into the soil.....

40. Compost Processing 6/7/04 8:02 AM

If you don't like the confusion in which the world of composting is stuck, then be part of the solution, instead of continuing to confuse the situation. It doesn't help the world of composting if you are not willing to define things clearly. Compost has to have been processed properly. That term MUST be reserved to mean something specific. I don't care that some people have applied the definition incorrectly. Start using the term correctly, now, and you will begin to help instead of hinder. Aged manure - if it has been composted, then, call it compost.

If manure has NOT been composted, then call it aged manure if it has sat around for a time. How long? What are the conditions that define aged manure becoming.... soil? When might manure sit long enough, with adequate microbial processes, that it now becomes soil? But if it is processed in that fashion, it is not compost. Stop trying to muddy the waters and call it compost. Stop with the some people do it this way, others that and isn't it all compost? It is NOT compost unless specific conditions are met. If dung beetles have processed manure, then perhaps there is no difference between dung-processed material and earthworm castings. But how would you KNOW? It would be useful to get dung beetles recognized as having a commercial importance.

What terms that could be developed for all the permutations of partially composted material? HELP the world of compost by coming up with the categories, defining them clearly, working to develop a consensus, and developing the scientific database that is needed to define these semi-composted materials. Compost should be defined based on the starting materials used, and on the biological and chemical composition of the final product. IF we had data, we might be able to say that with a mix of certain starting materials, the final product ALWAYS has this biology and this chemistry.

Limits of the DATA are what push the NOSB and the USDA to their attitudes. They provide DATA that show that E. coli do not survive in thermal compost, in aged manure, in partially-composted materials (come up with better terms than that for each of the situations you want to have considered), in worm caste produced under whatever conditions. Define the conditions. Do not try to make one study. The Eastman study, in the limited conditions of that study, suffice for all worm compost made everywhere. If you can't afford to run experiments that show what happens to human pathogens in all these different conditions of storing waste material, or show what happens to helminthes when you treat wastes with worms, or dung beetles, or by heating with microbes, please recognize that you rely on rapid microbial growth to do the job. But who herds the microbes? Is it a turner, or worms, or dung beetles or enchytraeids doing the microbe herding?

Define what you are talking about. Help put this information into a useful form. Otherwise, you just keep spinning your wheels, getting nowhere. Define the kinds of composting, the kinds of storage. If you can't do the work, then read and put together a summary of all the data on composting. That would help give a basis from which to start a series of experiments. Put together categories, define the categories that you think would encompass your problems, and do some literature work. You put that together, and then I'll put together the proposal to submit to a funding agency to get the work done.

I'm asking for help of anyone out there wanting to work on this. Do the literature reviews, do the summarization, and define what you think are the important categories based on the knowledge we have. Hopefully, while you do that, I can publish the data I do have. We can then develop the next proposal. There just isn't enough time in a day for me to get to the literature review, especially since I try to answer questions on this list. Which is most important? Answering questions here, publishing data, or continuing to help growers do the biological conversion? All of the above. Then please help by getting the literature reviewed. Let us ALL work out the categories of what we think is important.

41. Raccoon Manure 5/31/04 1:44 PM

Just don't make it sound as if I encourage addition of raccoon manure as a normal thing to compost. ANY manure - raccoon or otherwise - has to be properly composted. Cows can have guardian, if they drink from infected streams. But raccoons are more likely to have serious infections. If any raccoon poop is in the compost pile, make sure it is composted properly. But how many of us have raccoons visiting our compost piles, unbeknownst to us, in the middle of the night, contributing their fecal material to our piles? Compost properly, always. Any animal can have helminthes; another set of organisms we worry about in the world of human health.

Compost MUST be properly heated in order to kill pathogens and pests. I am not aware of any information that shows that passage through an earthworm digestive system is adequate to kill helminthes, pathogenic protozoa, or virus. So most people go through a thermal compost phase before feeding material to the worms. Seems a little redundant, doesn't it? Thermal compost for a few days before you feed the organic matter to the worms.

Question: Why not just do the thermal composting?
Answer: Because letting the worms do the turning processes and finishing of the compost is less expensive than you having to play with turners, grinders, etc. But then you cannot process as much material as quickly with worms. There are tradeoffs. Heat is necessary as a first step in composting any material that has weed seed or possible virus, helminthes or protozoan contamination. So, if adding any kind of manure, you have to go through a heating period, 131 F for a minimum of 3 days and that means ALL the material has to reach that temperature for the WHOLE time. The outside of the pile has to be turned to the middle if doing pile outside. If doing plastic bag composting, you still HAVE TO TURN, or the inside of the pile gets too hot and turns the carbon to charcoal, while the outside of the pile, up against the plastic, may not be hot enough.

I hammer this a great deal, because new people on the list need to understand that putting organic matter in a pile for awhile will not give you compost. It gives you a pile of organic matter which may or may not be properly composted. You have to monitor temperature, although there are more and less labor-intensive ways to do the composting. There's information on the SFI website, www.soilfoodweb.com as well as good information in Rodale books. Track down some of the Sandbagger or Lube information on thermal composting. My opinion is that the Lobe's were the people who really got people to think about the important factors in composting. But for worm composting, see Mary Appleton's website, wormwoman.com. Her book on "worms Eat My Garbage" can't be beat for practical information. For those that want the more scientific level, read some of Clive Edwards' publications and compendiums. See the Ohio State University website for that.

42. Forms of Chitin 5/30/04 2:50 PM

Question: Doc E, like raccoon scat (because they eat insects..:) for chitins in composts.
Answer: I don't think I have ever recommended the addition of feces from any animal into the compost pile. Fecal material can be added in low concentrations, but I would choose some other form of chitin LONG BEFORE I would recommend animal feces -- shrimp shells, dead insects, anything containing chitin will help select for those fungi that attack and use chitin. This will increase the biomass of fungi that can attack chitin-cell-wall-containing fungi, as well as insects that may be the vectors for the spread of the SOD-causing organism.

43. Bacteria and Fungi Groups 5/16/04 10:15 AM

Question: To me there is contradicting data. There is SFI data then there is stuff from the bacteria/fungi group that talks about the types of stuff that grows on flours and grains.
Answer: Consider what the bacterial/fungal group are likely considering when they think about flours and grains. They are considering conditions where the microbial community has been limited severely by the conditions imposed. Stored flour and grain are in conditions that are very limited by dryness, possibly with additives to prevent any available moisture. Dust particles are loaded with spores of the fungi that cause seed-diseases. These conditions set the stage for the growth of a particular set of fungi. Some people call these fungi molds. One of the kinds of fungi that grow in these conditions are the ergot fungi. Alternaria, Aspergillus and related species are another set of fungi common in this environment, as I recall. Rusts, smuts and yeasts can be a problem too. When we add protein containing meal to GOOD compost, however, which should have the wide diversity of species that good compost should have, the conditions are NOT present for the growth of the bad fungi I mentioned above. Typically, ergot fungi, rusts or smuts can't even be isolated from decent compost.
Your bacteria/fungi group are probably un-aware of what is meant by good compost, properly made compost. Their experience is with stinky, smelly, putrefying organic matter, not with compost. Check it out, and see if that's not what they think of when they consider compost.

44. Hay and *Protozoa* 5/15/04 9:52 AM

Question: When referring to hay as a source of protozoa, what is the crown? Is it the top part with seeds or the bottom part near the ground?
Answer: The crown is the bottom near the ground, thick growth where the stems come from the roots. This is the area that the protozoa like, as well as the VAM fungi. You can find lots of VAM spores (if the plant is colonized with VAM), and lots of protozoa.

Question: Also, any idea if it matters whether the hay is green (freshly cut from the field) or dried (bailed)?

Answer: If the hay is stored properly, it doesn't make a difference. The protozoa go dormant, which means they encyst, and make it through the dry times. The dry hay is a bit safer, since then any diseases usually die off in the dry period, so you have less likelihood of transmitting any disease. Of course with the green, as long as you keep your eyes open, you should be able to see any diseased stems, and pull them out before growing the protozoa. Please realize that there is a protozoan inoculum on the market.

Question: I've been using alfalfa as a mulch in places and find it works quite well in maintaining moisture and bringing up earth worms.
Answer: Excellent! Thank you for the info! The earthworms are probably attracted to the fungi and bacteria growing on the alfalfa, and the moisture being maintained is helping them stay alive once there. Insecticides (white flies, aphids, leafhopper I suppose) and herbicides are about all I know of being applied to alfalfa.

45. Compost Smell 5/15/04 9:03 AM

Question: Why is the compost smelling sour?
Answer: That tells you what? Think back to what smell is produced when you mix acetic acid, butyric acid, valeric acid, putrescine, hydrogen sulfide, and ammonia. Sour smells are the result of what kind of metabolism? These are a mix of the organic acids produced when anaerobic metabolism occurs. The compost is likely too wet. The grey fuzz says, look out. Mix the compost to aerate it, and let the fungi start again. Hopefully this time you will get threads, and thick strands.

46. Molds, *Mycellium*, Fungi 5/10/04 5:53 AM

Question: As far as I could tell, the fuzzy stuff is not really a fungus but is an ergot.
Answer: Let's clarify the information about bread mold, ergots, and soil fungi. Common bread molds are found in soil, ergots are also found in soil. They are typically present as spores, not as active, growing fungal mycelium. *Mycellium* means the strands of fungal threads that make up the fungus body. Soil fungi include a huge diversity of literally hundreds of thousands of species of fungi. They range from beneficial fungi, like the ectomycorrhizal fungi, to the not-harmful-but-not-known-to-be-hugely-beneficial fungi, like most of the *hyphomycetes*, to the fungi we as humans would prefer not to have around, like mildew. But we do need them. Everything needs to decompose, and that's what most fungi do. They decompose things. If they didn't, we'd be buried in all sorts of garbage. If you found someone that said bread molds don't exist in soil, I'd like to take them on a little tour of the soil in their yard. I bet we'd find common bread mold there...And please note, all molds are fungi. You can usually tell someone with just plant pathology training, because they use the term mold to refer to fungi that cause disease. Many water molds, or fungi that produce motile zoospores, are plant pathogens, but many are not pathogens. There is no real restriction of the use of the term mold to those fungi that cause disease. All molds are NOT bad guys. If we don't use terms correctly, we end up not being able to communicate.

47. Nematodes 2/1/04 6:54 PM

Question: I'd love to increase the beneficial nematodes in my (vermi)compost and thus in my tea. If I add *Steinernema* or *Heterorhabditus* to my compost, how would I make them feel at home and willing to raise a big family? Should I worry about C:N ratio or temp or ph? Would the same environment encourage predatory nematodes?

Answer: *Steinernema* and *Heterorhabditus* are entomopathogenic nematodes, and thus they need insect larval stages to consume. You need to have the microarthropods in your worm compost. Mark Sturges does this all the time, and often has great *Steinernema* and *Heterorhabditus* populations in his worm compost. To get predatory nematodes, you have to have bacterial and fungal feeding nematodes, so the predatory nematodes have something to eat. You also need to NOT disturb the compost much. No turning, mixing. Also, you need to maintain the compost at ABOVE 50% moisture at all times. Predatory nematodes are slow-growing and don't often reproduce. You need a normal seasonal cycle to get the predatory nematodes to go through reproduction. But don't let them freeze, and don't let them fry. They are very much like the earthworms in their requirements to grow. Probably the best books on nematodes are in Dutch. Tom Bongers is a good resource. There's also a couple books by Gregor Yeates. Deb Neher at University of Toledo would be a great person to talk to! Alternatively, check with my husband, Russ Ingham at russ.ingham@comcast.net   He knows a lot about nematodes - grin!

48. EM, Bokashi, Chloroform Fumigation 1/25/04 4:06 AM

Question: I assume we are talking about Bokashi stuff?
Answer: Bokashi is one way of making EM, as I understand.

Question: I am giving this a try, mainly as a way to begin processing kitchen waste. Could it be useful to put the bokashi in the worm bin?
Answer: Not a good choice for the worm bin itself, better for the pre-worm bin heating step, or added into a thermal compost process. Worms require aerobic conditions, and if you let the worm bin go anaerobic, or even part anaerobic, the worms often (but not always) decide to leave. How anaerobic did the bin go? We need to better understand the impact of oxygen concentration, water-logging, and production of acid on worm-decision making processes.

Question: Or inoculate it (after initial processing) with soil?
Answer: Add EM into the pre-worm hot compost part of a thermal cycle, or process your waste doing the facultative anaerobe process of bokashi. I have noticed that adding EM bacteria, or other facultative anaerobe bacteria like EM (lactic acid bacteria for example), to a thermal compost pile, keeps the temperature of the pile lower. This is good, especially for us folks that work all week and don't have time to check the thermal pile very often. So, if you were careful about amounts of your finished bokashi you added to the worm bin, so you weren't driving things anaerobic, the inoculum would probably help. I think I've seen a couple recent papers on EM preparations being low in human pathogens.

a. Fish Hydrolysate

Here's another one I meant to talk about earlier - some data from Dramm that shows that fish hydrolysate also suppresses E. coli and human pathogens. So, if you have manure-based compost, can you add fish hydrolysate to the compost, or tea, and get suppression of the pathogens? Dramm has data showing this happened. Need more studies on this! But I'd bet that similar food web interactions were happening in bokashi as in fish hydrolysate. And it doesn't matter if molasses is used or not. If you have high sugar (glucose, sucrose, molasses, other sugars), it's going to be a problem, unless you use something to make the conditions in the compost or tea incapable of supporting human pathogen growth. And despite some folks disliking the plea for some solid data, really, folks, if you are making compost commercially, you need to test! If you buy compost from a commercial source, you need to insist on decent data. If you ever have trouble figuring out what some scientific data mean, just ask us about it. We should be able to help you understand what it means.

b. A Little EM

If you are doing back-yard gardening compost, a little EM in the pile can work to keep fluctuations in temperature from messing up an otherwise good compost. The most critical thing though is making sure you don't add too much high nitrogen containing material to the compost pile, but not too little either. Adding particular bacteria, like lactic acid producers, which are a large component of EM, and adding some other good guys like Bacillus which compete well with pathogens, and Pseudomonas which does well using proteins and decomposing pesticides, will keep things in the range between 131 and 155 F.

Question: My problem with EM production is that it must be in an anaerobic environment.
Answer: It is really interesting to try to figure out the shift from aerobic to anaerobic, back to aerobic, back to anaerobic, back to aerobic, and round and round a few more times, that can occur in bokashi production. You have to make sure you allow the material to get fully finished, so you are back at aerobic before applying. That generally takes longer when the temperature is cooler.

Question: This leads me to suspect that the organisms won't survive too well in the soil once applied.
Answer: The data that have been done to "show" that addition of bacteria to soil doesn't do much did not differentiate between bacteria that can grow on plate media, and bacteria that cannot grow on plate media.

Question: How many bacteria in bokashi actually can grow on the typical plate media used in the lab?
Answer: Pretty questionable whether it's the right media.

c. Chloroform Fumigation

When chloroform fumigation "microbial biomass" measurements are taken, they forget to realistically control the method, by solubilizing the kinds of carbons that chloroform solubilizes, but then adding in the fungal biomass which chloroform does nothing to make available. My experience is that chloroform fumigation is a laughable method for assessing what we need to know about bacteria and fungi, protozoa and nematodes in soil, or in compost. The answers people get using chloroform fumigation are meaning less, and quite inappropriate. But, the method gives a digital readout, so chemists like the method. If you apply an inoculum to a soil that has been nuked with pesticides and high inorganic fertilizer applications, the EM bacteria that grew while the bokashi was fermenting, do quite well in helping your soil move along and build structure, organic matter, and get nutrient retention started. Ciliates do well in bokashi, of course, but the flagellates and amoebae can be a problem to get established. So, a hay infusion to get the flagellates and amoebae. But once you get things turned around, once soil is being built, nutrient cycling is starting to go well, you need to think aerobic additions. Once the aerobic food web is well-established, then EM may be good as a food to feed the aerobes, as long as you don't push things too anaerobic.

Question: However, perhaps they are useful food for the existing soil life? (provided there is any...). I presume that having done their work, there are many bacteria there, all holding nutrients in a biological form? If this is so, then continued application might be beneficial to growing plants not so much for the living EMs, but for the form of the nutrients?

Answer: Hum, that's a thought. Probably won't harm anything, if care about not pushing things anaerobic, and the additions might help. As long as the price isn't too much, why not? So, the grower has to make the decision - cost versus benefit. Being a lazy grower, I don't like to add things if I don't NEED to add. There just isn't enough time in my life to do everything I want to do......

49. **Balancing Nutrients** 1/11/04 1:19 AM
There are important aspects of what you have to think about when trying to balance nutrients. You have to pay attention to all the nutrients. You will pay the consequences if you focus on just part of the whole.

Question: Bonemeal is high in Ca, but also has a serious PO4 load. Do you really need BOTH? Or are you contributing to the problem of polluted water instead of cleaning it up, as biological farmers should?
Answer: No number is right, unless all numbers are right. There is no one factor that can be used to grow plants, you have to be aware of all factors. Optimize everything that you can. Be aware that all chemicals come with contaminants.

Question: So, if not bloodmeal, what is the best, balanced nutrient you can use?
Answer: AEROBIC compost. It's made from plant material, so guess what? Properly made compost has the nutrients in balance..... But properly made, ok? Nothing that is putrefying.....

50. **Mushrooms** 1/10/04 8:21 AM

a. *Mushrooms in Forests*
I have been told by people who are experts on mushrooms that most mushrooms IN FORESTS are the fruiting bodies, or reproductive structures, of mycorrhizal fungi. I have taken that on faith, if you will, because there are some things that I just don't have time to research. So, most forest mushrooms are going to be good fungi. Try to take just one of the many mushrooms that are

present, and be careful about handling them. Each cap has billions of spores, and you don't need even that many. So, don't harvest all the mushrooms present, because then you deplete the diversity of the forest.

b. Mushrooms in Grasslands
Mushrooms in grasslands may not always be good guys. So, let's hold the fungus collection to getting the nice strands of fungi from the humus layer in forests, or in shrub areas.

A group of people that are great references for more information are Paul Stametz (his web site is Fungi Perfecti), Mike Amaranthus (Mycorrhizal Applications), Randy Molina (US Forest Service, and Dept of Forest Science, Oregon State University).

Question: Anyone have other suggestions on great resource people for this information?
Answer: Try your local University or college, and sometimes even the extension service. Look for someone who is a mycologist. Master Gardeners often have a mycologist they work with. Take a class on Edible Mushrooms, or Edible Plants to find out about what nutrients are in the plants around you.

Question: Many "weeds" are actually edible; why do we have it in for these plants?
Answer: They pop up in places we have cleared of other plants. Anyway, that tells you that you have prepared a great place to grow that plant, which we call a weed. The habitat is right for that plant. How about turning it into a bed of edible plants in your landscape?

So, do some looking around at who are the good guy fungi, versus who are the not-so-great in your area. This needs to be local knowledge. In general, avoid the fungi that are on sick plants. Get your fungi from the humus layer, because humus is food for the good guys, not the bad guys. The best fungi grow in good smelling humus. Not anaerobic. OK?

51. Hair, Feathers, Fungal Hyphae Enhance Keratinase 1/7/04 4:28 PM

Question: Look at this! Keratinase is indicated as the enzyme that decomposes prions! Good old Bacillus licheniformis! This is good news, because guess what compost abounds in?
Answer: If you use hair, feathers, fungal hyphae and other similar materials in the compost, you are enhancing keratinase! So, compost is a good way to deal with suspect materials. Phew!

Question: So, what concentrations are needed to make sure 100% reduction?
Answer: Well, that needs to be figured out.

52. Urea 1/5/04 10:05 PM

Question: Can I add Urea to straw based compost when there is little green material available?
Answer: Urea is high N, and will get the temperature in your pile going, but the break-down product of adding urea is NITRATE which is going to enhance bacteria, not fungi. Green material is added to maintain temperature, but not to give you the high peaks. You have to get temperature up in a thermal compost over 131 F for more than 10 to 15 days. So, you need the hi N, as well as

the green. Woody material is there to give structure, and allow air into the pile so you don't have to turn as much. And feeds fungi. Instead of urea, use coffee grounds, kitchen waste, grocery store produce waste (pre-consumer), potato cake, or other materials with sugars, proteins and carbohydrates in it. Green plant material of course contains this, but you don't always have green stuff. But remember, if you cut it green, and stored it without moisture, it is still green, even if the color went brown. The microbes have not decomposed the sugars, proteins or carbohydrates - they are still there. So dry hay is still green..... from a microbial point of view.

53. Worm Composting 12/30/03 12:56 AM
Get the castings out of the plastic barrels. They need to breathe. Make sure moisture is about 50%; add some fungal foods like humic acid, fish hydrolysate, oatmeal (per Jeff Lowenfels, as explained in the archives for this list with respect to amounts), or other protein meals like soy meal, or feathermeal, or alfalfa meal. Mix gently, keep warm (55 or higher), maybe even use a heated pad underneath. That should get the worm compost to resuscitate, grow some good fungi.

54. Fungi Appearance 9/22/03 7:55 PM
Rectangular? Where did that come from? Fungi often go into fruiting in the fall, after some rain, and cooler temps occur. You might be seeing the button stage of mushroom formation. Did they look like little buttons? Or fuzzy white cushions?

a. Fungi Are Most Likely Not in Most Soils
If a tea seller says there are lots of fungi in soil, laugh at them. Maybe lots of fungi in the old growth forest two, or twenty or two thousand miles away, but not your lawn, not your garden, not your crop fields, unless you can SEE the fungal strands growing in your soil. Most people have killed their fungi by using pesticides, fungicides, insecticides, herbicides, and inorganic fertilizer. They need to put fungi back in their soil, or they will never achieve the benefits they should be able to get from healthy soil. Can a bacterial tea help? Sure, But you are only getting step one, in a twelve step program. Why would you spend money on something that only gives you one-twelfth of the needed addition? When the whole program can be obtained at a lower price than the bacterial tea machines are selling theirs!

55. Types of Pathogens in Compost 7/26/04 11:59 PM
Typically when people talk about "pathogen-free" compost, they mean human pathogen-free. That is, E. coli free. And we see E. coli-"free" compost quite often. It just means that no E. coli were detected in the testing done. which means, the other human pathogens should not have been able to survive either. Plant pathogens are rather "in the eye of the beholder". I personally want pathogens of weeds in my compost. But no, or only low levels, of vegetable, grass or tree pathogens. I want to have my plants healthy, so they aren't stressed. Stressed plants get sick; healthy plants resist diseases.

56. Compost Ingredients 7/10/04 8:29 PM
I'd add SOME of the material to the cooling piles. Add more fresh material to your growth chamber material, and keep increasing diversity and growth. Try for the thick white threads. Look for more fungi in the litter under grape vines, hedgerows, shrubs or Acacia thickets - anywhere that litter accumulates on the soil.

57. Making Compost 6/24/04 5:21 PM

The compost needs to still be in active growth of the organisms phase. So, I like to add the calcium at the beginning of the composting cycle. With commercial compost, you need to turn 5 times, in a fifteen day heating
cycle, which means you have to get the original recipe right. We have people who are claiming back to ambient temp, using our approaches, in 15 days. Hum..... I want more data. Grin! Backyard, you use a different recipe, which allows one turn on day 7, and then you finish composting over the next 2.5 months. Arden Anderson, who is the co-conspirator on this approach, likes to add the lime toward the end of the composting cycle, as long as the compost is about 100 degrees when you add the lime, so the organisms are still active enough to immobilize the calcium on the biomass.

58. So, as Fungal a Compost, or Compost Tea as Possible, is Needed 3/27/04 7:22 PM.

With worm compost, this means that the worms need to be fed high amounts of fungal foods, such as paper, cardboard, fish protein, oatmeal, non-GMO soy bean, pea, bean, milk protein and/or melon rinds, carrots, stalks of vegetables. NO oranges, lime, lemon peels, or only a tiny amount. The worms will then end to help the fungal component increase, although you will still have great bacterial numbers, and some very beneficial bacteria, fungi and protozoa to boot.

59. Temperature Affects Worms 2/21/04 5:20 AM

Question: Could the really hot temperatures be affecting the worms?
Answer: The sun burn on my shoulders is really... ah.....affecting me!

60. Worms and Lettuce, Nitrogen Gas, Chlorine 2/21/04 2:48 PM

If the other foods you were adding were disappearing, then the lettuce has to have been sterile. Nuked in some way, possibly with nitrogen gas. The lettuce mixes they sell in the store are washed in chlorine, and then dropped into nitrogen gas atmosphere in the bags. This may drive things really sterile, but who knows for certain? May make them un-palatable for the worms, since the worms actually eat bacteria and fungi, not the plant organic matter.

a. High Temperatures

The high temps are not a problem for the microbes - unless you run out of water, or food. The microbes are really cranking, FAST, in this weather. It is hot and HUMID!!!

Chapter XI

TESTING
and
FIELD TRIALS

TESTING AND FIELD TRIALS

1. Compost Tea Standards 5/7/04 9:19 PM

Question: Since compost comes in all different varieties and constituents and tea is nothing more than a way to magnify the properties and constituents and distribute them in a different form, how do we come up with a standard?
Answer: We base the standard on the biology and chemistry required to see positive results in plants. There are different requirements for different plants, and different soils, but to some extent, BASED ON THE DATA WE HAVE COLLECTED AT SFI, as long as we at least reach a threshold, we will see positive results. If we help improve fungi, if the plants need fungi, or improve bacteria, if the plants require bacterial dominance, then we can obtain even greater benefits. So, the standards have to be based on PLANT RESPONSE. If the lab doesn't show you tests where they have clear impacts on plant nutrition, plant growth, etc, it isn't worth your time to continue with that testing.

The standards need to be PREDICTIVE. If you are going to do testing, the data better help you predict whether something needs to be fixed, or not, so that plant health will be improved, and improve nutrition, or yield, or flavor. We have standards for biology needed in compost, and compost tea, and in your soil. What we don't have is data on chemistry when biological systems are present and operating. Biology changes all you have learned about strictly chemical systems. We will all have to re-learn much of what we thought was the case with chemicals, once we put organisms back into the system.

2. Biomass Levels Relative to Plant Growth 4/30/04 6:44 PM

If testing of tea is done, it has to be predictive of whether higher or lower bacteria or fungi will benefit the growth of the plant. That's what we have done at SFI - showed that if you have certain minimal levels of organism biomass, then, when applied as foliar sprays, the leaf surface will be protected. That's why the bacterial and fungal testing can be useful. Same for soil - we have tested tea and compost to show that with organisms biomass at or above certain levels, we get benefit to the plant. It doesn't do us any good if we don't know what the biomass levels MEAN relative to plant growth. That's why everything at SFI has to relate back to the impact on the plant you are trying to grow. But, with the NOSB, we need to document pathogen levels in the compost and in the tea. So, can we put our heads together and develop a testing program that will put NOSB fears to rest. Once we have that human pathogen concern laid to rest, or at least a clear program of how to alleviate concern, then we need to get back to the demonstrations of benefit to plant growth, given different climates, soil types and plant cultivars.

3. Testing Tea 6/24/04 12:38 PM

A little microscope would help you with that question. You could test the tea before you added it to the sprayer, and then again just after you put the tea in the sprayer. Then you would know for certain if you'd done a good job getting rid of the toxic chemical.

4. Testing Each Batch of Tea 5/10/04 4:54 AM

We are working to test each batch of tea produced, so you know it contains the organisms you need:

1. to protect your plant,
2. to retain nutrients in the soil instead of having them leach,
3. to cycle nutrients into a plant-available form at the time and place the plant needs,
   4. to build soil structure so air passage-ways remain open into the soil and keep water infiltration adequate.

5. Testing for Good Sets of Organisms 5/7/04 9:32 PM

Question: I would think that we need to start simply: Compost + Air + Water and get each tested so we have some kind of baseline. Then we can add inputs. Now, we don't need extensive tea tests because we can assume, based on history, that compost with air and water will multiply microbes in the compost. What we are going to test for is pathogen growth. That's all. If we focus on that and get that under control, inputs may have little against them. So I would suggest we use traditional SFI testing for commercial tea when people are developing formulas and maybe use a more inexpensive test for pathogens. I'm sure SFI can provide such a test. It has to be cheap so a lot of people can use it and we can compile results.

Answer: We do need to document that there were good sets of organisms in the tea, and sometimes, things go wrong in a tea brew (the pump stopped because the electricity went off, but went on again before you came in the morning). But you don't know that happened. So, checking the tea for critters is important. And SFI provides pathogen testing. WE do EPA approved E. coli tests, AND we have just about finished the molecular probe testing as well – a 3 hour turn-around! Which do you need to have done? But be aware that other labs provide E. coli testing as well. But they need to be labs that deal with compost, or soil. OK?

6. Tea Definitions 6/10/04 7:29 AM

Let's go through definitions of good tea. When the tea has no biology to speak of (maybe just a few bacteria per field of view), that's BAD tea. Really, it's not tea. Guess which tea brewer often gives you that result?

a. Poor Tea:
If you see:
- 25 to 500 bacteria per field of view at 100 total magnification,
- no fungi even in 10 to 20 fields of view,
- no protozoa,
- no nematodes,
That's POOR tea. At least you have a decent amount of bacteria, but that's it. It's poor tea, because you only have bacteria, and they are probably anaerobic, or the fungi, protozoa and nematodes would be there. Guess which tea brewer usually gives this kind of result? And you can check this for yourself with the little microscope.

b. Adequate Tea:

If you see:

- over 500 bacteria per field of view,
- at least one strand of fungus in 10 to 20 fields,
- a couple flagellates and/or amoebae, or a FEW ciliates (flagellates, amoebae and ciliates are all kinds of protozoa),
- maybe a nematode or more in 10 to 20 fields of view

then you have ADEQUATE tea. This often happens when you add too much food for the aeration level you have. Or the water was too cold, still had chlorine residue in it, had some toxic something in your recipe, the tea machine wasn't cleaned properly. If you have only adequate tea, you need to be careful with the amount of tea you spray out - you may want to double or triple the dose. Make it 15 gallons per acre for a foliar, not just 5 gallons per ac.

c. Very Good Tea:

If you see:

- lots of bacteria per field (more than 500),
- a fungal strand in the first 5 fields you look at,
- all of the groups of protozoa in that first 5 fields
- maybe some nematodes in those 5 fields,

you have VERY GOOD tea. Use the 5 gal per ac amount for foliar sprays.

d. Excellent Tea:

If you see:

- huge numbers, thousands, of bacteria in EVERY field,
- a fungal strand in each field of view,
- many flagellates and/or amoebae in EVERY field,
- a nematode or two in the sample,

Then do a dance! This is EXCELLENT tea. This can be applied at less than 5 gal per ac. This tea can be "diluted".

Question: Guess which tea machines give us these kinds of results?

Answer: Australia, many folks have good machines, but you need to ask the Australia lab for that info. So, every one selling tea should get a little microscope, get trained to identify the critters, and take pictures of each tea brew, to be able to document what is in the tea brew. You still need to confirm activity and quantify biomass, so twice a year, have a tea checked by SFI to let you know you are getting the levels of active organisms that you need. Those of you buying tea, you should ASK the seller for this kind of information. Where is their proof that they are selling good stuff? Doing the little microscope approach takes about 30 seconds to put the sample on the slide and observe it. It can be done EVERY batch. You can even take a sample at say, 15 hours, and figure out if you need to do something to improve the tea, so it is EXCELLENT tea by the time you get to 24 hours.

7. Qualitative Assessment 5/30/04 3:43 PM

You can instantly tell a good tea, or a bad one. Stop by and take a look. You could pull a tea sample from your tank before you leave (it takes 30 seconds to do this), and pull one on the tea when you get back, and then you KNOW what happened. Remember, this is a qualitative assessment, but when it is a night and day difference, qualitative can be just as useful as quantitative. Take pictures of your tea before you leave, and then you safeguard yourself with respect to the quality of the tea that you are spraying out.

8. Organisms in Soil, Compost, Water or Tea 4/10/04 8:54 PM

Tea: AB—65   TB--11,008   AF--19.7   TF—102   HD--3.5

Humus: AB—191   TB—421   AF--34.4   TF—1228   HD2.5

Active bacteria (AB), total bacteria (TB), active fungi (AF) and Total fungi (TF) are measured by measuring length and width of these organisms in the soil, compost, water or tea you send in. That gives you bio-volume. We have measured the density of bacteria and fungi in soil for many years, and thus use the typical conversion for soil organisms to convert to biomass.

a. Comparing Numbers of Bacteria with Numbers of Fungi is Nonsensical
The largest organism on this planet is a fungus, and there are competitions going on for who actually has the largest individual fungus. So, comparing bacteria, which are among the smallest organisms on the planet, with individual numbers of fungi is just silly.

b. Comparing Biomass Makes Much More Sense
Because you take into account the mass of the organisms - you compare mass, not numbers of individuals. So, the values come as microgram per milliliter, if you are dealing with liquids, or micrograms per gram, if you deal with solids. We also report HD, which is hyphal diameter. The actual average width of the hyphae, which is an indicator of whether you have mostly "good guy" fungi, or typical fungi, or bad guy fungi. A generalization, yes, but most people like to have some idea of good, bad, ok, and here's a general indication. If the diameter in less than 2 micrometers, you have mostly not-so-good guys. 2 to 3 micrometers, the community of fungi is in the normal range - some good, some bad. 3 or above - life is good, pat yourself on the back, you have mostly the good guys.

c. Protozoa are Reported in Numbers of Individuals per Gram or Milliliter
Three groups - flagellates (F), amoebae (A) and ciliates (C). Flagellates and amoebae in soil are almost strictly aerobes, while ciliates prefer to consume anaerobic bacteria. So, there's a hint, if you high numbers of ciliates, that you may have anaerobic conditions present.

d. N is for Nematodes
Also reported in total number of nematodes per gram, or milliliter. We also identify to genus or species, and that is reported, although in this case, there were no nematodes, so no species ID.

e. Desired Ranges
We always report the "desired range" on the SFI report, based on years and years of collecting data from thousands of samples. Based on that knowledge, we came up with the desired range. Labs that don't have that background use the numbers that SFI developed. They have not done the tough

work, doing the assessments for years and years. They cannot justify the meaning of the numbers they put on their reports. They have no quality control of what they do. Samples were sent to several of the other labs. We used a gradient of samples from AG soils hammered with pesticides, to old growth forest samples. Clearly the nuked AG soils are the poorest soils, and the old growth forest soils are highest. Want to guess what the other labs reported? Did they get the gradient right? I'll be putting the data out in the next e-zine.

9. Testing Methods 5/7/04
The molecular methods are available. And we can quantify numbers of individuals of each of these species. At least the methods we are working on seem to be working fine. Only by using direct methods, and molecular methods can you figure this out, however. Plate counts.... sorry. When you limit carbon sources, temperature, moisture, humidity, types of N, P, K, Ca, etc, etc, etc, you don't get the majority of species. Any microbiology text book will tell you this.

10. Numbers of Individuals in Soil 4/12/04 7:09 AM
OK, here goes. That's not possible to say, really, for fungi. A fungal individual is difficult to know for certain. Plate counts mess up on that measurement, in general, plate counts give you "how many spores of fungi and pieces of hyphal strands were the fungi broken into when you shook your sample", which isn't really a useful piece of information.

a. Colony forming units
CFU - do not tell you if the fungal propagule was a spore, a tiny piece of hypha, or a mat of hyphae. You need to do biomass, that's all there is to it, when you are dealing with fungi. Especially when you want to compare fungi and bacteria, comparing numbers is just plain nonsense. We could tell you how many individual strands of fungi are present in soil, but that is dependent on whether the soil was just plowed, or not. It doesn't relate to anything useful.

Question: But what about bacteria?
Answer: Bacteria clump together, they like to form colonies. Just like people. People clump together in villages, towns, cities, etc.. The group helps each individual better. Think of a bacterial colony as being like a neighborhood of similar ethnic people.

b. Plate Count Approaches
Plate count approaches cannot separate all the colonies into the individuals, so plate counts always underestimate the actual number of individuals - but you don't know by how much.

Question: How many colonies were broken up when you shook your soil sample in buffer? How many were not, or were partially broken up?
Answer: Don't know.

Question: So, what are you getting when you run a plate count?
Answer: In direct microscopy, we count the individual bacteria that we can see, including the bacteria in colonies, measure length and width, and then using the typical density of bacteria in soil, determined over the years by lots of testing and which varies from soil to soil, season to season, we can determine biomass of bacteria in soil. We are working on differences in bacterial

254

and fungal densities, in the rhizosphere of different agricultural plants right now, so that will be put into the data that will be used to fine-tune the SFI report based on each plant that you tell us has been growing in the area you want to know about. A good test for a lab that says they are doing direct measurements, but are perhaps not actually giving good data because they don't work with the person who developed the direct microscopic techniques they purport to use, is to ask them how they figured out density of bacteria and fungi in soil -- what values do they use in their spread sheets, and how those values change with season? SFI labs direct that question to me, because I developed the knowledge. Sharing that knowledge, having someone able to understand that level of seasonal change, and understand how to do the assessment, generally takes a minimum of Ph.D. in microbiology. So, yes, other academics can tell you the reason you need to pay attention to this, but only by working with SFI labs will you get the knowledge that has already worked that one out. People who stopped by SFI and spent a week, or even a couple years, "training" with SF were not given this information. They can't explain where each value in our spread sheets comes from, and, of course, that's critical in order to change the seasonal parameters, the plant parameters, that need to be changed.

c. Numbers versus Biomass

Anyway, on to the numbers. Bacteria generally run about 1 million per gram (about a teaspoon) of dry weight of soil in conventional agricultural soil. Typically a plate count will overestimate the actual numbers of bacterial individuals, because the plate count will include dormant stages of bacteria, not just the active bacterial cells. That's a problem. If the information you need is - how many functioning cells in my soil - then you cannot get that knowledge from a plate count. Bacterial numbers in HEALTHY agricultural soil -- healthy defined by how the plant can grow without pesticides or inorganic fertilizer to help it survive (not on drugs, if you will) are typically about 600 million per gram dry weight of soil.

Question: Numbers of bacteria per gram in a conventional lawn, maintained by a chemical service?

Answer: You may have only disease - causers, and you may have only a few thousand per gram. Pesticides kill things. Oh, surprise. In a healthy lawn, which is disease-free, so not requiring any pesticides, we can find up to 2,000 million bacteria per gram of soil. But that should be balanced by a fungal biomass to balance nitrogen in a proper ratio to grow your perennial grasses. The proper biology does that for you. You must get the ratio of fungi to bacteria correct, for the plant you want to grow, or you may be setting the stage to grow weeds better than the plant you want to grow.

d. Field Soil

In a field of soil (about 2 million lbs of soil in the top ten inches in an acre of soil), that's well into the billions of individuals of bacteria, and possibly fungi. You need to be very careful when someone is talking about numbers of individuals of bacteria or fungi that you get the units correct. Did they say billions of individuals per gram of AG soil? Then they are not correct. Did they say billions of individuals per gram of soil in an old growth forest? They are correct. How productive a system are you talking about? If they say billions of individuals in an AG FIELD, then they MAY be correct. In an old growth forest stand of trees? They are being too conservative. And that's just bacteria and fungi.

Question: What about protozoa?
Answer: Add them in.

Question: Nematodes? Microarthropods?
Answer: You CANNOT have a healthy old growth forest without several hundred thousand microarthropods doing their thing, during the right times of the year. Seasonal processes are going on there, and we need to make sure they are there, in order to have a healthy forest. Much to understand. But not impossible, nor even all that complex, if you get an understanding of how it all works together. There's a great deal of "well, of course that's how it works", once you have someone explain the functions of the different critters for you.

11. Plate Count vs. Direct Count 5/9/04
What we need is to be able to PREDICT whether something will have an effect. We have tested compost tea over and over and shown that if the tea has at least these levels of bacteria and fungi, then we get positive results relative to disease, nutrient cycling, nutrient retention, erosion, plant yields, etc. With tea, ALL the teas applied over a period of time need to be at or above the minimal levels to maintain the desired results. So really, each batch of tea needs to be tested. That's why the development of the little microscope assay. You can test every tea, although you still want to confirm the activity of the teas every 10th brew or every three months, whichever comes first.

The Certified Compost Tea program at SFI sets up those testing requirements. A certifier comes out and looks at the tea making operation. Teas are tested four times through the growing season. The minimum levels of organisms have to be achieved with each test. If they aren't, we work with you to achieve the minimum levels.
But at a commercial tea operation, testing each batch of tea is a safe guard for the producer. Take a picture of each batch to document that each batch has adequate bacterial and fungal biomass. If the tea doesn't have the set of organisms desired, then you add more compost, or more foods, and brew longer -- or throw the batch out and start over. But figure out WHY the batch did not have the biology.

Question: Are the SFI standards cast in concrete?
Answer: No, because as we learn new things, the standards may change. If we learn that to GUARANTEE no mildew, you actually need twice as much ACTIVE fungal biomass, we'll up the standard level required. If we discover that bacterial biomass doesn't really need to be as high as we've set it, because you still get good black spot control with lower levels, we'll change the standard for black spot control. The standards were set based on ability to prevent disease on leaf AND ROOT surfaces. So, we have a standard that is based on results, from a plant's point of view. That's what you need, and that's what you have with SFI testing. You can't say that with any other testing methods that are out there.

a. Plate Count vs. SFI Method
At the last SFI introductory course, one of the people at the course related that they had sent in the same samples to SFI and to another lab that does plate counts. The samples were from soils where

they knew the productivity of the systems; so, for example, a forest, a good producing field, and a poor producing field of potato. The plate count lab index came back with a 0 for the forest, and the same index values, about 5 and 6, for the good producing field and the poor producing field. The plate count lab report stated that the forest soil must be from a desert, since there were no organisms growing on those plates. The good producing field was proclaimed to be less productive than the poor producing field, because the index was lower from what was actually the higher producing field. Hum...... SFI data showed good fungal dominated soil, but plenty of bacteria in the forest; the good producing field had about an equal biomass, above desired ranges (excellent!), for both bacteria and fungi. For the poor producing field, bacteria were barely in range, while fungal biomass was much too low.

Question: Which method of assessing soil organisms was predictive of productivity?
Answer: Forest soils have high fungal biomass. Those highly beneficial species do not grow well on any plate count media we know about.

Question: What grows well on the media chosen by other plate count laboratories?
Answer: Soil pathogens. Organisms that require highly disturbed environments. Once I saw what the person attending the course had done (I don't always think of everything, and further, I did not have the money to run this gradient before), SFI repeated this testing. The plate index showed very similar results to what the person had seen. Forgive me for not putting the actual numbers for the bacteria and fungi in here - I am doing this from memory, and we want to publish these results in a journal.

	Plate count	µg Bacteria	µg Fungi
Old growth forest	0	high	high
High production pasture	5	good	good
Low production pasture	6	ok	low
Good yield crop field (180 bu)	7	good	ok
Poor yield crop field (100 bu)	12	poor	very poor

So, our results bear out the results that were seen by the attendee to the introductory course. I want to repeat this again, before publishing, but it makes you really wonder about the usefulness of plate counts. And maybe really there should be no "wondering". Plate count media cannot grow most of the beneficial organisms in soil, so why would it be a surprise that the result would be as they are. We need to test other methods of assessing soil quality using gradients that are this clear with respect to productivity.

Question: Would FAME, or enzyme tests show similar kinds of relationships? Enzyme assays would be expected to increase as a soil became more productive, correct? Except, what if the specific enzyme being assessed is for a function that is less in an old growth forest than in a potato field? Is enzyme concentration linear as productivity increases? What about fatty acid methyl ester methods of assessing diversity? Is there a clear correlation between increasing production, going from a sick AG field, to an old growth forest, and kinds of fatty acids methyl esters?

Answer: I have never seen that kind of data reported in the scientific literature. The direct methods have their limitations - for example, when you are in highly productive soils and you have herds of higher level predators, which consume many, many bacteria or fungi. The biomass of bacteria, or fungi may be lower than expected, because they were eaten. You cannot look at just the bacterial and fungal biomass in those cases, you have to look at protozoa, nematodes and microarthropods as well. It has to be a sum of ALL the biology present.

A few studies have looked at bacterial biomass across a production gradient, and showed bacterial biomass leveling off mid-way through that production gradient. The researchers concluded that direct methods do not work. I think they showed their lack of understanding, or they were out to try to "prove" that their approach was better. Because, of course, bacterial biomass levels off half-way through succession. Fungal biomass is what increases after that mid-successional stage of production. But half-way through increasing forest production, fungal biomass can also level off, because nematodes or microarthropods increase. They eat fungi, and some bacteria, and hold the bacterial and fungal populations in check. But then the increase in soil biomass occurs in the predator populations. If ALL the biology is assessed, then the gradient becomes clear.

There is a series of papers from some work we did at the EPA terracosm project that shows this relationship. The papers are still in preparation, and the person doing the writing has told me that the statistics are just about finished. So, that data will finally be released, in a year or so. We need predictive ability. Whatever assay we choose to use, it has to be predictive of what we want to know. Direct determinations tell you if you have enough biomass to cover the leaf surfaces. So, it's easy to see why biomass can be predictive of whether the plant surface will be protected.

12. Assessing Compost Tea Quality 2/23/04

a. Plate Counts
When people do plate counts of bacteria to assess compost tea quality, there is no correlation between the plate count results and improvement in plant health. So, people doing plate counts and claiming that tells them whether the tea is any good are just fooling themselves. Plate methods cannot assess the true diversity in any sample. Plate methods are fine for doing counts of organisms that you know grow in certain conditions, but not for understanding diversity.

b. Bio-Log Determinations
At SFI, we are doing Bio-Log determinations, where different media are used to grow species of *Pseudomonas*, *Bacillus*, nitrogen fixing bacteria, etc. in certain conditions, and then we can tell you whether the species that grow in those defined conditions are beneficial or not. But this is not true diversity, just a means of telling you if you have beneficial species or disease-organisms. Please realize the limitations of this approach. Until we can do DNA methods, true diversity is very expensive to figure out.

13. Plate Methods vs. Molecular Methods   2/1/04 7:05 PM

a. Plate Methods

Krasilnikov used plate methods, which means he missed a whole bunch of organisms in the soil. About 99.9% of the bacteria and fungi in soil DO NOT grow on any medium we know about. So while the work is good from a human pathogen view, it is extremely limited from a soils point of view.

b. Molecular Methods

Molecular methods are being developed, and that's where we will really be able to address true soil diversity. There's a good relationship between total bacteria biomass and bacterial diversity, and total fungal biomass and fungal diversity. The relationship is pretty linear. But, of course, we can't say what species ARE present, just whether you have adequate levels of not. For the species listing, we can send you to molecular people who will give you the list of DNA sequences you have in your soil.

Question: So, what does that then mean?
Answer: You know the number of unique species you have.

14. Microscope Methods 1/20/04 11:17 PM

Yes, total bacteria is done by direct microscopy, but you need epi-fluorescent stains to be able to differentiate bacteria from clay colloids. The bright field scope can give you general ideas about critters in soil, compost and tea. Probably easiest for tea. However.. the methods are best for looking at "few bacteria" to start with, and an "increase" later on. Not methods that are highly quantitative, really, but they are useful for being able to say - darn, nothing happened in the brewing cycle. What went wrong....

15. General Biological Practices 1/20/04 11:35 AM

a. Test an Area

Choose an example garden, typical of the area you are in. Do soil chemistry and soil biology samples. Ah, but not just one kind of test -

b. Step one - do a total N, P, K, and total micronutrient test which is a total combustion followed by analysis. OR, do a USDA, or University, A&L type harsh-extractant test, which will give you TOTAL levels of nutrients, most of which are not plant available and won't become plant available for about the next 1000 years. But these results will tell you what is truly GONE from your soil.

Do this once, and it should be good for the next oh, 10 years. It may be that the local extension service already has this kind of data for your soils, or the local soil chemist at a local University. So check that resource first, ok? But interpret the result correctly. Don't imagine that the numbers mean that the nutrients are going to be available to the plants any time soon! This is just an assessment of what is held in the PARENT MATERIAL, and what may have been totally wiped out by conventional practices.

c. *Step two* - do an Albrecht kind of soil chemistry test. This tells you what nutrients will potentially be available over the next couple years. And it tells you if something is missing from what the plants will potentially be able to access. If the biology is right, these nutrients will become available next summer. Almost invariably, calcium will be WAY out-of-whack, because it has been leached from your soil over the toxic chemical era we've been through. Iron will be high, but completely unavailable, and without the right fungi to solubilize that iron, you will have moss in your lawn. Potassium is often lacking too, so that has to be fixed.

But the way to fix deficiencies or excesses are NOT by adding more chemicals. There's a reason you lost those nutrients to begin with - they were in your soil in Idaho, I guarantee it. The soils there are VERY young, and should have all the nutrients you need. But we have exited them because of the chemicals and tillage programs recommended over the last 60 years. We didn't know better, so let's not get into blame mode. Let's just move on....So, with the Albrecht test, you know what nutrients need to be added. But now, how to add them? In the compost or the compost tea. Easy. But let's do one more test, of what is available, right now, for your plant.

d. *Step three* - Reams testing tells you what is available to the plant in solution right now. If you put your seed in the soil today, are there enough nutrients to get it to germinate? If not, then yes, we need to add those available nutrients right now, and work on the biology at the same time to get the nearly-available nutrients (Albrecht test) into the available (Reams test) pool.

I'm simplifying here, but don't let's make this any more difficult for beginners to understand. We can get into the special cases and the exceptions once those exceptions are encountered, ok?

e. *Analyzing the Chemical Data*
So, now, you have data on: total nutrient pools, the soon-to-be-available pool, and the actually available pool. You will have recommendations to add all kinds of chemicals from these labs. Please realize, however, that many of them are tied into chemical sales, so they will push you strongly to "solve" your problems by adding in salts. Yep, all those inorganic additions they are telling you to make are salts. Which kill the biology. Which means you will lose those organisms that hold those nutrients, if you use those salts. And that leads to leaching, and further loss of those nutrients. Which means, you get to buy more next year.

Hum, the American way? If the consumer doesn't know any better, get them to buy more. Most chemical salespeople don't know what they are doing to soil health by adding these salts and toxic materials. Or they don't want to believe what they are doing. In the case of academics saying "there's no data", my conclusion is that they are flat out incapable of reading the recent scientific literature. They have their Ph.D., why should they have to keep up in the literature? Direct academics saying there are no data to the Ecological Monograph written in 1985, by Ingham et al (different Ingham, not me as senior author) on the impact of soil biology on plant growth. Or have them look at the SFI website and read some of the books on our reference list, or my list of peer-reviewed papers. But, moving along, now you understand, from the chemical tests, what is present in your soil, and what you need to add.

f. Step four - soil food web assessment. What biology is lacking in your soil? You can get a pretty good idea just by observing. The soil foodweb website goes over look-see information you should be paying attention to. I've written them up before for this list-serve, so please look at Chris Reid's document where she has summarized the topics on this list serve.

So, do not add salts to your soil. If you must add LOTS of nutrients, add them to your compost. The FUNCTION of biology is to, in part, increase the holding of those nutrients. So, reduce any recommendation from the soil chemistry labs by a factor of about 10 times less than what they recommended, and that addition goes into the COMPOST. Beginning or end of cycle seems to make no difference, as long as you give the biology at least a week to recover and retain.

Example: Albrecht test says you need 8 tons of lime per ac. Don't do that, you are wasting money, and harming surface and ground water. A ton is about 2000 pounds, so the recommendation is to put 1600 pounds of lime per acre. That's a chunk of change, plus think about trying to actually spread 1600 pounds. That's a chunk of change too.

g. General Recommendations
Instead, do what Arden Anderson and I have been demonstrating works. If the recommendation is 8 tons (1600 pounds) of lime, reduce that amount by 10 times (to 160 pounds). Add 160 pounds of lime per 1000 pounds (half a ton) of compost (or 80 pounds per ton). Let the organisms have a week or more to deal with that addition, and spread that compost out at a minimum of half ton per acre. A ton is better, 5 tons better, etc. It's really addition of carbon to your soil that makes the greatest difference. The calcium is just along for the ride, and you have it in the right proportion to the carbon in compost at this point. Not only to you get the equivalent of 8 tons of lime, but you enhance your biology. Make sure the compost was made with good fungal foods, so you get the organism that holds the calcium in the soil, and doesn't let it leach.

Add any other "lacking nutrient" to your compost - typically:

1) fish hydrolysate (please make sure you check mercury levels in the product - ASK the seller for the DATA before buying!). We have data on Neptune's Harvest, showing that it really enhances fungi. See the SFI website for the data. Organic Gem as well, and has good calcium levels. Add that to your compost instead of the lime, which is a salt and can kill some of the beneficials. Amount to add depends on the nutrients you need to add to the compost. Read the label on the fish to figure that out. Sandy at Neptune's Harvest, Ray Gore for Organic Gem, or Bob Posthuma for GeoFish can give you the recommendations given the amount of nutrient you need. Can't say anything about Dramm, I don't communicate with their salespeople.

2) kelp (cold water kelp has more nutrients in it than warm water kelp. Make sure the SALT level is ok - again, get the nutrient analysis from the company. Make sure salt is less than toxic levels.

Also, as I understand, Acadian kelp has lost their organic accreditation, because of too high acid extraction in their process or something like that. Sorry, I don't always remember everything anymore. But, look around for some other organically accredited kelp. Better for your compost organisms, and your plants. Strong acids denature the nutrients and prevent your plants from being able to obtain the nutrients.

3) soft rock. We've been looking at soft rock and rock dusts, and folks! LOOK OUT! Pay attention to the zinc, copper and lead levels in some of that material! Bad news! You MUST get the chemical analysis on these things. Most people understand they shouldn't be putting something toxic into their soils.

I don't tell anyone not to buy any particular machine. I just say, here are the data from all the different tea machines. If you don't believe those are the levels those machines get, test your tea. Over and over again, when we ask what happened to the biology in a low-fungi, low protozoa tea, the person confesses that they bought one of the machines that can't produce decent tea. Then we work with them to get them to understand how to make those machines give decent tea. They can be modified to be ok.

Your choice is to buy a machine that can't produce a compost tea with the biological levels established as giving full benefit. People always have the option to do whatever they please, but then don't complain to me when the tea from those machines doesn't give all the benefits you think you should be getting. If the tea lacks the fungal biomass, protozoa and nematode numbers that you need to achieve, you won't get all the benefits. Of course, making sure the compost has the fungi in it to begin with is very important.

4) compost usually has all the nutrients your plant needs, plus the biology, if it was made correctly. Aerobic, never stinky, temperature did not get above 155 to 160 F. Again, as a garden columnist, you might pull readers in by doing columns on how the local compost sources do their composting, and what the nutrients and biology therefore are in that "compost". Readers love it when they can go to a local source and find out what is the best.

You can rank composts by chemical and biology components, or by the process they use to compost - least smelly, temperature in a good range. Rank worm compost by the concentration of worms in the bins, time between adding wastes into the bin, and removal of material as finished worm compost.

You have to avoid saying "buy this because it is best" - that's law suit land. But you can rank things on objective things like how much nitrate (bad if it's above a certain level, and that level is established by USDA, although I enjoy that the acceptable nitrate level is going down, and down and down), biomass of beneficial fungi (level established by SFI based on if above this level of biomass, and with foods present, they will establish and grow in the soil), protozoan numbers, etc.

Standards should always go back to the plant response when that material is placed in or near the root system of the plant. That is what we do at SFI. If it doesn't give the benefits we talk about as being possible, then we'll point that out.

h. Standards
Hard to achieve? No, not if you are honest and willing to do the necessary work to get there.

Some people say that SFI standards are impossible and too complex, and that SFI plays favorites. They claim they only get in the club if they achieve the standards. Well, duh! That's the way it should be. Orange juice can only be labeled orange juice if it contains more than 51% orange juice. What an impossible standard! And you can only get into the orange juice club if you pass that standard! Gasp!

If people can't achieve the standards, then they claim that the standards aren't real? What does that in fact tell you about the person doing the criticizing? That perhaps they can't achieve the standards, and anything they can't achieve must be stupid? Sour grapes, anyone?

SFI standards are based on getting plants to grow without disease (so no pesticides needed), on reducing weeds (so herbicides not needed), on reducing inorganic fertilizer use (so no inorganic fertilizer needed), reducing water use by the system (so less watering), on increasing yields (no disease, better water retention and nutrient retention), AND higher yields? Yep.

If the biology isn't right, the benefits won't occur - all of the benefits. If part of the right biology is achieved, will only part of the benefits occur? Yes. And that's good enough for some people. But not for me. All of the benefits are possible and can be easily achieved, if things are done right.

Not willing to make decent compost? Or demand that compost bought from someone else is documented to have the biology needed? Where's the documentation?

There's a bridge that a salesperson I know would love to sell you. You can get a really nice deed and everything. Oh, you want to see the bridge first? Dang, asking for data....

i. Brewing Equipment
Not willing to make sure the tea machine is clean, which means cleaning the BOTTOM of all surfaces that are in the machine each time? Have a tea machine that accumulates grunge on the bottom of the tea machine while brewing? You aren't going to be able to deal with mildew when conditions are right for a mildew outbreak.

j. Black Spot
Black spot? Any bacterial tea can deal with that. But what if you are still having black spot problems even when you are using tea? It says you really don't understand what tea is all about, and the biology needed to do the job was killed before it could do the job. I've talked about the things you have to consider and the easy ways to determine this without testing.

k. Conclusion
Think about what you are doing, and seek advice from an SFI advisor, all of whom have had training in the things they need to think about when it comes to making great tea. Lots of potential factors to think about, but most gardeners don't need to go through the whole list. Think about gardening - there's a huge complexity to think about, but most people don't have to - they have you

to help them. That's why garden columnists exist. Growing plants can be a real mind-boggling experience what with all the details that COULD be playing a part. Using compost tea can be just the same, but just a little experience, and you can cut the list of things to consider.

16. **Plate Counts Shortcomings** 10/18/03 12:10 PM

Plate counts tell you nothing useful about the actual number of species present. Plate counts are not capable of giving you information on the number of individuals of any ACTIVE, metabolically functioning species in soil, compost, compost tea, or any environmental sample you want to talk about. Plate count information gives data on a minor subset of organisms that may or may not have been active, could have been present just as spores, and not active for decades. Chat with Eric Nelson, whose paper on comparing plate counts with what was going on in soil or compost samples with respect to pathogens demonstrates how useless plate counts actually are. Dr. Eric Nelson, Cornell University. The guru of composting for in turf. Just might know what he's talking about? His words, and as I recall this is an exact quote: "Plate counts are bogus when testing environmental samples."

a. Here's an example for you Plate count tests were done, the grower was given the data from 6 different media and told that the compost tea was good, the "index" was above 5 (what does that mean?). Fungal numbers were high. The "fungus" was mildew. Huge numbers of spores of mildew in the "tea". In the field? Mildew was much higher in the plots "with tea". Great, mildew took out the grape vines. It wasn't compost tea at all, was it? The tea was likely anaerobic, as it smelled. It was growing only a limited set of species of fungi. How can you call it compost tea, when what is growing is basically just mildew? Scares me what the reputation of "compost tea" is going to get to be when we have idiots pulling off this kind of "tea making" and "tea testing". Frightening.

b. Make Sure Tea Stays Aerobic

Measure aeration. Make sure the tea recipe you are using allows the tea to stay aerobic. Wish there were test strip papers we could use to dip and know that the tea was aerobic at 14, 18, and 20 hours into the brew, when, if the tea is going to go anaerobic, is when it happens. Any one know of anything like this? Maybe we need rental oxygen probes to go to people when they start making tea with tea makers that haven't been tested properly. But, when you use KIS brewers, we KNOW they stay aerobic if you use the amounts of foods recommended by the manufacturer. Clean after use completely. Use Monrovia tea brewers - same story. Use EPM machines, but clean carefully, and use the recommended ingredients. Use the Bitti-brewers, or the Alaska Giants, but clean well, and make sure you take the compost out after a couple hours. OK, numbers MIGHT not be as great, but at least you won't kill plants, and won't have the mildew debacle. If the tea stayed aerobic, then check your total and active bacteria, total and active fungi. You learn the right way to make tea, using this approach, and after one or two tests, you know you are doing good, and you don't have to test, except for the occasional test strip, and the occasional SFI test (e.g., once at year, when you get started in the spring) to guarantee quality.

c. Molecular Probe Testing

SFI is working on molecular probe testing to do the E. coli, Salmonella, Shigella, N-fixers, Pseudomonads, etc. Plate counts are not as reliable as these molecular methods, plate counts are more prone to false negatives and positives, and take longer, and cost more. Plate counts will soon be an outdated technology, something we think of Louis Pasteur having to do during the dawn of our understanding of microbiology, not something anyone would use to assess numbers of anything for real world samples.

17. Leaf Organism Assay   2/13/04 11:40 PM

a. SFI Technician Wrote: Please excuse my assumptions. The letter "codes" refer to B=bacteria, F=fungi, and tc=total coverage. This is in reference to a leaf bioassay in which a portion of the leaf is sprayed with a fluorescent stain, and living bacteria and fungi will take up this stain and glow under a epifluorescent light. It is a method used to examine living microorganisms. The numbers refer to the percent of leaf surface covered by F or B. Understand that this is not absolute % coverage. It actually refers to the number of squares on a grid that contain these glowing microorganisms. Please forgive me if this explanation is less than accurate. This is just my general understanding of the SFI leaf organism bioassay, and I'm sure Elaine could explain this much better than I have, but you should get the general idea.

b. Elaine's further explanation: Ah, let me explain the activity assay. A leaf is held in FDA solution for the correct period of time, then observed using the epic-fluorescent microscope. Actively metabolizing organisms will actively transport the stain into their cells, hydrolyze the acetate from the fluorescein, and accumulate the fluorescein in the cells. We know that aerobic bacteria will produce glue layers around their bodies, and thus the area that they will cover. We can see the areas around the hyphae as well, and so the organisms don't have to be "chock-a-block" stacked up to each other. After all, if you put 100 people in a phone booth, there is still space in the booth, right? But we'd all agree that all the space is reasonably well occupied. Right? Same with what we do for the leaf assay. The leaf is reasonably well occupied at 100% coverage, about 70% coverage has some space empty, 50% coverage has half empty spaces, etc. We find that less than 70% coverage can be a problem. We want 5% of the leaf covered with fungi, and 65% covered with bacteria. More is better.

18. E. Coli Testing 3/27/04 12:32 PM
The methods that SFI uses for doing the Leaf Organism Assay -- we add FDA staining to pick up the active organisms. We also use molecular probes for doing the E. coli, Salmonella and Shigella, N-fixers, and will add more probes in the coming months -- 3 hour turn-around to enumerate E. coli and other pathogens. We will be adding the rapid E. coli assay to SFI assays and will add the ability to do these tests to the other SFI labs through the coming year. Most likely the recommendations to the NOSB will allow assessment of E. coli as a method of checking your tea and making sure the tea is low in human pathogens as a way to allow use of that tea on any plant material. So, we have a way now that you could make your tea, test it at 21 hours, and be able to put it out on food plants once you know it is documented E. coli-free. Of course, the tea would have to be sprayed within the next 24 to 36 hours, with adequate aeration during that time period. If held longer, you would need to run another test, most likely, to guarantee no problems. If you are putting on non-food plants, you don't need to worry about this. Enough new data are coming out; human pathogens don't survive on aerobic leaf surfaces so we can be pretty certain that they won't survive more than a few hours to a day.

19. Bio-Log Samples 2/21/04 5:02 AM
We have been running Bio-Log samples from materials, which allows ID of species of bacteria that will grow on a number of different media. If you would like to have us test your material, and ID the bacteria that grow on those plates to species, we can do that at SFI Corvallis. Price depends on how many species grow on the plates.

20. Testing Tea for the Home Brewer 2/21/04 5:02 AM
Several approaches for the home person:

1. Stain for adding to the tea to test coverage and activity.
2. Microscope so you can test each brew. Occasional check-up with SFI recommended.
3. "Bad smell" test in 24 hour, ambient temp, sealed bottle.

The bad smell test has been described. The other two are in testing phase. Testing on the stain is coming along.

21. Epi-Flourescent Microscope 1/22/04 8:41 PM
The epi-fluorescent microscope is only needed if you want to be precise and accurate. If you just want a general idea of "no one home", "not-good", "low", "ok", not-too-bad", "good" and "wow", then a bright field or phase contrast microscope is ok. The epi-fluorescent units are really for those of us that want to be at a commercial level.

22. Assessing Tea 1/20/04 8:26 AM

Question: I actually have some saline but wasn't sure exactly how to use it.
Answer: Use the saline in place of the tap water or distilled water. The match with physiological cell concentrations of salt will give more accurate number assessment.

Question: I can't tell what type they are only that they are there. I look at this frequency; then I look to see how this frequency transfers to the soil. I don't test immediately but wait a while. I can only get trends, of course, but if those trends can be repeated with regularity, I feel more confident.
Answer: Yes, this is one kind of information, and quite useful. If you know the soil had 100 bacteria, and 5 micrometers of hyphae (assess types based on morphology - that's how you determine actinobacteria from true fungi) before you added any compost or compost tea, and then a week later, you had 1000 bacteria and 20 micrometers length of hyphae, and a change in morphology, you know the tea improved things.

Question: But, what if you saw fewer organisms after you added the tea?
Answer: You might mistakenly assume that the tea was "no good", when in fact it was fine, but there was a toxic material in the soil that killed your organisms. Tillage, too much water, too little water, pesticide or herbicide residue, drift, air pollution, all can harm the organisms in the soil, or on leaf surfaces. So, don't jump to the wrong conclusion. One way to know the tea was good is to look at the tea and assess bacteria and fungi in the tea. Then you would know the tea was "good"

or not (lots of organisms, or lacking lots of organisms, for example), and can better fine-tune what the low organism numbers in the soil means.

Question: I can't even be sure that two batches of tea are the same.
Answer: But you can look at the biology in the tea, and at least have an idea that numbers of bacteria and hyphal length were high, low, or average.

Question: I can, of course, shoot for diversity but even with the best compost, I can't be sure of total similarity from batch to batch.
Answer: So, also look at the compost with the microscope.

Question: So I have to rely on trends. If I see certain bodies in my tea and they transfer to the soil and the plant analysis comes back showing improved use of nutrients and the soil food web is established, I have to think what I am doing is working and repeatable to a degree.
Answer: And you are correct.

Question: I'm not against training but, quite frankly, do not have the resources to throw myself or someone else into a training program which, I figure, would cost me somewhere in the range of $25K without the $20K microscope. I have to pay the person taking the training, pay for the training and compensate for the time they are not here generating capital.
Answer: Well, it does cost money. But your son might be able to train on one thing at a time, like just total bacterial biomass, or total fungal biomass, so he would know what he is looking at, and the correct morphology so he could ID what he was looking at. Training at SFI is about $1000 a week, and in a week, he can do quite a bit of learning - not only about morphology, but the other tricks of the trade, such as buffers, prepping samples correctly to know what the volume of soil is being observed, etc. We do ask for a non-compete, and a continuing quality assurance program, which is related to the number of samples being looked at. We want to make sure your morphological assessment doesn't go off on a tangent.

Question: He right now has developed a formula to try and predict how many more and the complexity of organisms he is plotting to see if he can predict growth from sample time to sample time.
Answer: Quite interesting! As I recall, trying to predict growth based on initial numbers was tried and is written up in either Sylvia's microbiology text book, or Thimann's book on the Life of Bacteria. As long as all growth conditions are held the same from time to time, then the prediction holds well. You have to know the conditions well. It's what we've done at SFI when we look at soils, climate, growing conditions all over the world. There is a decent relationship between biomass and diversity - usually directly linear as long as there is no toxins in the soil.

23. Assessing Activity 1/19/04 7:20 PM

Question: I use distilled water. However, it is not pharmaceutical grade.
Answer: This is a problem. Distilled water lacks physiological balance. You need to use a buffered physiological solution, like physiological saline, or phosphate buffer, or citrate buffer.

Question: I am looking through the whole cycle. I look for what is in my tea and see if it is replicating in my soil. That means fungi (look just like the textbooks show) protozoa and bacterial/fungal eating nematodes.

Answer: In your post you said bacteria, which is why I responded saying fungi too at the very least. So, great that you look at all of them, but this is where you really need the ability to assess activity. Many of the hyphae in soil are not active, and can be "left-over" from a long time ago. You need to distinguish *actinobacteria* hyphae from *oomycetes*, from *ascomycete*, from *basidiomycete*. All based on morphology, of course. Some training would be a good idea, since these things are not usually pointed out in text books.

24. Ecoli Testing 4/29/04 7:43 AM

The place to go for the standards for E. coli testing is the USEPA website. They only approve a few methods for doing the testing for fecal E. coli. You need to ask whatever lab you choose for the testing if they use EPA approved tests. If you have trouble finding the US EPA website, check the SFI website, www.soilfoodweb.com. In our testing methods section, we list the source, since we do E. coli tests using both the EPA approved coli-blue method as well as a molecular method (faster turn-around, and more accurate at lower numbers). If you can't find that on the website, call SFI and chat with Matt about the reference for the test.

25. Fecal E Coli Tests 4/26/04 3:05 AM

The testing being required is simple FECAL E. coli tests. Not coliforms, not the other pathogens, but the normal indicator of fecal contamination. Compost tea brewers will need to test compost used in compost tea, and if that is pathogen-free, then life is fine, use the tea without restriction. If pathogens-levels are below restricted levels in the compost, but still present, then either do not add anything to the compost tea brew that will allow pathogen growth in the compost tea - such as molasses or other sugars - or test the final compost tea to make sure you did not grow pathogens in the tea. Please note that SFI is just about finished developing a 3-hour turn-around test for E. coli using molecular probes. We will be able to do Salmonella, Shigella and other human pathogens as well. I just have to get back to the lab, and finalize the testing, to get this one available at all SFI labs around the world. You will be able to test your compost tea at 18 hours into the tea brew, and get the data back before you need to use the tea. Believe me, the Idaho lab is chomping at the bit to get this test! They can guarantee that each tea brew sold is E. coli-free, or at levels below any concern by the USDA or EPA. We HAVE to finish the testing that shows the aerobic conditions, with proper aerobic beneficial organisms, result in NO pathogens in the compost tea.

26. Pathogen-Free vs. Below Detection Level 7/29/04 12:49 AM

Question: I'm fine with "no pathogens detected", but I don't like "pathogen-free" because it is too much like marketing-speak, and it most likely is not true. From the way that you put things in this post, I suspect that you understand my objection to the term "pathogen-free". It is linguist ally taking one step beyond what the facts support.

Answer: I agree with you completely. Although I sometimes fall prey to the "market-speak" that gets used. I have been known to say "pathogen-free" because it is shorter than saying "human pathogens were below detection level". It's short-hand (short-speak?) Still, we should use language that is crystal clear whenever we are talking to folks that may not know the short-hand. So, "below detection level" is the proper term.

27. *Actinobacteria (actinomycetes)* 5/17/04

Actinobacteria (used to be called actinomycetes) are truly bacteria. But they are unique, in that they grow in strand forms, and so branch like fungi. But they fall apart quite easily when disturbed. They are very slender hyphae as well - only 1 to 1.5 micrometers in diameter. So you can tell them pretty easily in a microscope. The slender, slender "hyphae" are the actinomycetes.

28. Formazan for Dehydragenase Enzyme Test 5/10/04 4:47 AM

Formazan is the product tested when doing the dehydrogenase enzyme test. Dehydrogenase is an enzyme in the final steps in cytochrome respiration. Any organism that uses respiration based on the kreb's cycle generally also uses a cytochrome cascade to generate energy through ATP production. One of the steps in this cascade requires the generation of dehydrogenase to perform energy production. Dehydrogenase can, instead of doing its job in cytochrome energy formation, strip electrons from tetrazolium salts, and result in the formation of formazan.

Question: Therefore, the formazan test is a measure of respiration. Ah, but whose respiration?
Answer: Roots will cause formazan to form, as will bacteria, fungi, protozoa, nematodes.... they all use respiratory cytochrome systems. There are some bacteria and fungi that do not use dehydrogenase as an enzyme in respiration. So you miss those species altogether.

Question: Are they important species?
Answer: Some of them are common in soil. And, to make things more interesting, there are a number of bacteria that are killed by the concentration of formazan used in most of these tests. In order to generate enough color in a 24 hour test which is used to tell you how much respiration occurred (formazan is an interesting purple-violet color), toxic levels of tetrazolium chloride (otherwise known as TTC) have to be used. Some people have tried to use less toxic materials than TTC, but no one has demonstrated that these other materials are in fact less toxic, when ALL bacterial species are considered. As you might expect, it is difficult to actually demonstrate that nothing has been killed when we can't grow all these organisms to determine whether they are truly active.

Use of these alternative electron acceptors is, of course, detrimental to the organisms. When energy generation in organisms is disrupted by adding a compound that causes dehydrogenase to work on the TTC, instead of on the cytochrome system it normally is supposed to work on, the organism does not generate adequate energy, will be severely stressed, and often does not survive.

There's also the question of activity level. If one organisms is extremely active, and also resistant to the TTC salt, then that one organism may cause reduction of say 100 units of TTC to formazan during the 24 hour incubation period required. But another organism is not as active (not as much food, for example), and thus may reduce say 10 units of formazan, and not 100. Another organism, which succumbs to the toxic effect of not-getting-the-energy-it-needs-to-stay-alive, will reduce say 5 units of formazan, and then die.

Question: Thus the formazan produced is a sum of all the activity of all these organisms. What information exactly are you getting? Does this assay tell you what you want to know?
Answer: Up to you to decide. As far as I am concerned, there are too many questionable aspects to the assay. Please, formazan is a toxic material, so how do you dispose of the material generated in the testing process?
Too many problems with the formazan assay. Using fluorescein diacetate is much easier. It doesn't kill anything. It does not produce a toxic end-product so I am not destroying the environment by using fluorescein diacetate.

29. Electrical Conductivity 1/20/04 10:46 PM

We have just added the ability to do electrical conductivity to the list of assays that we do. So, we can check for lots of kinds of problems with compost or soil. If the biology is happy and healthy, then you probably don't have serious chemical problems. But, we can have heavy metal tolerant, or salt-tolerant communities of microbes, and so the EC assay will let us know about that problem. It's easy enough to buy an EC meter for those who want to add that ability. The meter costs about $270 from Pike Agri lab, and you just need de-ionized water to mix one-to-one with your soil or compost sample. The SFI test will cost about $5.00 per sample, because it takes time to mix the sample, do the assay, report the results via e-mail or FAX.

30. Organisms in Soil 1/10/04 2:07 AM

Please recognize that AG soil, not healthy soil was tested. So the 5,000 species is much less than what we find in soil where we have good organic matter. Aerobic compost, with a good diversity of different food resources contains more than 5,000 species of bacteria. And then there's fungi, protozoa and nematodes in there too. Not just bacteria. When we look at soil from a conventional AG field, we don't find the biomass or diversity of bacteria, fungi, protozoa or nematodes that are found in soil with good organic matter, where no toxic chemicals were used. Many bacterial species don't produce dormant stages, and thus they cannot survive being blown about for days, or even hours, or even minutes. We find that adding inocula of bacteria, fungi, protozoa and nematodes improves soil life.

a. Chloroform Fumigation and Plate Counts

Please do not be mis-lead by chloroform fumigation methods, or plate counts methods. Plate counts miss over 99.9% of the species of bacteria and fungi. Most of the species of organisms in soil, compost, or compost tea do not grow in the lab on the limited food resources used in any lab medium. Consider that in the lab one temperature is used, one moisture, one humidity, and thus these conditions are entirely WRONG for most soil biology to grow. Fumigation cannot differentiate bacteria from fungi, and in fact, misses fungal biomass almost entirely. The fumigation method cannot control for the carbon released by chloroform solubilization. You know that chloroform alters the solubility of many carbohydrates, oils, lipids, etc. And thus fumigation has more to do with organic matter levels than bacterial or fungal biomass.

At the recent Soils meetings, a report was given that there was no difference in microbial biomass between a soil without added inoculum, and a soil where inoculum was added. Of course not, using the methods they used. Most of the bacteria in the inoculum don't grow on the medium chosen. Fumigation won't detect fungal growth. So, of course the conclusion was made that addition of a microbial inoculum doesn't improve soil life. But look at the growth of the plants. Greener, less disease, higher yields, used less water. No measurable fertilizer N, P, or K was added. The added organisms had a significant, positive impact on plant growth. Inocula can make a great deal of difference. We've killed a great deal of the life in our soils. They are not in the soil a mile away, or ten miles ,or 100 miles. So if they aren't there, and can't survive the trip anyway, they can't blow back in.

31. Labs and Back-up 12/7/03 12:41 PM
There is the New York lab, and you can talk to Paul Wagner about what he sees. Talk to Eric Nelson at Cornell University. He's looked at these methods, and knows that direct estimations are the way to go, given what we need to know. Talk to the people who do direct determinations in Australia, New Zealand, Holland, and soon opening, Mexico, and Canada. They are independent labs, I don't tell them what to think. But the technology needs constant and consistent quality control. That's why the labs are linked. When visual methods are used, you have to maintain a solid frame of reference about what a fungus looks like. And that's what the SFI lab system does - we maintain a constant testing system. Which may be another reason that one lab has such bizarre numbers in their direct counts. One person without any back-up, makes mistakes. My lab folks are always checking with each other, and with me, about what they are seeing. Is this a ciliate? Or what is it? You have to have the back-up and the knowledge to know what you are doing.

32. SFI Testing Methods 11/20/03 8:02 AM
At SFI this fall, we did a phone survey of the clients we have worked with over the last few years:

1. About 25% said that they test with SFI once a year, because they have achieved the reduction in pesticide and fertilizer applications that they were told were possible. They make good compost, and/or good tea, and use them the way SFI recommends. Some of them are the people we worked with to develop the program. It is possible to get completely off of the toxics using the right biology. But you have to be willing to make certain the right biology is present and functioning properly for the plant you are trying to grow. If you never check, then when nature throws you a loop, it's guess and by gosh to know what to do to rescue the biology correctly and get your plant back into a condition of health quickly.

2. Another 50% of our clients are having partial success, and they realize they need to improve their biology in some fashion. So they are testing a bit more frequently than once a year.

3. The remaining 25% had various reasons they were testing more, or less. Some are having trouble obtaining good tea results, and as a result, their plant results are less than what they should be able to obtain. We work fairly closely with some of these folks. The tea machine maker they bought their machine from tries to work with them, and I think most of them have moved forward in the tea production arena.

4. Some are re-thinking the whole paradigm shift. It takes effort to change, and some people just like the easy road. It's their choice to continue to be part of the problem, and not the solution. Given the shocking condition of water in this country and around the world, all of the "easy-

271

roaders" will be back in a few years to learn from those of us who are at the cutting edge now, figuring out the solution to contaminated soil and thus water.

There will always be people who try something, don't follow the directions, and give up when they can't get it to work. Tea requires attention to the machine, to the compost used, and to the added foods for the microbes. Tea requires attention to the sprayer and application methods. That's why this list is so useful. A community of people working out what is needed. I don't know everything, especially the mechanical, engineering end of things. Most of the documentation that tea machines can extract and grow the beneficial aerobic organisms should be carried out by the company making the tea machine. Follow the directions for the machine you decide on, make good tea. Clean the tea maker properly, and keep making great tea. Don't use machines made by those who cannot document that their machines extract or grow the desired organisms. If someone says SFI doesn't know what they are doing, you should probably suspect that they are from a company that cannot get decent biology in their tea or compost.

a. Numbers Provide Evidence

Any grower should be wise enough to ask for the numbers showing decent biology before they purchase anything. That's where growers have clout - before they buy. No evidence that the product does what the machine maker says it can? Don't buy the product. No evidence that the compost is actually compost? Keep searching. Your nose is quite helpful in obtaining data whether the compost is decent or not, but the final proof has to be in whether the bacteria, fungi, protozoa and nematodes are in the compost. The company you buy the compost from should be expected to have data documenting the biology. So, failure is rare when there's just a bit of checking out the situation. But if you are making statements without checking out the truth, failure is the likely outcome.

b. SFI Does Not Culture Organisms

At Soil Foodweb, we do not culture organisms. We use particular activity stains, or total biomass stains, and ID and count organisms using microscopes. What we do is called direct enumeration. Any time you want to visit an SFI lab and see what we do, you are welcome to stop by. It takes about 20 minutes to prepare your sample, and get it to the microscope so you can look at your organisms in your own sample. We'll give you a quick tour of the lab while the sample is being weighed out, stained, and put on the microscope slide.

c. Most Organisms in Soil, Compost or Compost Tea Cannot be Cultured

Most of the organisms in soil, or compost or compost tea cannot be cultured in the lab. But anytime you want, you can look at them using a microscope. Think about how you determine if a person is a person. You don't have to grow them, or culture them, you look at them. Do they have the basic human shape? Then they are human. (How good a human they are is another story....) That's what SFI does with total bacteria, fungi, protozoa, nematodes and mycorrhizal fungi biomass measurements - we make sure they have the correct morphology, then measure their length and width.

d. Activity Stain Determines Active Biomass

We use an activity stain to determine active biomass. We know the normal activity and total biomass needed to grow different kinds of plants at different seasons in different soils. On the SFI report, we tell you what our database of well over 100,000 samples from around the world shows to be the minimum desired range for each organism group in order to grow your plants without pesticides, or high amounts of inorganic fertilizers. Those numbers change with season, with soil type, with crop, etc.

e. Soil Health May Take Years

If you want to take years to get your soil to a condition of health, and maybe never actually get there, that's your choice. If you want to get to a healthy condition rapidly, reduce costs (pesticides no longer needed, no more fungicides, insecticides, nematicides, etc), reduce watering needs, reduce compaction in your soil, then you need to know what's in your soil, and what needs to be "fixed", brought up to the right levels so your plants aren't stressed.

f. Testing to Improve Plant Growth

Everything SFI does is relative to improving plant growth. We have done that testing. So for someone to say there's no relation between the SFI assays and what's going on with plant yield is a total mis-representation.
Fact: if you do a whole Soil Foodweb test, the cost is about $250. That includes total bacteria, active bacteria, total fungi, active fungi, flagellates, amoebae, ciliates, nematodes identified to genus and feeding group, and mycorrhizal colonization of the roots, and assessment of disease on the roots. You can't get that level of knowledge from plate counts (which cost more than whole foodweb assessments). You can't begin to get the knowledge from a soil chemistry test that will help you get the soil into a condition that toxic chemicals are no longer needed. Soil chemistry tests try to tell you that you need MORE toxic chemicals, usually.

The four basic assays, active bacteria, total bacteria, active fungi, total fungi are about $100 (pre-discount for filling out the paperwork completely). If you want to get started, do just that set of four tests to make sure the base of the foodweb is right first. Then once those are in shape, after you have fixed them to be right to support the plant you want to grow, then work on protozoa, nematodes and mycorrhizal fungi.

Statements that someone knows lots of people who have tried tea and have given up is sad. Why would someone say that, without offering any solid information? There will always be nay-sayers. The rest of us get to forge ahead without them. They'll come along when they notice that no one is listening to them

33. Tea in Fall 11/2/03 12:39 PM

a. Northern Hemisphere

This is the time of year, in the northern hemisphere, to be getting down that last tea application to the soil, to get the proper set of organisms on the residues of your plants. If you make sure the good guys are decomposing the plant residues left from harvest, then you deplete the disease-

273

causing organisms, especially the fungi and will typically reduce foliar diseases by 70% next spring, and reduce root diseases by as much as 90% next year.

b. Southern Hemisphere

Now, in the southern hemisphere, things are in full swing for spring. But it is still time to be doing a soil drench application, because if that 30% of the foliar diseases made it through the winter, then you need to start combating them now. Make sure the disease causing organisms have a tough time finding food, because someone else beneficial is there first. Make sure you get down the protozoa, nematodes and encourage the microarthropods in your soil by giving them the fungi they need to be happy (full tummies, lots of reproduction, lots of kids to feed), and consume the spores of the disease-causing fungi. That way the diseases don't spread to your leaf surfaces. So, spring or autumn, tea is still a first order of business.

c. How to Test Tea

To test the tea, get a plastic water bottle (drink the water), rinse with a sample of your tea, then put in several dips of tea from around the whole tea brewer. Paul Wagner recommends taking a little bit of tea when you first start to transfer the tea to your sprayer, another bit a third of the way through the transfer process, and another bit at two-thirds of the way through, and a final bit at the end. Mix those together, fill your clean, tea-rinsed plastic bottle a bit less than half-full, seal, put in plastic bag (salable), as Autumn recommended, put in shipping container, and send overnight mail to SFI. New York or Corvallis? Doesn't matter - whichever is less expensive and fastest. The point is to know that you are making good tea. I'm happier with the molecular probes for E. coli, Salmonella, Shigella, N2-fixers, and Pseudomonas. They will be in the final testing process the next two weeks, and we should be able to offer the 3 hour turnaround time on these bacteria by the first of December.

34. Pathogen Interaction Trials 10/9/03 7:54 AM

We can do testing in the lab in simple interaction trials. We are right now developing the lab set-up to do these comparisons. The design is:

Obtain the *Agribacterium vitis* culture, preferably from the vines so you have the local culture. Plate the organisms on a agar medium allowing for it to grow - there are specific media for these different organisms so check the scientific literature to determine the correct medium. Order from Difco.

Grow the A. *radiobacter* in the commercial culture on another plate of the medium. On a third plate, put squares of the pathogen around the outside of the plate. In the middle of the plate, put a square of the potential bio-control. See if the bio-control actually suppresses or prevents the growth of the pathogen.

You need to be able to autoclave the plates once you are done, so you don't spread a huge inoculum of the disease all through the landfill. OK? We have the ability to do these kinds of tests at SFI. So, those of you who want this kind of work done, the cost depends on the hours it takes to culture and grow the organisms. Probably on the order of $300 to $800 per paired (pathogen - bio-control) test.

35. Pathogen Testing 10/9/03 5:41 Am

I have worked with the person who isolated and tested the bacterium you are interested in. Yes, it should grow in compost tea, and it likes amino sugars. So, reasonably complex sugars should work. A little testing with an SFI lab would tell you which food resource should work best. For example, bring a tea to the New York lab. Look at the organisms in the tea (takes about 5 minutes to prep, about 20 minutes to look at the sample to see what's present). Add in the bacterial inoculum, find out what the bacterium looks like. Split the tea into a number of smaller portions, depending on how many foods you want to test. Place a small amount (like one crop of food in a 500 ml container) of the different foods in the containers with the tea and *Agrobacterium*. Let the samples incubate while you go eat lunch, come back and look at the samples to see whether the *Agrobacterium* started to grow. Let incubate overnight, and check again. That way you know what food will feed the organisms. You might want to then test concentration of the food to add - for example, add 2 drops, or 4 drops, or 8 drops of the best food, so you get a better idea of what increasing foods do. When the brew runs out of air overnight, then the organisms won't grow, and you know you added too much food. Or get an oxygen probe and test that way.

36. Publishable Data 10/1/03 7:43 Am

The only way to know the effect of any material is to test it. If you wonder about effect on tea organisms, you have to make a tea, pull two volumes, treating them just exactly the same, and add the test material to one of the volumes, and not to the other. Remember to add the same amount of water to the CONTROL (no PRODUCT added) as you added to the test volume. Send BOTH in to have the biology tested. With a soil applied material, take two areas that are exactly the same. To one, apply the product, to the other, apply the same volume of water without the product. You might want to wait for a month before sampling when doing soil, to see the long term impact and the effect on the mycorrhizal fungi on the roots. That's the only way to go on anything that we don't know what it does. OK? If you want to have SFI publish the data, then you have to repeat the same control - treatment comparisons THREE TIMES. Preferably three control - treatment pairs at the same time, and then three control- treatment pairs at three different times of year. The replication is absolutely necessary when doing science. If you do all that, I'll be happy to write up the manuscript and get it published.

37. Testing Particulate Settled Matter 9/17/03 6:24 PM

I'm not aware of anyone taking their samples by letting the particulate material settle to the bottom of the tank and taking material from the settled tea. But it is not representative of the tea that will be sprayed out on your plants. Why would anyone take a sample this way, except to trick the tests into looking good, when in fact the tea isn't that good? As if people buying the tea or the machine don't then have trouble obtaining the numbers the tea maker is claiming..... so this approach to testing will back-fire on the person doing this, when people either don't get the numbers, or the benefit to their plants that the tea should be giving.

38. Testing for Human Pathogens 9/13/03 1:12 AM

The concern about consuming CT comes form the compost used. If the compost is not fully composted, which means it didn't pass through or touch worms enough (vermi-compost), or the compost didn't reach 131 F for a full three days in all parts (thermal compost, and it means ALL of the outside has to be turned to the inside of the pile to reach temp for 3 days, minimum), then you have to test the pile for human pathogens before use.

Of course, if you didn't put anything that would contain a human pathogen in the pile, you are pretty safe that the compost won't have human pathogen problems. So the composts that must be carefully dealt with are those containing manures or post-consumer waste materials. Human are great at contaminating food with pathogens. So, with manure-based or human garbage-based compost, there's a serious concern to make sure composting went correctly. If you know the compost was fine, or even if you had minimal levels of E. coli in the pile, the ACTIVELY AERATED tea brewing process will maintain the high diversity of bacteria, fungi, and protozoa needed to compete with the pathogens' ability to get food, have space, or obtain nutrients. Slow the growth and competitive ability of these organisms down by letting the oxygen drop too low, and now you can have growth of the human pathogens.

There's been some silliness about molasses CAUSING E. coli to grow, but what seems to really be the problem there is that molasses at concentrations about 1% or higher results in such rapid growth of the bacteria that oxygen in the liquid is used up, and the brew becomes anaerobic, letting E. coli win. Some brews that we ran showed at 5% molasses, the fungi were able to out-compete the bacteria, and reduced bacterial, and increased fungal growth occurred. That has not been repeated by other people, so some other factor was also operating in our trials at that concentration of molasses. More to learn. Need to keep eyes open to figure out what allowed the KIS brewer to give these results, where other brewers do not seem to be able to give those results.

39. 20% Coefficient of Variation 9/2/03 3:52 AM

We have data on repeated tests from the same tea brew taken at the same time, and over time. In general, variability with the assays we do have a 20% coefficient of variation. So, if the active bacterial reading you got was 20 ug, the variation would mean the actual value could have been as high as 24 or as low as 16. If the total bacteria was 1300 ug, then variation could have given values between 1040 and 1560 ug. This gives you the ability to compare other samples and figure out if they were significantly different or not. If that confuses anyone, let me know and I'll try to find a different way to express the concept. OK? This is written up in a few of the publications on the methods - work by Stamatidiatis, and the paper by Lodge. On my CV (resume) if anyone is interested.

40. 5% Molasses Test 9/2/03 3:52 AM

The data on which I based the 5% molasses test growing more fungi was with the 5 gal KIS brewer. The data have been submitted to journal, and I'll let you know when the paper is published. Maintaining aerobic conditions can be a problem. Both bacteria and fungi grow with the higher molasses content, but fungi grow more than bacteria, relative to a 1% solution. E. coli did not occur in the 5% tea, they were present in the 1% tea. Same compost source used in both teas. Same machine. Same water, etc.

41. Biovolume Calculation, Not Weighed 9/2/03 3:52 AM

The bacteria are counted, length and width measured, and biovolume calculated. Bacteria in general have about the same bulk density, and so convert to biomass. Not weighed. Dry weight basis, figure bacteria are about 80% water.

42. Three Conditions for E.Coli To Be Present 8/26/03 3:41 AM

As I keep saying, over and over, until I'm a bit tired of saying this, and WISH people would listen, read, pay attention! The tea has to have SEVERAL conditions before human pathogens will be reduced. Got that everyone? SEVERAL conditions, not just keeping the tea aerated.

Question: What else is needed besides maintaining conditions above 6 ppm? What are the THREE conditions necessary to reduce human pathogens in tea? What's the difference between a coliform, a fecal coliform and E. coli? Which ONE is of concern?
Answer: It's in the Compost Tea Brewing Manual, third and fourth editions. Please go check it out.

43. DNA and Molecular Analysis 8/19/03 8:33 PM

We work with researchers at Cornell University - Janice Thies for one. We also work with people at Southern Cross University in New South Wales, in Australia. They, of course work with many other people, so the network is pretty good. There's a company in Australia, Vistoria I think, offering DNA analysis of soil. They are looking specifically at the pathogens, and the cost is $75 Australian. So the ability to do diversity using realistic methods is happening. SFI hopes to offer the molecular approach once it gets to be a reasonable price. We have people working on these methods. Just keep your eyes peeled with respect to who will be first! Um, we will be putting together a CD on how to do tea assessment using a small microscope. This is just for tea (can't do leaf surface yet), and only for relative numbers of bacteria, fungi and protozoa. The activity work and leaf surface assessment is yet to come.

44. DNA Analysis 8/19/03 5:49 AM

Question: How do you know there are 25,000 species of bacteria present in a gram of healthy soil ? Or am I assuming something I shouldn't here? Seems like they're named when identified (like after the researcher).
Answer: When we ID a unique DNA strand, we don't know which bacterial species that belongs to. We don't know its culture requirements. We don't know if it was performing it's function in the soil. We have to combine the FDA method with the DNA method, and no one has figured out how to do that - yet. So, we don't have a good way to name bacterial species identified by DNA work. We have a sequence identifier, and those sequences are in databases. The next step is to figure out what the bacterial species that has that DNA does for a living.

a. DNA Analysis Parameters
When doing DNA analysis, one can find 25,000 - or more - unique DNA sequences of DNA. We count as different those sequences that are really different, not just one or two base changes in the sequence. So, there's an assumption that if the DNA sequence is significantly different, that it is a different species. Microbiologists are still arguing about that, and it's where I usually step away

from the argument. It just seems that there's a huge amount of species in natural samples that we cannot culture. But we can say there are LOTS of species present, much, much more than we can grow on plate culture media in the lab. So, trying to assess diversity of the bacteria in any samples by using plate culture media is laughable. When labs try to say they are at least getting a handle on changes in diversity, just ask yourself if getting less than 0.1% of the opinions in any city give you an idea of the diversity of opinions in that city on any topic.

b. Plate Counts for a Specific Species

Some labs claim that they can assess changes in functional groups, because different plate media are chosen, each of which assesses a function. That's like saying we can look in one pool hall in order to assess the diversity of kinds of sports that exist in that city. Less than 0.1% of the species that can do a function grow on any single medium in the lab. That is not adequate to even begin to understand how many kinds of species or individuals are performing sports in that city, or the number of kinds of sports. If you want to know about a specific sport, or function, and you know, for example, that all the soccer players will show up for a practice if each player gets their favorite food, then maybe you'll get a good idea of how many soccer players live in that part of the city. Plate counts for a specific species are like that. If you make the conditions such that all the E. coli will grow, then you can count all the E. coli in that sample.

c. Molecular Methods

So, molecular methods are the way to go to assess diversity. Total biomass of bacteria has a relationship with diversity, usually. The more individuals of bacteria, the greater the probability that diversity is high. Not perfect, but a better assessment of diversity than plate count determinations.

45. Diverse Microbial Communities 8/17/03 7:15 AM

Soil does not have the variety or amount of organic matter that compost has. The diversity of species, and the activity of the organisms is much lower in most soils than in correctly-made compost. Notice I did not say all soils; there are exceptions. I'm talking soil, in general, and more specifically, conventionally farmed soil. Also note that I specify CORRECTLY made compost. Please don't include putrefying organic matter in the category of compost. Making compost on-site is better than buying compost from three states away, because the species in the compost will be site-selected. Adding in a handful of HEALTHY soil from your own land is good, and it is something that Ron Stewart would always do. Anyway, soil doesn't have the diversity that compost has, unless you add diverse organic matter to the soil. So some tropical soils have huge diversity, if there are 50 to 60 species of trees per acre, plus three to four layers of understory plants below that canopy. That kind of diversity just doesn't happen in conventional agriculture fields......

Question: Can we culture this kind of diverse microbial community in the laboratory?
Answer: Current DNA analysis suggests that there may be millions of species of bacteria in the world, and tens of thousands of species in any gram of soil. We can culture, or grow, only a drop in the bucket of the enormous number of species of bacteria and fungi that exist in any soil. When we limit growth conditions, we limit the species that can and will grow. So, plate cultures are inappropriate when it comes to determining species diversity, and whether it is actually adequate or not.

Compost has a wider set of conditions and food resources for microbial growth than any culture medium people can put together. So compost is a great way to grow a huge set of the desired species. But even there, we don't get ALL the species possible. Making compost that is started at different times of the year (and therefore has different starting foods in the mix), and adding compost made at different times of the year, will continue to expand the diversity present in the soil you add the compost to. So, keep adding.......Maximize diversity. Let the plant feed the organisms it needs to protect the root and foliar surfaces. We can't pretend that we know, or can even begin, today, to name all the species that a single plant needs, much less in different soils, or climates.

Will we be able to do that someday? Maybe. Need those molecular methods. At a cost that growers can afford. Molecular biology is the only hope for figuring out all the species of bacteria and fungi in a soil, or compost. DNA analysis needs to be married with RNA analysis, and activity assessment. Don't ask that of culture methods. Plate counts just don't make it. Even a range of culture media just don't allow growth of the diversity needed.

46. Bulk Densities of Organisms 9/3/03 3:30 AM

Questions about bulk densities of organisms. We just held our second Annual Keshena Landscape Management Workshop, The theme was: "Building Soil": the ecological foundation for productive landscapes. I bring up two items from that workshop that I feel important for the international Holistic Management movement:

1. We were asked to challenge some prevailing theories on "root-pruning": recent studies in plant physiology indicate that root-pruning may have more to do with local compaction than a severe pruning above ground... How much of our rangeland wisdom comes from the study of dysfunctional or functionally impaired situations? (As I now understand it: lacking soil-biology/structure can lead to the collapsing ground and localized compaction causing anaerobic conditions and the forming of alcohol in the root-zone... this rather than a severe above ground pruning will cause "root pruning"..... We viewed one example in a rocky area where the roots of severely grazed grass went down 1.5 meters to water... The implications at least for us on Kachana are far reaching...)

2. Is Compost Tea a new tool for the "tool box"? As I understand it at this stage: We can compliment (if not super-charge) the effectiveness of our large animals by managing the "micro-herds" in our soils. The reverse could/should also apply... we will be looking into this.

So this on average, one bacterium of 1 micrometer width, 2 um diameter, weighs 0.2 picograms. This is based on work by Eldor Paul, Paul Voroney, M. Alexander, and others. Active bacteria have a greater density, about 0.41 ug per cubic centimeter, based on work by a researcher at Sapelo Island in Georgia. Sorry, can't remember his name, been too many years.

a. Fungi
Fungi have a greater variability in density than bacteria, and so their length and width must be measured, and the conversion to biomass from biovolume based accordingly. Empty hyphae may

be quite light, around 0.20 ug per cubic centimeter, while active fungi may weight 0.44 ug per cubic centimeter. Series of papers on this way back in the 1980's, and if I remember correctly, Van Veen published a paper on this.

b. Protozoa Values

Protozoa values are in Darbyshire's book, and nematode values are published in Ingham et al, 1985. See the sfi website for the list of pubs in my CV. The density of different nematodes vary depending on the functional group of nematode.

47. Sampling 8/14/03 6:19 AM

a. Organisms in Tea

Do testing on the tea to make sure you have the organisms in the tea - total and active bacteria, total and active fungi.

b. pH

SFI can do this if you want.

c. Organic Matter

Have to go to a soils lab for this. SFI is thinking about a color-based test. The darker the color, relative to the parent material, the more HUMUS. That's probably the more useful test.

d. Root- Depth

Visual thing. Use a ruler to measure depth to bottom of root zone. Take pictures to document root thickness, color

e. Soil Structure

Sieve through increasingly small size sieves. Or drop a 6 inch square of the soil from waist height, and look at the size of the chunks. More structure, the fewer "clods", the better the 1 to 2 cm aggregates. Again, pictures.

f. Soil Depth

Also take a metal rod, and push into the soil, record the depths where it gets harder to push the rod into the soil. You can put a pressure gauge on the top of the rod, and a couple handles on the pressure gauge. That way, you can record the pressure needed to push the rod into the soil. As you improve soil structure, and decrease compaction, less pressure is needed to push the rod into the soil, the fewer compacted zones you will hit.

48. Representative Test 8/14/03 6:19 AM

The point is to have a representative test. Many small samples mixed together and then observed for the organisms. No different than sampling for pathogens in blood, milk, sewage, or water. The microscope being referred to is one that can be used to assess leaf coverage by a compost tea. We're working on it, not quite ready yet.

49. Testing Scrutinized 8/14/03 6:19 AM
Composted means many small samples mixed into one.

a. Live organisms tests
FDA is the simplest. Must have a high intensity UV lab in order to see the stain though. That's what is taking time.

b. CT Scrutiny
And I agree about why is CT being subjected to so much scrutiny, when other things that have been shown to have much greater risk are not prevented. People die from exposure to pesticides, and all we get are warning labels on the containers. There has never been a documented case of CT causing a human death, and we are told that CT is the same as raw manure. Hopefully that will be changed by the CTTF.

50. Pathogens and Sugars 8/7/03 9:58 Am
Yes, anything containing fairly diverse sugars and proteins would substitute for molasses. Check the past archives for info. But realize that there has been a concerted attack on molasses as a food resource. If people try to "outlaw" molasses as a food resource in compost, or tea, because supposedly molasses causes E. coli to grow, then we'll lose all sugars eventually. The point is that sugar, whether those sugars in molasses or other simple sugars, provides for RAPID bacterial growth. As the bacteria grow that rapidly, oxygen is used up, and the normal AEROBIC organisms that compete with human pathogens are no longer functioning. Plate count methods to differentiate aerobic from anaerobic are really silly as well. Aerobes don't all die because oxygen has become limiting. Many aerobes just go to sleep. Although no longer functioning, they will still grow on plate media if they are put on plates in an aerobic incubator. Plate counts don't allow you to determine if the aerobes are FUNCTIONING. Plate counts tell you if the organisms are present, but the organisms may be present as dormant stages. Plate count determinations are useless for differentiating aerobic versus anaerobic growth. If aerobic bacteria and fungi are no longer functioning, then bacteria that do better in reduced oxygen conditions get first chance at the food resources. So, if molasses, or other sugars, are present in high enough concentration, after reduced oxygen conditions shut down the activity of the competitors of the human pathogens, then the human pathogens can grow.

Again, without competition, the human pathogens can win in competition for foods. When the human pathogens are out-competed by normal aerobic organisms, the pathogens don't grow. In order to REDUCE the human pathogen numbers, predators like the protozoa must be present to consume the human pathogens. Yes, there must be some attrition of the human pathogens if they aren't winning for food, but that can be a long term process of attrition. Having the predators present means the reduction in bacterial biomass is rapid. So, don't fall for the line that if we outlaw molasses in compost tea, we'll solve the problem. It's just not that simple.

51. Academic Mind Set 5/7/04 7:53 AM
Isn't it interesting that NONE of the work by Raoul France, or Anne France-Harrar, or Howard, or Eve Balforth, or even the Luebkes was ever pointed out in any class when I was a graduate student working in the area of soil ecology? Perhaps that explains why there is such a dichotomy between

what people learn in Universities in the US, and what soil ecologists do in other countries in the world. The mind set of many academics in the US has been limited, restricted, and made narrow by the training they received. They dis-regard, disrespect, and pooh-pooh these other sources of information. There are individuals in the academic world with broader minds, and we need to work with them.

Question: How do we do that?
Answer: We need funding to be able to provide them with support. Where we can, we need to incorporate all knowledge into the replicated studies we do. Even with transmutation, there is a core of fact there that needs to be understood. But please understand that people mis-took "disappearance" and "appearance" of soil nutrients from "no-where" as elements being transmutated.

a. Transformation not Transmutation
In fact, it was transformation from one form of the element - such as oxygen - to another form of the same element - carbon dioxide. No need to invoke transmutation. They needed to realize that their extraction methods were inadequate. Another example - ammonium is released when protozoa eat bacteria. This is not a case of nitrogen being transmuted from some other element, such as boron. That's just not possible without the release of a great deal of energy. But because nitrogen "appeared" in the soil, suddenly, some researchers interpreted that appearance as being explained by transmutation. Not the case. Their extractions procedures ignored the bacterial source of N. It did not "appear" suddenly from no-where, but from a source they were ignoring. Their view was "how could bacteria be important -- they are so small and insignificant". But bacteria make up in numbers what they lack in size. That was their mistake, to ignore the capacity and ubiquitous nature of bacteria and fungi, protozoa and nematodes, in soil.

b. Government Funded Testing Needed
We need the pressure that all of you can provide to make funding become available from the US government to work on how to prevent human pathogens in compost, and in compost tea. How to KNOW for certain that the process you follow will result in no problems. We have to provide evidence that those who intentionally have tried to make a bad name for compost and compost tea, who SAY they composted correctly, but in fact never aerated the compost pile, are brought to understand that they did wrong. We have to make those who say they used "finished compost" when in fact they did not use anything even close to finished, realize that they are harming the world of compost and compost tea when they do that, and rescind the "science" they reported as being inaccurate.

We have to provide the evidence that making compost tea without control of aeration will result in a material that is so variable in potential outcome that it is useless to growers. That is part of what the current go-around of the compost tea task force was all about. There are people who want to reject compost tea altogether, because the outcomes from not-adequately controlled compost tea making have proven harmful. And then there were those who had an agenda - from a money-making point of view - to prevent compost tea from being given a green light.

52. Active and Total Organisms 8/8/03 9:50 PM

Question: Is this correct, the SFI inactive B or F test result number distinguishes B and F that could be activated from dead B or F?

Answer: The readings are active and total. The inactive, which can be obtained by subtracting active from total, could be just slow, sleeping, or dead. The active organisms are the really active ones, such as marathon runners. Most of us aren't marathon runners, and as I sit here at my computer in Lismore, Australia, on a nice Saturday afternoon, I would not be counted as active, since I am not metabolically active enough to take up and stain fluorescently in a three minute period of time. In fact, I'm seriously considering taking a nap here in a few minutes, so I am really not metabolically active at all. I can only hope this message is still in the realm of understandable to the rest of the compost tea community. So, activity as measured by the SFI method requires REALLY active organisms, ones that are modifying the soil, or tea, or whatever ,because they are that active. Organisms just waiting to get going do not stain, just as ones that were running hard, but have now slowed down, do not stain either. Anaerobes do not take up the stain either. With the ratio of active to total, over time, you need to be a bit careful. If the total biomass didn't change much from time 1 to 2, and activity went down, then the percent activity is a reflection of a lower number of active organisms. But, if total biomass increased, and activity stayed the same, then the ratio would decrease. But it's just a reflection that you grew more biomass over that time period.

Question: If I brew a tea that comes back with great numbers, and inactive means "potentially active", and I add a tiny amount of fish hydrolysate to activate them, then my tea at the time of application could actually have a higher active B and F, couldn't it? Can I count on this activation in gauging how potent the tea will be?

Answer: Right, the difference between active and total can be viewed as mostly "potentially active". Good term. You add more food, and some of the critters will wake up and grow, where they would not have woken up before. The organisms will continue to use that food, even after applied to the soil or plant surface, and thus you will allow more organisms to make the transition to the real world alive, active and functioning.

53. Anaerobic Brews 5/7/04 7:53 AM

Question: What are the conditions that allow an anaerobic brew to remain pathogen-free?

Answer: I BELIEVE that with the lactic-acid bacteria is promising. But we need solid data on that potential. Belief is not adequate proof.

Question: What are the conditions that small scale growers can use to produce material that can be applied to food stuff without concern? And not just one person's way of doing things, what are the parameters, clearly understood, that allow this?

Answer: Testing of the parameters, and which one is most important in which condition, is what needs to be funded. The public needs to demand that the funding be provided TO THE PUBLIC to understand these things. Given the condition of who actually controls University systems, the money cannot be given to them.

54. Training for Starting an SFI Lab 1/20/04 11:17 PM

We typically train people who want to start an SFI lab. We ask that people sign a non-compete, non-disclosure agreement. We don't want people to train with SFI, learn our methods, and how we manage to do the work so efficiently, and then go out and start a competing lab. I also want to make certain everyone doing direct assessment maintains the search images, so we ask that quality assurance be performed. Also, we keep improving the methods as equipment gets better and better. I want methods and equipment to be as cutting edge as possible, and I want constant checking so everyone has the same definition of the morphology of the different organisms.

We typically start people out doing active bacteria, total and active fungi. It takes about a month to get that really under your belt, and look at enough different soils to have a good idea of the variability you are going to see. We usually have about 100 different soils and plants that each person needs to look at so they really have an understanding of the differences that can occur. Usually no lab other than the main lab sees that range of variation, but better to be over-trained than under-trained! We then work on total bacterial assessment, and then protozoa. Takes another month to get good at these assays. So, to do a lab that can do most of the foodweb takes about 2 months of training, or about $8,000. Mostly that is technician time to show the trainee what needs to be done, and then practice, practice, practice!

Mycorrhizal fungi take a good month to get the search images worked out, because you need to be able to identify VAM, other *endo-* and *ecto-myccorhizal* fungi. so we usually get the lab going on the activity assays, and the next winter train the *mycorrhizal* fungi. The next winter we start nematode training. We usually get you to be able to count and pick, then begin to work on the morphology over a month time period, let you practice for a year on your own samples (while sending nematodes samples into SFI main lab for the actual ID), then another month of training here at SFI the next winter. Then until you agree with ID with what our experts do, SFI main lab confirms all IDs. Then, of course, there is on-going QA. As we do soil chemistry, and species diversity, we will work out training methods. Not quite there on the molecule probe methods yet, so can't quite say how long to train. Working with the folks at Cornell University and another group in Europe on these methods, so just stay tuned....

Chapter XII

SAMPLE TEMPLATES for REPLICATED TRIALS

BASIC INFORMATION NEEDED FOR RELICATED TRIALS

Control Group: Always use a control set where you just water and do nothing else to that group. This is done to simply see how that plants grow and survive for comparison to the treated groups.

Number of Replicates: A minimum of three plants, seeds, trees, vines, rows, etc. are needed within each group. Five or more is recommended.

Types of Seeds, Plants, Trees, Vines, etc.: Record the common name and the botanical name and any other information about germination, sun/shade requirements, planting time, temperature, etc. Examples of types of plants/seeds to conduct trials with are: turf, tomato, lettuce, onion, radish, peppers)

Randomization: Do mathematical randomization of plots, plants or pots, or simply number sheets of paper and draw numbers for placement of initial treatment groups and within each group. Rotate pots weekly.

Location of Experiment: Specify the address, state, county, and country of your field trial.

Treatments: In the case of compost tea trials, use the same kind of soil, and the same kind of water for each treatment group. Then use compost tea on one treatment group, and a conventional fertilizer on another treatment group. Make sure water is chlorine or chloramine free is preferable. Have the water tested if necessary.

Placement of Groups: Place your groups as far away from each other as possible. If they are outside and wind is a factor, think about placing your compost tea group downwind so as not to cause possible cross over of microorganisms. Try to keep all other environmental factors as equal as possible, same shade, sun, elevation, etc.

Records: Keep a very accurate journal recording exactly what you do to each group and when and the results. Take photos whenever possible. Number your plants so the numbers are visible in the photos.

Testing: Test soils before and after treatment if possible for microbiology, NPK, plant available nutrients, pathogen presence, leaf organism assays, etc.

Procedure: Describe how you will be conducting your experiment. A basic sample below:

1. Count Number of seeds going into each pot
2. Count number of seeds that germinate
3. Record time seeds germinate – shoots come up
4. Day 0 = the day planted
5. Record time for shoot to reach certain height (for example: 5")
6. Record Green Index #1 – 5 (find samples of different shades of green to use for reference)
7. Weight pots = moisture value

Experimental Design for Potted Plants Trials for Enhanced Growth of _____utilizing Compost Tea and Conventional Fertilizer

Experiment Commencing _____ through _____

1. **Type of Plant::** _____*Seeds* will be used for the experiment.

2. **Size of Containers:** 18 three inch pots.

3. **Location of Experiment:** The experiment will be conducted at _____.

4. **Randomization**:

    a. The pots will be set up as follows in three groups:
        i. Control Group A (Compost)(6 pots)
        ii. Treatment Group B (Compost Tea and Compost)(6 pots)
        iii. Treatment Group C (Conventional Fertilizer and Compost)(6 pots)

    b. Each pot will be numbered for each mini-greenhouse as follows:
        i. Control Group C: (Compost) numbers 1 – 6
        ii. Treatment Group A: (Compost Tea and Compost): numbers 7-12
        iii. Treatment Group B: (Conventional Fertilizer and Compost): numbers 13-18

    c. Numbers will be randomly drawn for placement of Treatment and Control Groups.

    d. Numbers will be randomly drawn for pot placement within each group.

    e. Numbers will be redrawn and pots will be replaced once a week within each group.

5. **Treatments:**

    a. Control Group C - No Compost Tea or Conventional Fertilizer, (water as needed).

    b. Treatment Group A – Compost Tea once a _____(week, month, etc.), (water as needed).
    c. Treatment Group B – Conventional Fertilizer according to directions, (water as needed).

6. **Measurements**

    a. Count the number of seeds going into each pot.

    b. Count the number of seeds that sprout in each pot.

    c. Record the number of days that it takes the seeds to sprout (photos).
       (Day 0 is the day the seeds are planted)

    d. Record the day the pots are thinned and the number of sprouts remaining (photos).

    e. Record the time it takes for the plant to reach a certain height (3 inches, 5 inches, etc.)
       (photos)

Experimental Design for Row Crop Trials for Enhanced Plant/Tree/Vine Growth of_____ utilizing Compost Tea and Conventional Fertilizer

Experiment Commencing _____ through _____

1. **Type of Plants/Trees/Vines:**: _____ will be used for the experiment.

2. **Size of Plants/Trees/Vines:** _____.

3. **Location of Experiment:** The experiment will be conducted at _____

4. **Randomization**:

   a. Each row of trees will be numbered as followed:
      i.   Control Group A (no Compost Tea) Row _____(_____ trees/vines).
      ii. Treatment Group B (Compost Tea) Row _____(_____ trees/vines).
      iii. Treatment Group C (Conventional Fertilizer) Row _____(_____ trees/vines).

   a. Each tree will be numbered in each row as follows:
      i.   Control Group A: numbers 1 through_____.
      ii. Treatment Group B: numbers _____ through _____.
      iii. Treatment Group C: numbers _____ through _____.

4. **Treatments:**

   a. Control Group A -- No solution (Water as needed).

   b. Treatment Group B -- Solution (Water as needed).
      1) Compost Tea (20 Gallons per Acre) applied Spring and Fall.
      2) Compost Tea (5 Gallons per Acre) applied every _____.

   c. Treatment Group C -- Solution (Water as needed).
      1) Conventional Fertilizer (per directions per Acre) applied Spring and Fall.
      2) Compost Tea (per directions per Acre) applied every _____.

4. **Treatment Products - Microbiological Testing:**

   a. Laboratory tests will be conducted on solution and compost for microbiological content at the beginning and completion of the experiment.

7. **Plant/Tree/Vine Height, ____, ____, ____ and Microbiological Testing in the Field:**

   a. Measure Plant/Tree/Vine height and green index from each group each month.

   b. Soil will be tested at the beginning and end of the experiment

   c. Leaf Organism Assays will be conducted to determine microbiological coverage on tree leaves.

Chapter XIII

DR. ELAINE INGHAM'S PROFILE

Dr. Elaine Ingham, Bio

Dr. Elaine Ingham
Address: c/o Soil Foodweb Inc.
*   1750 S.W. 3rd St., Suite K, Corvallis, OR 97333*
Phones: W: (541) 742-5066; Cell: 541-460-4026
E Mail: info@soilfoodweb.com

Professional Background

Dr. Elaine Ingham is currently *President and Director of Research* for *Soil Foodweb Inc.,* a small business that grew out of her *Oregon State University* research program. Her research is on:

- What organisms are present in the soil and on the foliage of your plants?
- Which organisms benefit which types of plants?
- Which organisms harm plants?
- How can these organisms be managed to grow plants with the least expensive inputs into the system while maintaining soil fertility?

Behind her user-friendly approach lies a wealth of knowledge gained from years of research into the organisms which make up the soil food web. Her goal is to translate this knowledge into actions that ensure a healthy food web that promotes plant growth and reduces reliance on inorganic chemicals. Elaine also offers a pioneering vision for sustainable farming, improving our current soils to a healthier state, without damaging any other ecosystem.

Dr Elaine Ingham is an energetic, easy-to-understand speaker who explains what life in the soil is all about. Behind this 'user-friendly' approach lies a wealth of knowledge gained from years of intensive research into the organisms, which make up the soil food web. Elaine not only understands the soil food web, she has knowledge on how to ensure a healthy food web to promote plant growth and reduce reliance on inorganic chemicals.

While truly an academic, Elaine is also passionate about sharing her knowledge and research findings with those at the grass roots level of working with soils. That includes not just farmers who grow crops, but also those who graze cattle, sheep and other livestock, fruit and vegetable growers, greens keepers, parks and gardens workers, nursery operators – in fact anyone who grows things, even if it's just plain old lawn grass. Elaine offers a way forward for sustainable farming. A way of improving the soils we work with now and a way to keep soils in this healthier state without damaging any other eco-system.

Professional Background – Earlier Years

1986-1991
In 1986, Elaine moved to Oregon State University, and joined the faculty in both Forest Science and Botany and Plant Pathology. For several years, Elaine's "home" department was Botany and Plant Pathology. In 1991,because the number of samples from outside Elaine's immediate program being sent to her for

analysis were becoming a large component of what she was doing, Elaine opened a service through the University called the Soil Microbial Biomass Service. The Service offered researchers and commercial clients the ability to have soil samples analyzed for soil foodweb organisms. During this time, Elaine became known as an energetic and easy-to-understand speaker who explained what life in the soil was all about, and she started speaking to groups throughout the United States about the Soil Foodweb.

1996-2005

By 1995, the number of samples coming into the Soil Microbial Biomass Service was close to 8,000 samples a year, and the amount of lab space required to process this number of samples was greater than originally planned. The head of Elaine's department asked that the commercial portion of the Biomass Service be taken off-campus. Thus, in the fall of 1996, Soil Foodweb Inc. became a commercial enterprise. With the move into a private lab, Elaine's focus turned more to grower-related issues, focusing on the expense of intensive chemical use as well as the damage these chemicals inflict on beneficial organisms in the soil and on foliage. The research and practical understanding and application of soil organisms continue at Soil Foodweb Inc., while much of the academic side of her work remains at the University.

2000-2005

In December 2000 a new Soil Foodweb lab was opened in Australia, at Southern Cross University in Lismore, Australia so that grower's down-under could have overnight access to the assays they need to improve plant production without the use of high levels of inorganic chemicals. The Lab Director at the Australia lab is Merline Olson, Certified Soil Foodweb Advisor. Her publication, The Compost Tea Brewing Manual, is updated periodically to include the latest results in compost tea work.

Key Accomplishments

- Her work with biological products with *Lyndon Smith, Wayne Woodward* and *Jim Johnson* of *Huma-Gro* and with *Tom Piatkowski* of *Helena Chemical Company* is leading the way for understanding which bio-stimulant products work best, and how much material is needed to achieve desired improvements in soil organism functions.

- Work with *Ken Warner* of *Frontier Industries* and *Ron Ste*wart of *Columbia Gorge Organics* on how to make the best humus material possible shows that establishing biological components of the foodweb, and giving the biology the foods needed, long-term benefits for plant growth are achieved.

- Since 1996, *Dr. Ingham* and her staff (*Nedra Olson, Twila Henderson, Brian Pearson, Diane Johnson, Kelsi Fitch, Robert Shepard* and *Matthew Slaughter*) have developed three new methods. These methods more rapidly assess soil and foliage-related organisms, and are a major break-through for easily assessing how soil and foliar biology changes with different management practices.

- Recent improvements have been with Beneficial Organism Identification and Quantification. Working with *Holmes Enviro, Lab, SFI* is offering a new assay using selective media and molecular methods to identify whether 20 of the most beneficial bacteria are present in your soil, compost or compost tea.

- Working on compost tea with many people around the world has brought a greater understanding of how to properly manage thermally produced compost, vermicompost, and compost tea to guarantee disease-suppressive, soil-building, nutrient-retaining composts and compost teas.

- Dr. Ingham has worked extensively on genetically engineered organism issues with a non-governmental organization called the *Edmond's Institute*, directed by *Beth Burrows*. Elaine is a strong advocate of sound ecological testing of all genetically engineered organisms before they are released into the environment.

- Dr. Ingham maintains a website where the results of work done at *Soil Foodweb Inc* and in her University research program are posted.

- Her current projects range from working in citrus groves in Florida, to cotton and avocado in Australia, turf and golf courses in many places, roadside restoration in California and just about every other plant system in between.

Educational Background

Elaine started her academic career at *St. Olaf College* in Northfield, MN with a double major, cum laude, in *Biology* and *Chemistry* in 1974. Elaine earned her *Master of Science in Microbiology* in 1977 at *Texas A & M University* and her *doctorate degree* from *Colorado State University* in 1981. Elaine's doctorate is in *Microbiology* with an emphasis on soil.

Elaine was offered *Post-doctoral Fellowship*, along with her husband Russ (who also has a doctorate from Colorado State University in Zoology, emphasizing nematology), at the *Natural Resource Ecology Lab* at *Colorado State University*. In 1985, Elaine accepted a *Research Associate Fellowship* at the *University of Georgia*.

Published Works

Over 2000 pages of published journal articles are listed on the www.soilfooweb.com website.

Personal

She writes occasional columns for a variety of magazines and papers. In her spare time, Elaine publishes scientific papers, writes book chapters, gives talks at meetings and symposia around the world and has a family. Elaine and her husband Russ (who also has a Doctorate from *Colorado State University* in *Zoology*, emphasizing nematology,) live in Corvallis Oregon.

Attendance at Elaine courses is always very high with a broad cross section of people taking advantage of her knowledge sharing. It is exciting that a speaker with such a depth of knowledge and dynamic presentation style, who is respected the world over as a leader in research of the soil food web is sharing this information with us.

Chapter XIV

DR. ELAINE INGHAM'S PUBLICATIONS

Peer-Reviewed Journal Articles

1. Ames, R.N., E.R. Ingham and C.P.P. Reid. (1982). Ultraviolet-induced auto fluorescence of arbuscular mycorrhizal root infections: An alternative to clearing and staining methods for assessing infections. Can. Jr. Microbiol. 28:351-355.

2. Ingham, E.R. and D.A. Klein. (1982). Relationship between fluoresces in diacetate-stained hyphae and oxygen utilization, glucose utilization and biomass of submerged fungal batch cultures. Appl. Environ.Microbiol. 28:351-355.

3. McClellan, J.F., D.C. Coleman, K.A. Horton and E.R. Ingham. (1982). The effect of chloroform on protozoa and other soil inhabitants. J. Protozool. 29:491.

4. Ingham, E.R. and D.A. Klein. (1984). Soil fungi: Relationships between hyphal activity and staining with fluoresce in diacetate. Soil Biol. Biochem. 16:273-278.

5. Ingham, E.R. and D.A. Klein. (1984). Soil fungi: Measurement of hyphal length. Soil Biol. Biochem. 16:279-280.

6. Ames, R.N., C.P.P. Reid and E.R. Ingham. (1984). Rhizosphere bacterial population responses to root colonization by a vesicular-arbuscular mycorrhizal fungus. New Phytol. 96:555-563.

7. Ingham, E.R. and D.A. Klein. (1984). Phosphatase activity of *Penicillium citrinum* submerged batch cultures and
its relationship to fungal activity. Plant and Soil 81:61-68.

8. Ingham, E.R. and D.C. Coleman. (1984). Effects of streptomycin, cycloheximide, fungizone, captan, carbofuran, cygon and PCNB on soil microbe populations and nutrient cycling. Microbial Ecology 10:345-358.

9. Ingham, R.E., J.A. Trofymow, E.R. Ingham and D.C. Coleman. (1985). Interactions of bacteria, fungi and their nematode grazers: Effects on nutrient cycling and plant growth. Ecological Monographs 55:119-140.

10. Ingham, E.R. (1985). Review of the effects of twelve selected biocides on target and non-target soil organisms. Crop Protection 4:3032.

11. Ingham, E.R., D.A. Klein and M.J. Trlica. (1985). Responses of microbial components of the rhizosphere to plant management strategies in semiarid rangeland. Plant and Soil 85:65-76.

12. Ingham, E.R., C. Cambardella and D.C. Coleman. (1986). Manipulation of bacteria, fungi and protozoa by biocides in lodgepole pine forest soil microcosms: Effects on organism interactions and nitrogen mineralization. Can. J. Soil Sci. 66:261-272.

13. Frey, J.S., J.F. McCellan, E.R. Ingham and D.C. Coleman. (1986). Filter-out grazers (FOG): A filtration experiment for separating protozoan grazers in soil. Biol. Fert. Soil 1:73-79.

14. Ingham, E.R., J.A. Trofymow, R.N. Ames, H.W. Hunt, C.R. Morley, J.C. Moore and D.C. Coleman. (1986). Trophic interactions and nitrogen cycling in a semiarid grassland soil. Part I. Seasonal dynamics of the natural populations, their interactions and effects on nitrogen cycling. J. Applied Ecology 23:597-614.

15. Ingham, E.R., J.A. Trofymow, R.N. Ames, H.W. Hunt, C.R. Morley, J.C. Moore and D.C. Coleman. (1986). Trophic interactions and nitrogen cycling in a semiarid grassland soil. Part II. System responses to removal of different groups of soil microbes or fauna. J. Applied Ecology 23:615-630.

16. Hunt, H.W., D.C. Coleman, E.R. Ingham, R.E. Ingham, E.T. Elliott, J.C. Moore, C.P.P. Reid and C.R. Morley. (1987). The detrital food web in a short grass prairie. Biol. Fert. Soil 3:57-68.

17. Moore, J.C., E.R. Ingham and D.C. Coleman. (1987). Inter- and Intraspecific feeding selectivity of Folsomia candida (Willem) (Collembola, Isotomidae) on fungi: Method development and ecological consequences. Biol. Fert. Soil 5:6-12.

18. Ingham, E.R. and K.A. Horton. (1987). Bacterial, fungal and protozoan responses to chloroform fumigation in stored prairie soil. Soil Biol. Biochem. 19:545-550.

19. Coleman, D.C. and E.R. Ingham. (1988). Carbon, nitrogen, phosphorus and sulfur cycling in terrestrial ecosystems. Biogeochemistry 5:3-6.

20. Hunt, H.W., E.R. Ingham, D.C. Coleman, E.T. Elliott and C.P.P. Reid. (1988). Nitrogen limitation of decomposition and primary production in short grass, mountain meadow and lodgepole pine forest. Ecology 69:1009-1016.

21. Carpenter, S.E., M.E. Harmon, E.R. Ingham, R.G. Kelsey, J.D. Latin and T.D. Schowalter. (1988). Early patterns of heterotroph activity in conifer logs. Proc. Roy. Soc. Edinburgh 94B:33-43.

22. Ingham, E.R., M.V. Wilson and C.D. McIntire. (1988). Social and economic concerns with respect to the choice of critical terrestrial Ecosystems. USEPA.

23. Cromack, K., Jr., B.L. Fichter, A.M. Moldenke and E.R. Ingham. (1989). Interactions between soil animals and ectomycorrhizal fungal mats. Agric. Ecosyst. Environ. 24:155-169.

24. Ingham, E.R., D.C. Coleman and J.C. Moore. (1989). Analysis of food-web structure and function in a short grass prairie, a mountain meadow and lodgepole pine forest. Biol. Fertil. Soils 8:29-37.

25. Stamatiadis, S., J.W. Doran and E.R. Ingham. (1990). Use of staining and inhibitors to separate fungal and bacterial activity in soil. Soil Biol. Biochem. 22:81-88.

26. Coleman, D.C., E.R. Ingham and J.C. Moore. (1990). An across ecosystem analysis of seasonal effects and faunal reduction on decomposition in a semiarid prairie, meadow, and lodgepole pine forest. Pedobiologia 34:207-219.

27. Ingham, E.R., R. Griffiths, K. Cromack and J.A. Entry. (1991). Comparison of direct versus fumigation incubation microbial biomass estimates in ectomycorrhizal mat and non-mat soils. Soil Biol. Biochem. 23:465-472.

28. Lodge, D.J. and E.R. Ingham. (1991). A comparison of agar film techniques for estimating fungal biovolumes in litter and soil. Agric. Ecosyst. Environ. 5:31-37.

29. Griffiths, R.P., E.R. Ingham, B.A. Caldwell, M.A. Castellano and K. Cromack, Jr. (1991). Microbial characteristics of ectomycorrhizal mat communities in Oregon and California. Biology and Fertility of Soils 11:14-20.

30. Ingham, E.R., D.C. Coleman, R. Parmelee and D.A. Crossley. (1991). Reduction of microbial and faunal groups following application of streptomycin and captan in Georgia no-till agro ecosystems. Pedobiologia 35:297-304.

31. Ingham, E.R. (1993). The functional significance and regulation of soil biodiversity: An executive summary of the Soil Ecology Society meeting. Soil Ecology Society Newsletter 5:2-9.

32. Klopatek, C.C., E.G. O'Neill, D.W. Freckman, C.D. Bledsoe, D.A. Coleman, D.A. Crossley, Jr., E.R. Ingham, D. Parkinson and J.M. Klopatek. (1993). The sustainable biosphere initiative: A commentary from the U.S. Soil Ecology Society. Bulletin of the Ecological Soc. of America. 73:223-228.

33. Colinas, C., E. Ingham and R. Molina. (1994). Population responses of target and non-target forest-soil organisms to selected biocides. Soil Biol. Biochem. 26:41-48.

34. Ingham, E.R. 1994. Soil Organisms and Forest Health. Pages 12-15 in Headwaters Journal, Spring (1994).

35. Ingham, E.R., D.C. Coleman, and D.A. Crossley, Jr. (1994). Use of Sulfamethoxazole-Penicillin, Oxytetracycline, Carbofuran, Carbaryl, Naphthalene and Temik to Remove Key Organism Groups in Soil in a Corn Agro ecosystem. J. Sustain. Agric. 4(3):7-30.

36. Ingham, E.R. and H. Massicotte. (1994). Protozoan communities around conifer roots colonized by ectomycorrhizal fungi. Mycorrhiza. 5: 53-61.

37. Ingham, E.R., J.D. Doyle and C.W. Hendricks. (1995). Assessing interactions between soil foodweb and a strain of Pseudomonas putida genetically engineered to degrade 2,4-D. Applied Soil Ecology. 2:263-274.

38. Ingham, E.R. and W.G. Thies. (1996). Soil foodweb responses in the first year following clear cutting and chloropicrin application to a mature Douglas-fir forest to control laminated root rot. Applied Soil Ecol. 3:35-47.

39. Rygiewicz, P.T. and E.R. Ingham. (1997) Soil Biology and Ecology. IN Fairbridge, R.W. and D.E. Alexander (eds) Encyclopedia of Environmental Science. Van Nostrand Reinhold. NY.

40. Sances, F.V. and E.R. Ingham. (1997). Conventional and organic alternatives to methyl bromide on California strawberries: Effect of Brassica residues and spent mushroom compost following successive chemical fumigation. Compost Science and Utilization. 5: 23-37.

41. Griffiths, R.P., J.A. Entry, E.R. Ingham, and W.H. Emmingham. (1997).Chemistry and microbial activity of forest and pasture riparian-zone soils along three Pacific Northwest streams. Plant and Soil 190:169-178.

42. Ingham, E.R. and W. Thies. (1997). Changes in rhizosphere microflora and microfauna 10 years following Douglas-fir live tree injection with chloropicrin or methylisothiocynate. Can. Jr. For Res. 27:724-731.

43. Hendricks, C.W., M.T. Holmes and E.R. Ingham. (1998). Foodweb methodology to assess ecological effects of anthropogenic stressors in soil. Trends in Soil Science. 2:181-189.

44. Massicote, H.B., L.E. Takaberry, E.R. Ingham, and W.G. Thies. (1998). Ectomycorrhizae establishment on Douglas-fir seedlings following chloropicrin treatment to control laminated-root rot disease: Assessment of 4 and 5
years after out planting. Appl. Soil Ecol. 10:117-126.

45. Ingham, E.R. and J.Barlow. (1998). Sustainable Agriculture and the Ecology of Soil Perspectives on Business and Global Change. 12:31-42.

46. Ingham, E.R. (1998). Soil organisms and their role in healthy turf. Turf Grass Trends. 7:1-6.

47. Wilson, M.V. and E.R. Ingham. (1999). Mycorrhizal requirements of six wetlands herbaceous plant species. Mycorrhiza.

48. Ingham, E.R, Seiter, S., and R.D. William. (1999). Dynamics of soil fungal and bacterial biomass in a temperate climate alley cropping system. Appl. Soil Ecol. 12: 39-147.

49. Doyle, J.D., Hendricks, C.W., Holmes, M.T., and E.R. Ingham. (1999). Effects of Klebsiella planticola SDF20 on soil biota and wheat growth in sandy soil. Appl. Soil Ecol. Vol.11issue 1: pg 67-78.

50. Ingham, E. R. (1999). The Soil Biology Primer. Chapter 1. The Soil Foodweb. NRCS Soil Quality Insitute, USDA. 48 pp.

51. Ingham, E.R. (1999). The Soil Biology Primer. Chapter 2. Soil Bacteria. NRCS Soil Quality Institute, USDA.

52. Ingham, E.R. (1999). The Soil Biology Primer. Chapter 3. Soil Fungi. NRCS Soil Quality Institute. USDA.

53. Ingham, E.R. (1999). The Soil Biology Primer. Chapter 4. Soil Protozoa. NRCS Soil Quality Institute. USDA.

54. Ingham, E.R. (1999). The Soil Biology Primer. Chapter 5. Soil Nematodes. NRCS Soil Quality Institute. USDA.

55. Ingham, E.R.(2004). The Soil Foodweb: It's Role in Ecosystems Health: The Overstory Book Cultivating Connections with Trees 2nd Edition; Editor Craig R. Elevitch.

56. Ingham, E.R. and M.D. Slaughter. (2005). The Soil Foodweb – Soil and Composts As Living Ecosystems. International SoilACE Conference in Soil and Compost Eco-Biology. Leon, Spain. 1: 127-139.

Book Chapters
57. Ingham, E.R. and R. Molina. (1991). Interactions between mycorrhizal fungi, rhizosphere organisms, and plants. Pages 169-197 in Microorganisms, Plants and Herbivores, P. Barbosa (ed). John Wiley and Sons, NY.

58. Ingham, E.R. and R. Molina. (1991). Interactions between mycorrhizal fungi, rhizosphere organisms, and plants. Pages 169-197 in Microorganisms, Plants and Herbivores, P. Barbosa (ed). John Wiley and Sons, NY.

59. Ingham, E.R. (1994). Soil Protozoa. Agronomy Society of America. In Methods in Agronomy, P. Bottomley (ed). Agronomy Soc. Am.

60. Ingham, E.R. and A. Moldenke. (1995). Microflora and Microfauna on Stems and Trunks: Diversity, Food Webs and Effects on Plants. pp. 241-256. IN Gartner, B. Plant Stems. Academic Press. NY.

61. Ingham, E.R. (1997). Soil Microbiology. pp. 114-131. IN Sylvia, D. and Hartel, P. Soil Microbiology:Environmental and Agricultural Perspectives. Oxford University Press.

62. Edmonds Institute (10 authors). (1998). The Biosafety Handbook. Edmonds Institute, Bellingham, WA

Refereed Reports
63. Wilson, M.V., E.R. Ingham, C.D. McIntire and M.L. Scott. (1988). Report on the selection of several potentially critical terrestrial systems. USEPA.

64. Ingham, E.R., M.V. Wilson and C.D. McIntire. (1989). A general model of biotic interactions. Special Report to the USEPA, CR-813570-01-0, 36 pp.

65. Thies, W.G., M.A. Castellano, E.R. Ingham, D.L. Luoma and A.R. Moldenke. (1991). Bioresponse of nontarget organisms resulting from the use of chloropicrin to control laminated root rot in a northwest Conifer forest. Installation of study. pp. 81-84. USEPA Special Publ.

66. Ingham, E.R., W.G. Thies, D.L. Luoma, A.R. Moldenke and M.A. Castellano. (1991). Bioresponse of nontarget organisms resulting from the use of chloropicrin to control laminated root rot in a northwest Conifer forest.
Evaluation of bio-responses. pp. 85-90. USEPA Special Publ.

67. Linder, G., E.R. Ingham, C.J. Brandt and G. Henderson. (1992). Evaluation of terrestrial indicators for use in ecological assessments at hazardous waste sites. USEPA/600/r-92/183.

68. Ingham, E.R. (1993). Use of soil foodweb structure and function to assess superfund sites. USEPA Ecological Site Assessment Program. Corvallis Environmental Research Lab.

69. Ingham, E.R. (1995). Standard Operating Procedure for Microbial Population Dynamics. USEPA Global Climate Change Program. Corvallis Environmental Research Lab.

70. Ingham, E.R. (1994). Standard Operating Procedure for Total Bacteria. USEPA Global Climate Change Program. Corvallis Environmental Research Lab.

71. Ingham, E.R. (1995). Standard Operating Procedure for Nematode Population and Community Structure. USEPA Global Climate Change Program. Corvallis Environmental Research Lab.

72. Ingham, E.R. (1995). Standard Operating Procedure for Protozoan Populations and Community Structure. USEPA Global Climate Change Program. Corvallis Environmental Research Lab.

Books

73. Ingham, E.R. and M. Alms. (1999), The Compost Tea Handbook 1.1

74. Ingham, E.R. (2000) The Compost Tea Brewing Manual. Sustainable Studies Institute, Eugene, OR. 60 pp.

75. Ingham, E.R. (2001) The Compost Tea Brewing Manual Second Edition, Soil Foodweb Inc, Corvallis, Oregon 68pp

76. Ingham, E.R. (2002) The Compost Tea Brewing Manual Third Edition, Soil Foodweb Inc, Corvallis, Oregon 78pp

77. Ingham, E.R. (2003) The Compost Tea Brewing Manual Fourth Edition, Soil Foodweb Inc, Corvallis, Oregon 88pp

78. Ingham, E.R. (2004), Compost Tea Quality: Light Microscope Methods, Soil Foodweb Inc, Corvallis, Oregon 47pp

79 .Ingham, E.R. (2004) The Field Guide for Actively Aerated Compost Tea (AACT), Soil Foodweb Inc, Corvallis, Oregon 178pp

80. Ingham, E.R. (2005). The Compost Tea Brewing Manual, Edition 5, Soil Foodweb Inc, Corvallis, Oregon 79pp

Technical Reports (Not Refereed)

81. Ingham, E.R. and M. Holmes. 1995. Biosafety Regulations: A critique of existing documents. The Edmonds Institute, Edmonds, WA.

82. Ingham, E.R. 1995. Biosafety Regulation. Edmonds Institute, Edmonds, WA.

Magazine Column in BioCycle

Monthly column including discussions of: Anaerobic Bacteria and Composting, The Good, the Bad and Facultative Anaerobes, What Organisms are in Compost?, What is Compost Tea?, Methyl Bromide Alternatives, Fungi and Disease-Suppression, Vermicompost versus Compost - What's the Difference?

Numerous other magazine and newspaper publications since 1999. Please see the SFI website: www.soilfoodweb

Refereed Reports

64. Wilson, M.V., E.R. Ingham, C.D. McIntire and M.L. Scott. 1988. Report on the selection of several potentially critical terrestrial systems. USEPA.

65. Ingham, E.R., M.V. Wilson and C.D. McIntire. 1989. A general model of biotic interactions. Special Report to the USEPA, CR-813570-01-0, 36 pp.

66. Thies, W.G., M.A. Castellano, E.R. Ingham, D.L. Luoma and A.R. Moldenke. 1991. Bioresponse of nontarget organisms resulting from the use of chloropicrin to control laminated root rot in a northwest Conifer forest.

67. Installation of study. pp. 81-84. USEPA Special Publ.

68. Ingham, E.R., W.G. Thies, D.L. Luoma, A.R. Moldenke and M.A. Castellano. 1991. Bioresponse of nontarget organisms resulting from the use of chloropicrin to control laminated root rot in a northwest Conifer forest.

69. Evaluation of bio-responses. pp. 85-90. USEPA Special Publ.

70. Linder, G., E.R. Ingham, C.J. Brandt and G. Henderson. 1992. Evaluation of terrestrial indicators for use in ecological assessments at hazardous waste sites. USEPA/600/r-92/183.

71. Ingham, E.R. 1993. Use of soil foodweb structure and function to assess superfund sites. USEPA Ecological Site Assessment Program. Corvallis Environmental Research Lab.

72. Ingham, E.R. 1995. Standard Operating Procedure for Microbial Population Dynamics. USEPA Global Climate Change Program. Corvallis Environmental Research Lab.

73. Ingham, E.R. 1994. Standard Operating Procedure for Total Bacteria. USEPA Global Climate Change Program. Corvallis Environmental Research Lab.

74. Ingham, E.R. 1995. Standard Operating Procedure for Nematode Population and Community Structure. USEPA Global Climate Change Program. Corvallis Environmental Research Lab.

75. Ingham, E.R. 1995. Standard Operating Procedure for Protozoan Populations and Community Structure. USEPA Global Climate Change Program. Corvallis Environmental Research Lab.

Technical Reports (Not Refereed)
Ingham, E.R. and M. Holmes. 1995. Biosafety Regulations: A critique of existing documents.
The Edmonds Institute, Edmonds, WA. Ingham, E.R. 1995. Biosafety Regulation. Edmonds Institute, Edmonds, WA.

Magazine Column in BioCycle
Monthly column including discussions of: Anaerobic Bacteria and Composting, The Good, the Bad and Facultative Anaerobes, What Organisms are in Compost?, What is Compost Tea?, Methyl Bromide Alternatives, Fungi and Disease-Suppression, Vermicompost versus Compost - What's the Difference?

Numerous other magazine and newspaper publications since 1999. Please see the SFI website: www.soilfoodweb.com

Chapter XV

References

Abbasi, P.A., Al-Dahmani, J., Sahin, F., Hoitink, H.A.J., and Miller, S.A. (2002). Effect of compost amendments on disease severity and yield of tomato in conventional and organic production systems. *Plant Disease. 86*(2), 156-161.

Al-Dahmani, J.H., Abasi, P. A., Miller, S.A., and Hoitink, H.A.J. (2003). Suppression of Bacterial Spot of Tomato with Foliar Sprays of *Compost Extracts* Under Greenhouse and Field Conditions. *Plant Disease. 87*(8), 913-920.

Alvarez, M. G. S. and Antoun, H. (1995). Effect of compost on rhizoshere microflora of the tomato and on the incidence of plant growth-promoting rhizobacteria. *Applied and Environmental Microbiology. 61*(1), 194-199.

[Anon.]. (2005). Needed: *Compost Tea* Research Findings. *Compost Science & Utilization. 13*(2), 87.

Boehm, M.J. and Hoitink, H.A.J. (1992). Sustenance of microbial activity in potting mixes and its impact on severity of phthium root-rot of poinsettia. *Phytopathology. 82* (3), 259-264.

Brown, M.W. and Toworski, T. (2004). Pest management benefits of compost mulch in apple orchards. *Agriculture, Ecosystems & Environment.* {Online}.

Breeson, L.M., Koch, C., Le Bissonnais, Y., Barriuso, E., and Lecomte, V. (2001). Soil surface structure stabilization by municipal waste compost application. *Soil Sci. Soc. Am. J. 65*, 1804-1811.

Bulluck, L.R. and Ristaino, J.B. (2002). Effect of synthetic and organic soil fertility amendments on southern blight, soil microbial communities, and yield of processing tomatoes. *Phytopathology. 92* (2), 181-189.

Clark, G.A., Stanley, C.D., and Maynard, D.N. (2000). Municipal solid waste (MSWC) as a soil amendment in irrigated vegetable production. *Transactions of the ASAE. 43*(4), 847-853.

Cox, D., Bezdicek, D. and Fauci, M. (2001). Effects of compost, coal ash, and straw amendments on restoring the quality of eroded Palouse soil. *Biol. Fertil. Soils. 33,* 365-372.

Cronin, M.J., Yohalem, D.S., Harris, R.F., Andrews, J.H. (1996). Putative mechanism and dynamics of inhibition of the apple scab pathogen Venturia inaequalis by compost extracts. *Soil Biology and Biochemistry. 28* (9), 1241-1249.

Easton, V. (). The Murky Side of Mulch. *Horticulture. 102*(2). 50-53.

Edwards, L., Burney, J.R., Richter, G. and MacRae, A.H. (2000). Evaluation of compost and straw mulching on soil-loss characteristics in erosion plots of potatoes in Prince Edward Island, Canada. *Agriculture, Ecosystems and Environment. 81,* 217-222.

Eghball, B., Weinhold, B.J., Gilley, J.E., and Eigenberg, R.A. (2002). Mineralization of manure nutrients. *Journal of Soil and Water Conservation.* Nov./Dec., 470-478.

Eghball, B., and Gilley, J.E. (2001). Phosphorus risk assessment index evaluation using runoff measurements. *Journal of Soil and Water Conservation. 56*(1), 202-206.

Elorrieta, M.A., Suarez-Estrella, F., Lopez, M.J., Vargas-Garcia, M.C. and Moreno, J. (2003). Survival of phytopathogenic bacteria during waste composting. *Agriculture, Ecosystems & Environment. 96,*141-146.

Emino, E.R., and Warman, P.R. (2004). Biological assay for compost quality *Compost Science and Utilization. 12* (4), 342-348.

Faucette, L.B., Risse, L.M., Nearing, M.A., Gaskin, J.W., and West, L.T. (2004). Runoff, erosion, and nutrient losses from compost and mulch blankets under simulated rainfall. *Journal of Soil and Water Conservation. 59*(4), 154-160.

Fokkema, N.J. (1993). Opportunities and problems of control of foliar pathogens with micro-organisms. *Pesticide Science. 37(*4), 411-416.

Funt, R. and Bierman, P. (2000). Composted yard waste improves strawberry soil quality and soil water relations. *Acta Hort. 517,* 235-240.

Glanville, T.D., Persyn, R.A., Richard, T.L., Laflen, J.M., and Dixon, P.M. (2004). Environmental effects of applying composted organics to new highway embankments: Part 2: Water quality. *Transactions of the ASAE. 47(*2), 471-478.

Grandy, A.S., Porter, G.A., and Erich, M.S. (2002). Organic amendment and rotation crop effects on the recovery of soil organic matter and aggregation in potato cropping systems. *Soil Sci. Soc. Am. J. 66,* 1311-1319.

Hoitink, H.A.J. and Boehm, M.J. (1999). Biocontrol within the context of soil microbial communities: A substrate-dependent phenomenon. *Annual Review of Phytopathology. 37,* 427-446.

Janzen, R. A., Cook, F. D., and McGill, W. B. (1995). Compost extract added to microcosms may simulate community-level controls on soil microorganisms involved in element cycling. *Soil biology & biochemistry. 27,(*2), 181-188.

Janzen, R.A., Xing, B., Gomez, C.C., Salloum, M.J., Drijber, R.A., and McGill, W.B. (1996). Compost extract enhances desorption of alpha-naphthol and naphthalene from pristine and contaminated soils. *Soil biology & biochemistry. 28, (*8), 1089-1098.

Kim, K.D., Nemec, S. and Musson, G. (1997). Effects of composts and soil amendments on soil microflora and Phytophthora root and crown rot of bell pepper. *Crop Protection. 16*, 165-172.

Kochba, M. Ritvo, G. and Avnimelech, Y. (2004). The effect of municipal solid waste (MSW) on the replacement of sodium in sodic soil models. *Soil Science. 169*(8), 567-572.

Libmond, S. and Savoie, J.M. (1993). Degradation of wheat straw by a microbial community--stimulation by a polysaccharidase complex. *Applied microbiology and biotechnology. 40*(4), 567-574.

Linderman, R.G. and Davis, E.A. (2001). Vesicular-arbuscular mycorrhizal and plant growth response to soil amendment with composted grape pomace or its water extract. *Hort. Technology. 11*(3), 446-450.

Litterick, A.M., Harrier, L., Wallace, P., Watson, C.A., and Wood, M. (2004). The Role of Uncomposted Materials, *Composts*, Manures, and *Compost Extracts* in Reducing Pest and Disease Incidence and Severity in Sustainable Temperate Agricultural and Horticultural Crop Production—A Review. Critical Reviews in *Plant Sciences. 23(*6), 453-479.

Lodha, S., Sharma, S.K. and Aggarwal, R.K. (2002). Inactivation of *Macrophomina phaseolina* propagules during composting and effect of composts on dry root rot severity and on seed yield of clusterbean. *European Journal of Plant Pathology. 108*, 253-261.

Mondini, C., Contin, M., Leita, L. and De Nobili, M. (2002) Response of microbial biomass to air-drying and rewetting in soils and compost. *Geoderma. 105*, 111-124.

Movahedi-Naeini, S.A.R. and Cook, H.F. (2000). Influence of municipal waste compost amendment on soil water and evaporation. *Commun. Soil. Sci. Plant Anal. Vol. 31(*19 & 20), 3147-3161.

Palmroth, M.R.T., Pichtel, J., and Puhakka, J.A. (2002). Phytoremediation of subarctic soil contaminated with diesel fuel. *Bioresource Technology. 84*(3), 221-228.

Persyn, R.A., Glanville, T.D., Richard, T.L., Laflen, J.M., and Dixon, P.M. (2004). Environmental effects of applying composted organics to new highway embankments: Part 1: Runoff and Erosion. *Transactions of the ASAE. 47*(2), 463-469.

Quarles, W. (2001). Compost tea for organic farming and gardening. *IPM Practitioner. 23*(9), 1-7.

Reuveni, R., Raviv, M., Krasnovsky, A., Freiman, L., Medina, S., Bar, A., and Orion, D. (2002). Compost induces protection from *Fusarium oxysporum* in sweet basil. *Crop Protection. 21*, 583-587.

Sackenheim, R., Weltzien, H.C., and Kast, W.K. (1994). Effects of microflora composition in the phyllosphere on biological regulation of grapevine fungal diseases. *Vitis. 33*(4): 235-240.

Scheuerell, S.J. ; Mahaffee, W.F. (2004). Compost tea as a container medium drench for suppressing seedling damping-off caused by Pythium ultimum. *Phytopathology. 94*(11), 1156-1163.

Scheuerell, S. and Mahaffee, W. (2002). *Compost Tea*: Principles and Prospects For Plant Disease Control. *Compost Science & Utilization*. Vol. 10 Issue 4, p. 313-339.

ScholssP.D., Hay, A.G., Wilson, D.B. and Walker, L.P. (2003). Tracking the temporal changes of bacterial community fingerprints during initial stages of composting. *FEMS Microbiology Ecology. 46*, 1-9.

Suzuki, G., Takigami, H., Kushi, Y., and Sakai, S. (2004). Evaluation of mixture effects in a crude *extract* of *compost* using the CALUX bioassay and HPLC fractionation. *Environment International. 30*(8), 1055-1066.

Tang, C.M., Waterman, L.D. and Smith, M.H. (2001). The cel4 Gene of Agaricus bisporus Encodes a beta-Mannanase. *Applied & Environmental Microbiology. 67*(5), 2298- 2304.

Tang, J., Kanamori, T., Inoue, Y., Yasuta, T., Yoshida, S. and Katayama, A. (2003). Changes in the microbial community structure during thermophilic composting of manure as detected by the quinone profile method. *Process Biochemistry*. {Online}.

Utkhede, R. and Koch, C. (2004). Biological treatments to control bacterial canker of greenhouse tomatoes. *Biocontrol. 49*(3), 305-313.

Welke, S.E. (2004). The effect of compost extract on the yield of strawberries and the severity of *Botrytis cinerea Journal of Sustainable Agriculture. 25*(1), 57-68.

Zhang, W. ; Han, D.Y. ; Dick, W.A. ; Davis, K.R. ; Hoitink, H.A.J. (1998). Compost and compost water extract-induced systemic acquired resistance in cucumber and Arabidopsis. *Phytopathology. 88*(5), 450-455.